ELLERY QUEEN'S
PRIME CRIMES

ELLERY QUEEN'S

PRIME CRIMES

CASTLE

Grateful acknowledgment is hereby made for permission to include the following: *The Hand* by H.R.F. Keating, © 1985 by H.R.F. Keating, used by permission of Literistic Ltd.; *Gone Fishing* by Gerald Tomlinson, © 1985 by Gerald Tomlinson, used by permission of the author; *Tell It to Lucretia* by George Baxt, © 1985 by George Baxt, used by permission of the author; *Bygone Wars* by Shaun Usher, © 1985 by Shaun Usher, used by permission of the author; *Jack Huges* by Robert P. Mills, used by permission of the author; *Tillie, the Ex-Con* by Ernest Savage, © 1985 by Ernest Savage, used by permission of Scott Meredith Literary Agency, Inc; *Dead of Night* by Anthea Cohen, © 1985 by Anthea Cohen, used by permission of John Farquharson Ltd.; *Keep It Clean* by Ron Goulart, © 1985 by Ron Goulart, used by permission of the author; *Nobody's Fool* by Randye Lordon, © 1985 by Randye Lordon, used by permission of the author; *It's Best Not To Listen* by Shizuko Natsuki, © 1985 by Shizuko Natsuki, used by permission of Wood Bell Co., Ltd.; *The Visitor* by Kozo Igarashi, © 1985 by Kozo Igarashi, used by permission of Wood Bell Co., Ltd.; *The Cremona Varnish* by Lawrence Treat, © by Lawrence Treat, used by permission of the author; *A Very-Special-Occasion Dress* by Donald Olson, © 1985 by Donald Olson, used by permission of Blanche C. Gregory, Inc.; *The Line Between* by Barbara Owens, © 1985 by Barbara Owens, used by permission of Scott Meredith Literary Agency, Inc.; *Each Man Kills* by William Bankier, © 1985 by William Bankier, used by permission of Curtis Brown, Ltd.; *Death at Gopher Flats* by Patricia Matthews, © 1985 by Patricia Matthews, used by permission of the author; *A Public Duty* by Warren B. Murphy, © 1985 by Warren B. Murphy, used by permission of the author; *Jericho and the Lady Jogger* by Hugh Pentecost, © by Hugh Pentecost, used by permission of Brandt & Brandt Literary Agents, Inc.; *Rings On Her Fingers* by Frances Davis, © 1985 by Frances Davis; used by permission of the author; *Fish Out of Water* by Malcom McClintick, © 1985 by Malcolm McClintick, used by permission of the author; *The Third Possibility* by John F. Suter, © 1985 by John F. Suter, used by permission of the author; *The Benefit of the Doubt* by Robert Edward Eckels, © 1985 by Robert Edward Eckels, used by permission of the author; *Fonsy Noonan's Story* by H.R.F. Keating, © 1982 by H.R.F. Keating, used by permission of Literistic Ltd.; *Kill Before Publication* by Martin Russell, © 1985 by Martin Russell, used by permission of Curtis Brown Associates Ltd.; *Trumpetbird in the Cop Car* by Janwillem van de Wetering, © 1986 by Janwillem van de Wetering, used by permission of the author; *A Little Late Theater* by Jean Darling; © 1986 by Jean Darling, used by permission of the author; *Roberta* by Ian Stuart, © 1986 by Ian Stuart, used by permission of Curtis Brown Associates Ltd.; *Hearts and Flowers* by Nancy C. Swoboda, © 1986 by Nancy C. Swoboda, used by permission of the author; *Boots* by Antonia Fraser, © 1984 by Antonia Fraser, used by permission of

Contents

Introduction

A young woman revolts against the cruel game of selection practiced in singles bars.

The dynamic president of Studio 5 1/4 goes missing during a business trip to Milwaukee.

Baffled in the Bronx appeals to Dear Lucretia for help with her formidable problem.

Ed Nisbett, shabbily elegant, with guileless eyes in a scrubbed face, deals with Militaria from his shop in a London suburb.

Unpleasantness enters the easygoing Gopher Flats Campground for recreational miners.

A Japanese housewife is shunned by her neighbors, who believe she has betrayed a friend's confidence to the police.

A woman with an uncanny talent offers her services to a campaigning politician.

Sam Train takes on a new case and John Jericho solves the sinister disappearance of a young woman jogger.

This volume of Ellery Queen mystery short stories never before published in book form begins with a light story by H.R.F. Keating and ends with a longer, darker story by this same venturesome, versatile author. In between are twenty-two stories of varying lengths and shadings. Murder, espionage, theft, extortion, a puzzle or two, and more than a half dozen psychological suspence stories, two of which—Anthea Cohen's "Dead of Night" and William Bankier's "Each Man Kills"—are very strong stuff. "Not for the squeamish," as the saying not particularly accurately goes. The same, come to think of it, actually holds true for the "light" Keating story, "The Hand," referred to earlier. However, such stories can be read with great satisfaction provided the reader is given fair warning.

H. R. F. Keating
The Hand

James never much liked the days when he had to come back from school on the bus. It didn't happen often—really only when the car had to go in for service. But when it did, James had to keep stuffed down inside himself a little voice that wanted to say to his mother, Please, can't you come and fetch me?

It was funny. He hadn't minded his first journey home on the double-decker at all. It had been a special treat for his eighth birthday actually, after he had been asking if he could go on a bus on his own for months and months. And that first trip had been great fun. Only the next time he had just sat worrying and worrying about everything and hadn't enjoyed it at all. There wasn't any special reason. Perhaps it was just because no one else from school went back that way. And each time afterward it had been the same.

But he wasn't expecting anything more awful than usual on the day that it happened.

When he got on and clambered upstairs as he always did, because that first time he had sat up there and it had been super, he found that there were two people already on the front seat on the right that he usually bagged and there was an old lady on the one on the left.

Still he decided that he would go and sit next to her instead of taking somewhere farther back where he wouldn't see as much.

Right from the moment he sat down beside her he began to be sorry, though, because she turned out to be one of the talking sort.

"Hello," she said. "How nice for me to have a nice little boy come to sit beside me."

James nearly said, I'm not a nice little boy, but he knew he shouldn't be rude and so he gave the old lady a sort of smile and said nothing. But that didn't stop her. She opened the enormous handbag she had on her knees with a loud click.

"I wonder if there's a little boy somewhere about who'd like a peppermint," she said.

James knew all about never taking sweets from strangers, and the old lady was certainly a stranger. But she was old and he thought that if he accepted he would have a jolly good excuse while sucking away not to have to talk. So he said, "Oh, yes, please" in a very enthusiastic voice and "Thank you very much" in an even more enthusiastic voice and dipped into the rather crumpled paper bag the old lady held out and took one of the peppermints. It was the very strong sort he didn't really like, but he kept on with it so as to be able to sit quietly and look out of the window, checking how much of the journey had gone by, making sure not to miss his stop, although it was miles farther on really.

But the old lady just went on talking even if he didn't and soon he

10

realized that she wasn't just a talker—she was a bit batty, too. More than a bit even.

"I'm on a mission, you know," she said. "A very important mission, just like those spacemen."

And she leaned forward in her seat and peered out, a bit as if she were steering a spaceship or something. As she did so, the handbag on her lap, which she had not fastened up again after she put the peppermints back, came wider open and James looked down into it. He knew it wasn't a polite thing to do, but he felt he could do it because the old lady was such a nuisance.

The bag was a terrible mess, like all ladies' handbags, only even worse. There was a big ball of knitting in a horrible shade of purple wool with two long knitting needles stuck into it. There was a scarf, a bright-blue woolly one instead of the bright-green silky one the old lady had 'round her neck. There was a spare pair of woollen gloves in pillar-box red. And there was one of those folding umbrellas, although the old lady already had one of the long sort dangling from her wrist.

But there was something else right at the bottom that he couldn't quite make out. It was greyish or pinkish and seemed to be half wrapped up in a big hankie, a white one with red splotches on it.

All the time, the batty old lady was rattling on.

"Oh, look, there's a doggie. Don't you wish you had a doggie? I know I do. But perhaps it's a good thing I haven't got one just at this moment. They don't always like going on buses, you know, and it's terribly important for me to be on this bus now."

She was speaking so loudly that James was glad the two people on the other front seat had got off and the whole top of the bus had emptied. He wondered if he could slip across to the vacant seat but thought that would really be too rude to the old lady, even though she was batty. And it probably wouldn't stop her talking anyhow.

But he did feel that the way she was going on made it all the more right for him to twist 'round and have a better look at what the thing at the bottom of her handbag was.

He twisted and looked.

The moment he had done so he wished the idea had never come into his head.

The thing was a hand.

The second he got a good look, there was no mistaking it. It was someone's hand. It had been cut off at the wrist. The red splotches on the handkerchief it was lying in were blood.

James felt horrible. First he went cold as cold. Then a moment later he went all hot. He could feel sweat sticking to his trousers where he sat. Then he went cold again and began to feel sick.

What was he going to do? Why did the old lady have it in her bag? There could be no proper reason. The only possible thing was that she had somehow cut it off someone.

How she could have done it—she was quite weak-looking—James

couldn't imagine. But he knew it was what she had done. She was someone who had done a murder. It was the only explanation. He was sitting next to a person who had done a murder.

He kept quite still and forced himself to think properly. It was all true. Here he was, James, on his way home from school, and he was sitting next to an old lady who had murdered someone and cut off their hand afterward, or—he began to think a bit more—who had perhaps seen someone she knew murder the person and was helping them now.

But, even worse, the old lady had not stopped for a moment chattering on and one in her batty way. She didn't seem in the least worried about what she had in her bag. About what she had done.

"Now, that reminds me, did you do your good deed today? All little people should do their good deeds every day, you know. I always do one, too, except when I forget. And I always ask any nice children I meet if they've done theirs. It's terribly important, you know. So, now, have you done your good deed for today?"

She was really wanting him to answer this time. He felt even more awful. He was going to have to talk to her. He would have to or she might realize he had seen what was at the bottom of her bag.

He swallowed the last stingy bit of the peppermint. "No," he managed to choke out. "No, I haven't."

But it didn't seem to be enough. The old lady jerked 'round and peered at him hard.

Did she guess?

"Goodness, how pale you're looking all of a sudden."

Had he given himself away, after all?

He crossed his arms over his stomach and pressed as hard as he could. It was a way he knew of making yourself go red in the face. But he had a nasty feeling it wasn't going to work this time. He felt so sort of ill inside.

"You didn't see that awful accident just before you got on the bus, did you?" the old lady went on, and James realized he had escaped for the time being anyway.

"No," he blurted out. "No, I didn't."

And at once he was furious with himself for not thinking of saying yes. It would have been the perfect explanation for being pale.

But at least she was going on talking, and he could try to work something out. He had to decide what he was going to do. He hadn't realized it until now, but he was going to have to do something about the old lady. He had to. He was the only person who knew what she had in that bag.

There was a part of him, a big part he knew, that wanted not to do anything at all, that wanted this ghastly journey to be over, that wanted his stop to appear—although he knew it was really miles away still. Then he could just get off the bus and pretend he'd never seen what he had. Perhaps on the news one night there would be something about the police catching a terrible murderer and it turning out to be an old, old lady. And then he would be able to tell himself that what he had seen had been true, and it wouldn't matter.

But it did matter now. He hadn't just *thought* he'd seen what he had. He had seen it. With his own eyes. That hand was still there in the lady's bag. And he, James, had to do something about it.

What? It wouldn't be any use calling the conductress, even if she did come up to the empty top deck. She was the young one he sometimes had and she wouldn't be able to arrest anybody, even an old lady. No, he had to get hold of a policeman, a proper policeman. Because, even though it was an old lady, it was someone who had done a murder, a murder he knew about.

So the only thing to do, he thought, was to keep a jolly good lookout. Perhaps sooner or later he would spot a policeman down on the pavement on one side or the other. Or he might see a police car. That would be better. Sometimes on the bus or going home in the car—how he wished this hadn't been one of the days the car was in dock—he had seen a policeman, and quite often there had been police cars. Not roaring along with siren sounding but just going by like ordinary cars only a bit more slowly with two policemen sitting in them.

If only the bus would pass one now, perhaps he would be able to do what he would have to do. Just get up, say goodbye to the old lady so as to keep her from suspecting, and then get off the bus at the next stop and signal to the car or even, to make sure, step out into the road in front of it—if he could do that and still give it plenty of time to stop— and then just tell the policemen in the car what he had seen. A police car could easily overtake the bus and then one of the policemen would just go up to the old lady and arrest her.

Only there wasn't any sign of a police car, or even of a policeman walking by.

And then, quite suddenly, after he had been trying to block from his ears the sound of the old lady's voice chattering on—she was saying something about going to Mars now—he saw he was almost at his stop. Somehow the journey had gone rushing by. So he could just get off and pretend it was all some sort of dream, after all.

Only he couldn't. Because it wasn't.

Far from being able to get off, he was going to have to stay on right past his stop and hope and hope he could spot a policeman somewhere or, better still, a police car.

"Here, love, aren't you past your stop?"

It was the conductress, calling from the top of the steps.

"No," he called back quickly. "No, it's all right." Then an idea came to him. "I've got to go much farther today," he said. "To see my granny." His granny really lived up in Scotland, but inventing that she had a house somewhere near the end of the bus route was a good reason for staying on as long as he had to.

The conductress went back downstairs, and for a moment James went hot at the thought that all the time she had known where he had to get off and had been keeping an eye out for him. But that didn't matter now, not when he had something much, much more important to worry about. It was up to him—him alone—to tell the police about a murder.

And then, almost as if just by thinking hard enough he had made it happen, there was a police car. It was parked by the curb and the bus was having to go 'round it.

He jumped up.

"You aren't getting off already," the old lady said.

And James thought that suddenly she didn't sound as friendly as she had sounded up till now, in spite of her being so batty. Had she guessed somehow that he had seen what she had? And what would she do if that was so? Would she grab hold of him and not let him get off? She couldn't murder him, too, not on top of a bus. But she might do some-thing terrible to him, something that would somehow stop him telling anyone about her ever.

"I thought you said to that nice conductress that your granny lives much farther along," the old lady said, still sounding as if she was accusing him of something but not as horribly fierce as she had seemed the moment before.

"Yes," he answered, surprised at what was coming straight into his head in the emergency. "Yes, my granny does live farther along, but I've just remembered I've got to go back home first to take her a pot of marmalade my mum made yesterday."

"Well, that can be your good deed for today," the old lady said.

"Yes. Yes, it could."

And James ran all the way to the back of the bus and down the stairs before she could say anything else to stop him.

He still had to wait a minute or two before the bus got to its next stop. He worried for every moment in case the old lady came hopping down the stairs after him and perhaps took one of those long knitting needles he had seen in her bag and jabbed him to death.

But she didn't. And the bus just drew up at the stop as if nothing unusual was happening.

James jumped off and stood for a second watching it pull away. I've done it, he thought. I've got away. And I still know the secret.

He set off running back toward the police car, and as soon as he reached it he tapped on the nearest window. The policeman sitting there wound the window down and James, although he was very out of breath, began explaining.

"Now, come on, sonny," the policeman said. "An old lady with someone's hand in her bag? Are you trying to be funny?"

For a moment James wanted to give up. If the policeman wouldn't believe him after all he had gone through to get to him, why shouldn't he just walk home and this time really forget the whole thing?

But then he thought of what he had been through—he had seen that awful, impossible sight and he'd had to talk to a person who had done a murder, he had had to make all those excuses so that he could get away from her and tell the police—so he was not going to be stopped now, not just because the policeman thought he was trying to be funny.

He took a deep breath. "I know it sounds as if I'm telling stories," he said, "but I'm not."

This time the policeman did seem to believe. He opened the back door of the car and told James to hop in, and in hardly a minute they were pulling up in front of the bus so that it had to come to a halt. Then James was following the policeman 'round to where the conductress was looking out from the platform wondering what it was all about.

"Just an inquiry, love," the policeman said to her. "Something perhaps a bit wrong on your top deck."

He marched up the stairs and James went after him. The batty old lady was still sitting where he had left her. She was leaning forward, looking down at the police car with a very interested expression on her face.

Shouldn't she be more frightened? James thought. If she's got a murdered person's hand in her bag she should be much more frightened seeing a police car stop the bus.

But he didn't have time to try and work out why she might not be, because the policeman had gone striding up to her. "Excuse me, Madam," he was saying, "but I understand you may have an object in your handbag which has caused this young lad here some distress."

What will see do? James thought. Will she try to get past the policeman and escape? He took hold of the handles of the seats on either side of him and held on as tight as he could. That should stop her for a second or two anyhow.

But the old lady had not moved. "Oh, dear," she said to the policeman, "did he see the hand? I didn't think he could have done."

"It is a hand you've got there then?" said the policeman, sounding as if he didn't quite know what to do.

"Yes, of course it's a hand," the old lady said.

"Do you mind if I have a look, Madam?" the policeman asked.

"I think you'd better. In fact, it might be best if I gave it to you, with that nice car you have."

"Yes, well ... Well, we'll see about that, Madam."

The policeman peered into the bag which the old lady held wide for him.

"Yes," he said, "that's a hand all right. How did it come into your possession, Madam?"

He spoke a little more gruffly now. But the old lady answered with her usual smile. "From the accident, of course. Where else would I have found a hand? I saw them putting that poor man into the ambulance and then it rushed away at top speed, and the next moment I just saw the hand peeking out from the smashed motorcycle. Well, I've read all those stories in the papers about what they can do nowadays even sewing on *arms* that have been cut off, so I knew at once what I must do: take it to the hospital."

"Well, yes, Madam," the policeman said. "But on a bus?"

"You don't think," the batty old lady answered with a little fierce spurt, "that I can afford taxis on my pension, do you?"

Then the policeman just took hold of the hand in its blood-splotched handkerchief, brushed past James in a great rush, and went thumping down the bus stairs.

"Well," the old lady said, "I wonder if this means I haven't done my good deed for the day, after all?"

James wondered then whether he had done *his* good deed. Half of him thought he'd probably been very silly and half of him thought he might have been quite clever.

It was only when he had to go home by bus the next time that he thought that he must have done a good deed that day—because he didn't feel worried about the journey at all.

Gerald Tomlinson
Gone Fishing

Ed Marlin studied me across the clear walnut expanse of his desk. His story was of the Judge Crater variety.

"Dwight checked out of the Uhlaender Hotel in Milwaukee at nine in the morning," he said. "That was on August eighth, ten days ago. No one has heard from him since."

Marlin wore a concerned expression above his wide, loosely knotted silk tie, the kind my son calls a Bozo the Clown tie. But Ed Marlin was no Bozo. Executive vice-president of a company called Studio 5¼, he was a brisk, wiry, balding guy who cared more about state-of-the-art personal computers—and the bottom line that told the story of the company's hot-selling Citrus Micro—than he did about men's fashion.

I went over his story. "You're saying that Dwight Gill, your president here at Studio 5¼, has been missing for ten days. He'd scheduled a district managers' meeting at the Parsippany Hilton for yesterday morning and he didn't show up. That convinced you something must be wrong. You decided to thumb your way through the Yellow Pages and find a private investigator. Your finger stopped on me."

Marlin loosened his tie some more. "Basically, yes. Something's gone wrong out in Wisconsin. No doubt about it. Dwight travels a lot. He's out of touch with the office quite often. Some people think he goes fishing on company time. But he doesn't just jet off to Sudsville and play hide-and-seek with his district managers. He doesn't cut his secretary off without a phonecall."

"How about his wife?"

"No wife. He's been divorced twice. He lives alone in an apartment in Fort Lee."

"Which has been checked out, you say. Which is why I'm on my way to Milwaukee."

"Mr. Napier, that's what I would suggest. I don't see any other choice. We'll gladly pay your fee"—I concluded right then that I'd set my fee too low—"and we'll pay expenses. Studio 5¼ can go on for a while without Dwight, of course, but we need to know what's happened to him."

So it was that I found myself lounging in an aisle seat of a Boeing 737 at 37,000 feet, speculating on the strange leavetaking of Dwight Gill from his corporate duties. The Studio 5¼ VP had Xeroxed the story of his boss's life from an old press release and I had glanced through the bio at the terminal. Dwight, it seemed, was one of those miraculous young hackers turned businessmen, a high-tech chipwizard originally from the little town of Black River in northern New York, near Watertown.

17

In high school his first love had been photography, but he became
interested in computers early on. After earning an engineering degree
at Clarkson Tech in Potsdam, he joined a small New Jersey-based
computer firm. From there his career took off. He rose about as fast and
as far as the price of high-tech stocks. At 29 he founded Studio 5¼. At
40 he had enough money to buy out three of his most troublesome
competitors, which he did. When Studio 5¼ itself was acquired three
years later by GVA Industries, one of those grasping, many-tentacled
conglomerates, Dwight stayed on as Studio 5¼'s president. He was
already considered a grand old man of the industry.

He was also a "sweet, dear person," according to his secretary, a
trim, dressed-for-success lass of 25 or so, who added fondly, "And, you
know, he isn't one of those frail, refugee-looking types who grew up in
front of a CRT. He's an outdoorsman. For a couple of years he held the
world record for catching some kind of fish. A sunfish, I think. Still,"
she tacked on as a loyal afterthought, "he would never let fishing
interfere with business."

She hardly had to stress that he was a hard driver. The record spoke
for itself. This wonder-working Dwight Gill out of Black River, New
York, had come to New Jersey and had wrung out and mopped the
floor with most of his presumably equal peers. He had to have made a
few enemies. Even lovable Tom Carvel had his enemies, they say. And
computers are a tougher game than ice cream.

The one real lead I had after talking with Marlin was that Dwight
Gill, an inveterate traveler, spent a lot of time at the Milwaukee plant of
The Magic Box, Inc., one of Studio 5¼'s dozen or so subsidiaries. The
Magic Box outfit produced a state-of-the-art modem that in the re-
strained words of its ad agency put the Citrus Micro "on line with the
universe." Magic Box president Tony Oliveri should be able to help me,
I was told.

Not so. Big, grey-haired Tony Oliveri, who looked like a frostbitten
pumpkin in a pinstripe suit, knew nothing of Gill's supposed visits to
his bailiwick. "They told you he comes here a lot?" Oliveri growled,
hooking his thumbs under the rolling fat above his belt. "Dwight almost
never looks in on us, Mr. Napier. Oh, maybe he drops by once a year.
But if he keeps coming to Milwaukee, as you say, he must be calling on
somebody else."

I checked my notes. "He's been in Milwaukee eleven times this year.
Spent a total of thirty-two workdays here. That's a lot of company time.
Does Studio 5¼ have anything else going on in the area? Another
subsidiary?"

Oliveri shook his head. "Nothing. Dwight doesn't even have a sales
rep in town. The nearest one is out in Eau Clair. A guy named Ike
Whiting. Handles both Wisconsin and Minnesota."

"Okay," I said. "The fact is, Dwight Gill has been in Milwaukee
eleven times since January. We know that from his expense account.
What do you think he could be doing out here?"

He thought for a minute. "Fishing, maybe. Up north of here for muskellunge. Probably the Lake Chippewa Flowage—that's where the big ones are." Then he thought again. "No, I take that back. Dwight fishes, but I'm sure he doesn't let it interfere with his job. He's as singleminded about Studio 5¼—about business—as a shark is about blood. If he's been in Milwaukee, he's been here for something more important than muskies."

"And what could that be?"

"When you find him, I'm sure he'll tell you." Tony Oliveri stood up. "I'm afraid this is a busy day for me, Mr. Napier."

I took the hint.

The morning was still young and already I was trying to figure out what to do next. The Magic Box had put me on line with a vacuum. Who might know where Dwight Gill had gone after reaching Milwaukee?

I decided to try a long shot, the garage attendant at the Uhlaender Hotel. I knew that Dwight rented cars when he was in Milwaukee, and it might just be that the head car-jockey would have some idea of where he drove them.

The Uhlaender's garage attendant was a sharp-featured caballero with a thin moustache and an ongoing struggle with the English language. I showed him a photo. Did he know Mr. Gill? Yes, he recognized the face. Did he remember what use Mr. Gill made of the cars when he was at the hotel? He did. Not ony that, he volunteered the information. Straight out. In New Jersey it would have cost me a hassle and a cash outlay.

"Mr. Gill, he drive out to Port Wilder. Eighty-five miles. Always Port Wilder."

"Port Wilder? Why?"

"Why? Who knows? But this I know: Mr. Gill, he is not a poor man. He is not wanting for cash money. His room rent is paid night after night, and his car is where? Not here. Port Wilder. And he is the same place, right? I hear this from desk clerks. Also—" He eyed me shrewdly. "Mr. Gill, he tip very big." He let that news item sink in, then added, "I have to—how you say?—like, make it on tips." He smiled.

I gave him a ten. It wasn't so different from New Jersey, after all.

Port Wilder, Wisconsin, is no metropolis. It has 8,000 or so people. If the garageman had said Chicago, or even Madison, I might have doubted the value of a trip. But a small town was another matter. If Dwight Gill did much of anything around Port Wilder, I should be able to get some kind of fix on him.

By noon I had pointed my rental car west, without any clear plan of attack once I got to "the Gateway to the North," as the Port Wilder boosters put it. From the highway, the town looks like a hundred others. Fast-food chains, motel chains, supermarket chains, discount chains, here as elsewhere, have conspired to homogenize the landscape.

Where once there was rich diversity, now there is bland uniformity.
Only in the blighted downtown areas of most cities can the remains of
old businesses be found, home-owned and bankrupt. Even the bustling
malls are increasingly alike, with just a few local department stores
hanging on, holding out against the rage of alikeness.

But here and there you can find exceptions. One exception stood
right there before me on Route 16 on the outskirts of Port Wilder. It
created a skyline of sorts for the little town. It was called Big Badger Bait
and Tackle, a gleaming four-story glass building that could have been
designed by Eero Saarinen. It dwarfed the one-story tire dealer on one
side of it and the full-service, self-service gas station on the other.

I pulled up at the full-service pumps and gave the attendant the
thumb-up sign. When he came for my credit card, I handed him a photo
instead.

"Did you ever see this guy?"

The attendant, a gangling youngster with vermillion hair, had the
eyes of a bullfrog and the voice of a chickadee.

"Yeah, he looks familiar."

"How familiar?"

"Not very. But familiar. I mean, I've seen him. I think he works for
Badger." He gestured vaguely at the glass box next door. "Might be a
flunky there. Might be a salesman."

"So he's here now and then?"

"You got it. Now and then, off and on."

"You can spot the Badger regulars, I guess."

"Sure. The ones that buy Mobil, anyhow. I know Mr. Whiting." He
said the name semi-reverently, as if I'd recognize it. I did.

"Ike Whiting? Is that his name?" I recalled the line from *Alice in
Wonderland*—curiouser and curiouser.

"He's Isaac Whiting on his credit card. And over there"—he flailed
his arm again "—I hear he's the big badger himself."

"Whiting runs Big Badger Bait and Tackle?"

"If he don't, you could fool me. He drives this big blue Mercedes
around town and acts like he owns the state."

I handed him my credit card. "Thanks."

The nice thing about most of the neon miracle miles outyside many
small cities is that you can accomplish everything from banking to
boozing within half that distance. It being lunchtime, I aimed for the
golden arch and queued up, opting for fish nuggets over a beef patty.
It seemed only right within the shadow of a major bait-and-tackle shop.
I settled into an orange plastic booth and thought about progress.

Isaac Whiting is not a common name. It seemed likely that the Studio
5¼ rep out of Eau Clair and Big Badger's Mercedes-borne honcho were
one and the same. The matter bore looking into. If Ike Whiting and
Dwight Gill had some kind of business arrangement unrelated to New
Jersey computers—and that looked like a red-ripe possibility—I needed

to find out about it. The Wisconsin-Minnesota sales rep for Studio 5¼ might know a lot more about where Gill had flown than Magic Box boss Tony Oliveri had known.

After lunch I headed for Big Badger Bait and Tackle, that architectural marvel of the hinterland. I've always felt you can tell something about the state of a company by looking at the cars in the parking lot. If the company is on the skids, so are the employees' cars. If the company is prospering, the cars reflect it. If that analysis is right, then Big Badger had to be pulling in money faster than a baleen whale pulls in krill. I noticed more new and expensive cars than I'd seen since I staked out a convention of Amway superstars.

The place looked pretty prosperous inside, too. The ground-floor showroom had an updated Abercrombie & Fitch air to it, but I was interested in the upstairs offices. I asked the clerk in charge of reels where I might find Ike Whiting. He pointed toward a bank of elevators. "Third floor. Ask the receptionist there. I don't think Ike's in this week, though."

I went up in a mahogany-paneled elevator. The third-floor receptionist was a roly-poly young woman who seemed eager to please. "I'm terribly sorry," she said, "but Mr. Whiting won't be in today. Could I ask what your visit is in reference to?"

Sure. No secret. I produced the photo of Dwight Gill and said, "I'm looking for this man. I thought Mr. Whiting might be able to help me."

She almost squealed. "You don't need Mr. *Whiting* to help you. That's Mr. Gill. He's our president."

Startled by her response, I said, "I know it's Mr. Gill. The real question is, do you know where Mr. Gill is?"

She shrugged. "Well, he's not here today. In fact, I don't think I've seen him for a week at least. My guess is he's on a business trip. He does a lot of traveling."

"For Big Badger?"

She looked surprised. "Certainly for Big Badger. He's the president. He has to go everywhere."

I allowed it all to sink in. Dwight Gill was evidently the full-time president of two companies. Nice work if you can get it—and juggle it—and keep it. Did anyone at Big Badger know that Gill wasn't just a fishing-supplies mogul but also a tycoon in the computer industry? More important, did anyone know where Gill might be at the moment?

I posed the question: "Mr. Gill's secretary would know his whereabouts, wouldn't she?"

"It's a he," she informed me. "His secretary is Ray Xavier. Would you like me to ring him?"

"Yes," I said, handing her my card. "It's possible that something may have happened to Mr. Gill."

"Oh, dear." Her round face took on a worried expression as she called Ray Xavier and informed him of my presence. She hinted at my grave mission. Her voice shook a little. It must have made an impression on the secretary, because he arrived in the lobby about two minutes later, breathing hard.

"Mr. Napier?"

We shook hands. He wore a well tailored suit that did nothing to hide his athlete's shoulders. He looked more like a Big Ten running back than a secretary.

"Can I speak to you privately?" I asked.

"Yes, sir. Please come back to Mr. Gill's office."

He led me past what I suppose was his own small cubicle and into a stark-white office. What decor there was had to do with fish and fishing—a few watercolors, a print that looked like an original Currier & Ives, and a large Big Badger calendar, still turned to July, featuring a leaping brook trout. A small mounted fish hung on one wall.

"A green sunfish," I speculated.

Xavier nodded. "Not bad, Mr. Napier. You got it on the nose. Doesn't seem like much of a trophy, does it?"

"It looks to me like the one-time world record."

He motioned me toward an easy chair, then sat down on a sofa facing me. "Right," he said. "You've done your homework. From Stockton Lake, Missouri. Mr. Gill caught it on a business trip to Kansas City."

For the first time it struck me that this secretary, who I guessed was in his early twenties, bore a striking physical resemblance to Dwight Gill. But his manner was not that of an heir apparent. He asked, "What can I do for you?"

"I'm looking for your boss. He seems to have disappeared."

"Coffee?"

"No, thanks."

Ray Xavier hesitated for quite a while, as if trying to make up his mind what to say. Finally, he came out with it. "Okay, Mr. Napier. All this is going to get back to Studio 5¼, anyway. I guess even Mr. Gill can't run two companies at the same time. Not forever, anyway. You may as well know our problem."

I nodded. "I think I do know it."

Xavier said, "I guess you do. It's basically the same problem as yours. Except we have a second missing person—Hazel Varden."

"Who?"

"Joe Varden's wife. Joe's our new advertising manager. He joined us a few months ago. Hazel—Mrs. Varden—stayed behind until their house was sold. She just moved here the week before last. They bought a house up on Lakeview Terrace."

"Where did they come from?"

"Kingston, Ontario. Joe ran an ad agency there."

"And now both Dwight Gill and Hazel Varden have vanished, no forwarding address. Did they leave at the same time?"

"Apparently yes. It's a little hard to tell."

"Any idea where they've gone?"

"No," he said. "Not really. You'll have To ask Mr. Gill for the details when you find him."

"Could I ask you a pesonal question, Ray?"

"Sure."

"You look a lot like Dwight Gill. Same eyes, same ears, same chin. Are you related to him?"

Xavier nodded. "As a matter of fact, I am. He's my father. I'm the child of his marriage to Lauren Xavier. The first marriage. I use my mother's married name because she's the one who brought me up. My half sister, Eunice, works in Purchasing. She's nineteen. She's from the second marriage."

"What about the present marriage?"

"None. My father didn't go the show-biz route. He gave up on wives after two tries. Now he's wedded to Big Badger."

"And Studio 5¼."

"No. Just Big Badger. He *hates* Studio 5¼. GVA Industries is running the show there now, and ruining it. That's the whole reason he started Big Badger three years ago. He was losing control back in Jersey, watching his company being smothered by a conglomerate. This place is his escape from the corporate frenzy. It's his little backwoods bait-and-tackle shop. Of course, it's gone big-time now. Dad's such a great businessman he's turned Big Badger into a regular money machine. It grosses about half as much as Studio 5¼ already, mostly through catalog sales."

"So with all this success, where has he gone? Tripped out lightly with Mrs. Varden? A third inamorata? Another try for domestic bliss once he calms down his angry new advertising manager?"

"No way. He's not interested in a third wife. Forget the domestic triangle. Dad's more interested in a second world record." He glanced over his shoulder and pointed toward the mounted sunfish. "Believe me, I know."

"Trying to get his crown back, eh?"

Ray shook his head. "Not that crown. The green sunfish has always embarrassed him. It's so damn little. The record he really wants—the one he's wanted all his life—is the muskie record. Seventy pounds plus. Now, that's a tough one. It goes back to 1957, and it wasn't set in Wisconsin. It was set by some guy named Arthur Lawton in the St. Lawrence River, up around Clayton, New York. Dad's fished up there dozens of times. It's near his hometown. Once, he says, he caught a muskie off Wellesley Island that missed Lawton's record by four ounces. He had the fish reweighed about ten times. If you've got a decent expense account, Mr. Napier, I'd say go to Clayton and check it out. Dad goes there whenever he can. He's more likely to be there than he is in

the Lake Chippewa Flowage—assuming he's fishing, which I'll bet he is.
He wants to top Lawton's record, and I think he figures his best shot is
the St. Lawrence."

And so I went, high, fast, and east on a Boeing 737, winging my way
to Syracuse, thence to Watertown, thence to a rental-car agency whose
Olds Omega would carry me to the Thousand Islands—all this flutter
on the wings of a fishing-trip theory. It seemed like a far-fetched
venture, but Studio 5¼ wanted answers and my other options were no
more promising. If Dwight's son and private secretary didn't know
where the old man might be, who did?

The Thousand Islands were once one of the fashionable playgrounds
of America. The wealthy and famous bought islands and built comfortable summer homes on them. Glorious wood-hulled speedboats
plied the waters of the St. Lawrence. Much of that glamour is gone now.
The islands, lovely as ever, still attract summer visitors, some of them
with money, but the great days are past.

I drove north from Watertown, reliving my childhood days when
this same drive had been magical, when the Thousand Islands reflected a
faroff, iridescent style of life that awed me and seemed beyond any
reasonable ambitions of my own. Now, older and wearier, it seemed like
a pleasant drive, nothing more. I had long since ceased to envy the
people who owned those lush islands. My only desire now was to find
Dwight Gill. And that prospect drove me, because this was going to be a
cause célèbre—the remarkable saga of one man running two good-sized,
successful companies at the same time, and doing it in such a way that
the larger company had no knowledge of the smaller company. This
was moonlighting with a vengeance. The *Captain's Paradise* of corporate
navigation. The press would jump on it and I could use the publicity.

Ray Xavier had given me the name of Gill's usual motel in Clayton,
an unimposing riverfront inn with a Tudor facade. The desk clerk
recognized Gill right away from the photo, but hadn't seen him in
weeks. He said that Mr. Gill owned a nearby island—Pisces Island—a
significant fact that his son hadn't told me. The clerk said I could hire
a boat to get to the island if I wanted to. "Try Roberts Point," he
suggested.

I tried Roberts Point. A weatherbeaten oldtimer with a meerschaum
was more than eager to ferry me to Mr. Gill's castle, as he called it. I
thought he was kidding, but he wasn't. As we approached the dock, I
could see what looked very much like a small Rhine castle rising behind
the thick woods. A classy-looking inboard bobbed in the choppy water
at the dock. Somebody was at home.

I paid the captain and asked him to come back in an hour. It didn't
seem likely that I could expect a free ride to shore.

The friendly smell of balsam met me as I made my way along a
pebbled path toward the castle. If Dwight Gill was here, he was about

to be discovered. Maybe he didn't care. The worst that could happen was that Studio 5¼ would cut him loose with a golden parachute, and that might be exactly what he wanted. From what his son had said, and what seemed to be the truth, he was more interested in Big Badger Bait and Tackle, anyway.

Gill's home on Pisces Island was a castle, all right—the way they're supposed to be. As a kid I had visited Boldt Castle, the place built on Heart Island back at the turn of the century by a hotel magnate for his wife. Gill Castle, if that's what he called it, was smaller and it was a lot newer. The door had an enormous cast-iron knocker in the shape of a fish. A muskie. I knocked. No one answered. I knocked again.

When the door opened, I fully expected to see Dwight Gill. Or maybe Hazel Varden. The person who opened the door was a tall, lean, handsome woman, probably in her late forties, well groomed but rather hard-featured, blonde and straight as a Viking, who gave me the once over coolly, without speaking.

I've always been bothered by stonewall silence like this, more than a detective should be. I said, "I'm looking for Dwight Gill." I flipped open my wallet, handed her my card.

She examined it with painstaking care and stood aside. "Come in."

The interior was nothing at all like a medieval castle. Apparently the architect had been told to provide a Thirteenth Century exterior and a Twenty-first Century interior. Everything was antiseptically modern, the color restricted to white, grey, and black, the materials to glass, chrome, and plastic. It looked like an expanded version of Gill's office at Big Badger.

The lady motioned me toward the living room, and at her invitation I dropped down into a chrome-and-grey chair. She remained standing. She said, "What can I do for you?"

"I'm looking for Dwight Gill."

"So you said."

"Do you know where I can find him?"

"Yes, I do."

That was what I wanted to hear. Yet something in the response was clearly amiss. There was no hint of helpfulness in her voice or manner, just a flat statement of fact, along with a faint trace of antagonism.

I matched her verbal frost with a touch of tonal ice. "Where?"

"In Greenwood Cemetery, Watertown. The funeral was last Monday."

I leaned forward. My expression must have invited additional confidences.

"He died of a heart attack six days ago. He was out in the boat, fishing for muskies, I think. He may have hooked a big one—that's what a man in a nearby boat said—and just as he was pulling it in, fe fell back gasping. Or gurgling, which was the word used. His rod fell into the water and he was dead by the time the man got to the boat."

"Who was this man?"

She seemed reluctant to say, but after a pause she did. "His name is Fred Da Silva. He's from Watertown, but he owns the next island to the north and spends most of the summer here. He's a friend of mine."

"I see. Now, could I ask—" it sounded idiotic so late in the conversation "—who you are?"

"I'm Karen Gill. The widow."

I had to stop and think for a moment. "The mother of Ray?"

"No."

"The mother of Eunice?"

"No."

"Who, then?"

"The mother of nobody."

"But Dwight was married only twice and—"

"I beg your pardon," she said sharply. "Dwight was married once. To me. We eloped right after high school. I thought I was pregnant at the time, but I wasn't."

"You were divorced later?"

"Absolutely not."

I began to see the whole colorful tapestry. "But Dwight did marry again, you know. Twice. He does have two children."

"So Hazel Varden told me."

"Ten days ago."

"Approximately." Her mouth was as tight as a bowstring. "I wasn't amused, but I wasn't completely amazed, either. All of a sudden it was obvious that Dwight had been playing some very foolish games. Personal games, business games. Cruel games. He wasn't just fishing in New Jersey, or Missouri, or Wisconsin."

"How do you happen to know Mrs. Varden?"

"I've known Hazel Varden since childhood. She was in my high school class, along with Dwight. She was Hazel Weber then. When she married, she moved to Canada, but she used to come back to Watertown quite often. We never lost touch. You can imagine her bewilderment when she moved to Port Wilder and found Dwight running a company there. At first she simply couldn't believe it. But it was true, and so were his two ex-wives. She phoned me. I called Dwight and asked for an explanation. He said he would come here immediately."

"And did he?"

"Three days later. When he got here, he said that Hazel had been killed in a car accident outside Milwaukee."

Wait a minute, I told myself. An auto accident outside Milwaukee—and Big Badger unaware of it? A heart attack on the St. Lawrence—and Studio 5¼ unaware of it? No one except Mrs. Gill seemed to have knowledge about either death—and she the one true widow, the lady who stood to inherit everything. A nice spot if you can maneuver yourself into it—and stay there. I doubted that she could. What she was telling me hardly added up—or if it did, it added up to an indictment.

"Are you sure," I pressed her, "that you've got your facts straight? Isn't it possible that Dwight killed Mrs. Varden out in Wisconsin, or had her killed? Maybe out of fear or anger when she confronted him with the story of his one valid marriage? That marriage could have posed quite a problem for him. Bigamy. Criminal prosecution. I can see lawsuits all over the place, can't you?"

Mrs. Gill's gaze was unhelpful. "I have no idea what Dwight's thoughts or feelings were. I never did. He was charming, but he was also an enigma."

"Where do you think Mrs. Varden's body could be?" I asked. "Joe Varden at Big Badger obviously doesn't know."

She looked away.

I went on. "I assume you have a death certificate for your husband. Cause of death—heart attack."

"The death certificate will say that, yes. Dr. Pollack from Clayton arrived here within an hour of the attack. Dr. Pollack," she added, "is our family doctor. He's been a friend for years."

That came as no surprise. Hazel Varden had uncovered Dwight's secret. Hazel was dead. Mrs. Gill had uncovered her husband's secret. Dwight was dead. Coincidence can be stretched only so far. Never mind the convenient conclusion of Karen Gill's doctor. I wondered what an autopsy would show. I was pretty sure what an autopsy would show.

As far as I was concerned, the case was solved. I could tell Studio 5¼ where Dwight Gill was. Dead. I could tell Big Badger where Hazel Varden was. Dead. I could speculate on what had happened to both of them. But I had only suspicions, no proof. That was still to come.

I said, "Mrs. Gill, did you have any idea of how wealthy Dwight was? How successful?"

"No, not really. Not until a few days ago. I knew that he and I were well off. But it was infuriating to learn what a colossal fraud he was. What a liar. He must have been possessed. You probably think I'm a complete fool for not suspecting him, Mr. Napier, but let me tell you: Dwight was a very plausible man. He was a master of flattery. A con artist, if you will. He could make me think I was the only woman in the world. He did make me think that."

"The other wives came as quite a shock to you, then."

She smiled coldly. "I loved him, however strange that may seem. My only regret was that he was so seldom home. He traveled all the time. Still, I was willing to put up with it. Business was good, and I have to admit I enjoyed running things on my own. I've been doing it for more than twenty years. Dwight traveled, and I'm sure he fished a lot. I worked. But we both treasured the few days we could share here each year. Or so I thought."

"This business of yours," I said. "It's in Watertown?"

"Yes. Watertown has always been our home, Dwight's and mine. Dwight was brilliant at business from the time he was a teenager. A prodigy. He started the store while the two of us were still in high school and ran it right through college. His main interest was photography in those days. He made it pay off. The store prospered, and we branched out into mail order." She glanced sadly around the room. "The business bought this castle. It was good to us."

"It's too bad you felt you had to kill him," I said quietly. "Would you care to tell me how you did it?"

She looked directly into my eyes, her face immobile. "I have an excellent lawyer, if it comes to that." She went over to her handbag that was lying on the coffee table. "And I have no intention of letting Dwight's death interfere with business. I'll be back at the store tomorrow."

She pulled out a business card and handed it to me. At this point nothing about the Gill temerity could either amuse me or surprise me. It was abundantly clear that the Studio 5¼ chieftain had not been running *two* successful businesses at the time of his death. He had been running *three*. The card read:

Black River Photo Supply
"Number One in the Northeast"
Dwight Gill/President
Karen Gill/Vice President

George Baxt
Tell It to Lucretia

Dear Lucretia:

Just as you urge in your column, I am telling it to Lucretia at last. I've been a faithful reader of your column for more than five years now, every day except Sunday, and I can no longer carry my burden myself—and I trust you because you are like an old and faithful friend and I am an orphan. Please bear with me, as this will be a very long letter and therefore ineligible for publication, but if I don't get some help soon I will not be responsible for what I'm thinking of doing.

For eight months I've worked downtown in a very respected but dull law office. My boss, who is obviously a lawyer and I mean very obviously, is a crashing bore, but he pays well. We snap at each other a lot, especially when he makes snide remarks about Twinky stains on some of the briefs and how it looks like I'm gaining weight. (I am. More about this later.) Yes, I'm a married woman. In September we celebrate our fourth anniversary, though (as you will gather from this letter) I wouldn't count on it. My husband is in the merchant marine and therefore away from home for long stretches at time. He is now absent in the middle of one of these long stretches. He has been gone three months and I don't expect him back for at least another two. You can imagine what these long absences do to a woman as highly passioinate as I am. I really mean that, Lucretia, I smolder something terrible.

I'll bet you already understand what my problem is. I'm involved with another man (I will call him Albert as that is not his real name). Albert has an office in the same building in which I work. I saw him for weeks on the elevator and sometimes at the newsstand where I buy my Twinkies and he buys chocolate bars, to which I now know he is addicted. The first time we made eye contact, I went weak all over. I mean I really began trembling and I shook so badly a perfect stranger had to come up and steady me. The second time was on a crowded elevator. We were jammed up against each other, I know now not by accident, and I almost fainted. The third time I was trapped in the ladies room after office hours (I was working overtime) and it was Albert who kicked the door in and rescued me. He, too, was working overtime, thank God. It was that kick that did it. I fell into his arms from gratitude and suddenly I felt his hot lips pressed against my also hot lips. He knows a motel across the George Washington bridge in New Jersey and we went there immediately. I almost got fired from my job the next day because I worked overtime at the wrong thing.

Lucretia, as God is my witness, I thought this would be just a one-night stand, as Albert is very suave and sophisticated and (as I very soon learned) is mixed up with some other promiscuous young women.

(He calls us his harem. Isn't that awful?) But, no, Albert pursued me. He sent flowers to my office, which I made him stop doing after the first time because everybody knows I'm married and my husband is away. I explained the flowers by saying it was my birthday and so at five o'clock they surprised me with a cake and wine and I was so embarrassed, as you can well believe. But to get back to Albert.

Albert is a man of mystery. I really mean this. Oh, I know he, too, is a lawyer, but he is very chic and high class. He keeps dropping little items like he was at Elaine's last night and had a drink with Woody and Mia. Or he is going to Carnegie Hall for a concert his pal Lenny is conducting. Does he take me to Elaine's or Carnegie Hall? Like hell. Me it's the motel and the Carnegie delicatessen.

Well, after two months of our affair, which was the day before yesterday, Albert suddenly let drop he has a wife. Now don't think I was born yesterday—I suspected he was married all along. I mean, what lawyer as suave and sophisticated and as (I'm sure) rich as Albert is could be single—unless he has an aberration, which if he does, take it from me, you'd never suspect from those nights in the motel. I asked him how come he never told me about his wife before and he said it's because he hates her so much he can't bring himself to mention her name. He said he is her third husband and has often asked her for a divorce but she won't give it to him because the first two husbands cost her a lot of money and she's not about to pay off a third. (Do you suppose this means his wealth comes from her and not his law practice? Oh, see how confused I am!)

And now, Lucretia, here comes what I've been saving for last. I am p-r-e-g-n-a-n-t and you know what that means! That's why my boss is making cracks about my getting fat and that's why I'm eating all this junk food that will probably ruin my health. I told Albert about my condition the day before yesterday and of course you know what he told me to do about it. Well, I can't because it's against my religion. And I don't want to have to explain this to my husband (who I must tell you now is a very coarse and vulgar brute and understands very little except the comic books he reads, and his lips move when he reads). I think Albert should leave his wife and marry me. Please, Lucretia, I am enclosing a self-addressed stamped envelope. Although you know my real name from this, I still wish to sign the way all your published writers sign. Just call me

Baffled in the Bronx.

Dear Baffled in the Bronx:

What a sad, touching letter. I'm not calling you by your real name in case my letters to you fall into the wrong hands. You must take caution to see that they don't, as I have some very strong advice to give you. You see, dear B.I.T.B. (to save space), I am familiar with the Alberts of this world, who betray their wives and prey on other women. You can well imagine the thousands of letters I receive yearly from women who are in a plight similar to yours, and I have been conducting this column for over thirty years.

Let us begin with this blackguard, Albert. It is my suspicion that he is married to a woman a bit older than he is. I also get the feeling his wife is a very strong and very intelligent person and that he is afraid of her. I write this to you from past experience with other victims such as you. I also suspect he is not that successful in his profession and that he is dropping these half names to impress you and, psychologically, to impress himself. I have a strong suspicion he doesn't know any of these people personally, but that perhaps his wife does.

You have got to be a very brave girl, and I can well assume what courage it took you to take pen in hand and write me. Although I realize abortion is against your religion and a very difficult decision in any event, you must consider the possibility that you will have to undergo this suffering as I have a feeling Albert is not the type to give up a meal ticket easily. Perhaps you'll be lucky in one respect. A lot of Alberts of this world get themselves murdered in mysterious circumstances. And a lot of women are acquitted for murdering their faithless lovers. Be strong, and if you finally decide to have the operation demand the money from Albert. Threaten to go to his office and create a scene, if necessary. Don't hire a detective and have him tailed—it is a very expensive procedure and I know legal secretaries don't earn all that much. My poor, dear B.I.T.B., have strength, have courage. Believe in yourself as I truly believe in you. And keep in mind, of course, the possible consequences if your husband ever finds out about this. From your brief description of him I can well imagine what course of action he might take where you are concerned. Continue to let me know what is happening. Don't let Albert get away with this. As you can see, I am your friend and I care.

Your friend Lucretia

Oh, dearest Lucretia,

You are brilliant! Last night at the motel, eating from containers of lukewarm Chinese food (Albert referred to the food as "pure filth" and gorged on three of the chocolate bars he always carries for emergencies), I suddenly told Albert I was going to play a little game with him. I told him I was giving him a lot of thought lately (as I'm sure he well assumes!) and came up with some ideas about him. So he lit his pipe (the tobacco is a special blend he gets imported from London, England, which must cost plenty, I'm sure) and leaned back in bed and between nibbles on an eggroll I tell him the following: First I say I think he's married to an older woman. Right away I can see he's biting down hard on the stem of the pipe. "Go ahead," he says in a voice I don't quite recognize. I also tell him I think his wife is a very strong and very intelligent woman and that he is afraid of her. Right here his eyes narrowed into what looked like very dangerous slits. "Is there more?" he asks in a voice so weird I think he might be a dummy and behind him there's a ventriloquist. Anyway, I see I'm scoring points and from this I muster the strength and courage with which to continue.

I then tell him what you wrote in your wonderful letter to me (oh, no, I didn't tell him we are corresponding—he will never know that as your letter is well hidden in my secret hiding place in the apartment which even my husband doesn't know about). I tell him he does not really know these fancy names he drops and that it's probably his wife who mingles with celebrities and not him, and that his wife is rich and his meal ticket—and my God, Lucretia, the pipe dropped from his mouth and he started *strangling me!* (I am underlining for emphasis.) I scratched at his face and that's when he let go, and I fell to the floor sobbing and gasping for breath. Then I think he got frightened because he begged me to forgive him. Later I had these awful pains and the next day I was rushed to the hospital from my office and I lost the baby.

I hate him, Lucretia. I really hate him. I thought, now I'll have seen the last of him, but no, he's sending flowers again, and today he sent a box of chocolates, too, and phoned and said, "Tonight as usual?"

Lucretia, what shall I do? My husband will be home soon. I don't dare cheat on him while he's home, but Albert is becoming more persistent than ever now that I've lost our child. Can it be that I'm the only other woman in the world in his life? That even his so-called harem is a figment of his imagination?

To be perfectly honest, Lucretia (which believe me I have been all along), I am now very frightened of Albert. I have felt his strong hands around my neck and that was not very pleasant. I have an idea that Albert is very capable of committing murder. Please, my dear Lucretia, what do you think? What shall I do? Help me.

B.I.T.B.

Dearest B.I.T.B.:

What terrible suffering this monstrous Albert has inflicted upon you! Yes, you are strong, and yes you are brave, but I suspect, reading between the lines, that you have one weakness, and your weakness is Albert.

I suspect t his weakness is purely physical. You said in your first letter that you were terribly passionate, and from that line about your hot lips colliding in midair I suspect Albert is equally passionate. I am also positive about something I suspected about Albert but decided not to share with you until I was sure in my mind. Now I am sure and I must tell you I think Albert is a dangerous sadist. He gave himself away when he tried to strangle you. To add fuel to the fire, he sends flowers and candy to your office when of course I assume you warned him not to. I mean, how many birthdays can you have in a given year?

B.I.T.B., for your own sake, for your life (and I now fear for it, as either Albert or your husband might be driven to murder you), you must give up Albert before your husband finds out about this. If necessary, find another job and get out of that office building. You sound wonderfully young and alive and vivacious and of course passionate. (Have you ever consulted your doctor about nymphomania? Just a thought, nothing too serious to bother you now.) I'm sure you can make a beautiful new life for yourself, and perhaps even with your husband if you want to continue with your marriage. (Did you know that remedial comic books are available and might help broaden your husband's intellect?)

My dear young woman, take it from Lucretia—get rid of this Albert once and for all. Remember, B.I.T.B., I am your friend and I care.

Your friend Lucretia

My dearest, my wonderful, my good friend Lucretia,

I have taken your advice and gotten rid of Albert. A few minutes ago I stabbed him in the heart and he is very dead here in our motel in New Jersey. Don't think I did this in cold blood, as Albert was beating me up and I grabbed the knife off the kitchenette counter and let him have it. He must have died instantly—he is lying on his back with his eyes open, staring at nothing and the tip of his tongue is sticking out from between his once burning lips. (Please forgive this tacky motel stationery.)

I told him on the phone I never wanted to see him again and I was quitting my job to get out of that office building just the way you advised me. So help me, Lucretia, you should have heard him pleading and begging and whimpering. I couldn't believe he would carry on like this from his office, where certainly at least his private secretary could overhear. He said he was having a terrible time with his wife, who last night told him she had the goods on him at last and she knew all about me and this motel in New Jersey and my miscarriage. He said she probably had a private eye tailing him and if he is losing her he can't lose me, too. Oh, Lucretia, it was heartbreaking listening to him, so like the damn fool I am (and as I now realize you hinted in your beautiful letters to me) I agreed to drive out here and talk things over.

No such thing. There was no talking over anything. You were right. He wasn't about to give up his wife and the meal ticket. He was going to fight her tooth and nail, and if necessary ruin her career, which I still don't know what it is but it must be something big. He said he had plenty on her, too, but what worried me the most was my husband. Lucretia, I had a cable from him this morning saying he'll be home the day after tomorrow, much sooner than I expected. He's giving up the merchant marine. He's going to try and raise enough money to take us to Florida, where he wants to open a bar and grill in Key West. Oh, Lucretia, from the Bronx to Key West! From Albert to my husband! Anyway, one word led to another and we were screaming at each other. Then he started hitting me. He blackened my eyes and almost broke my jaw, so thank God for that knife.

According to my religion, I'll burn in hell. I certainly won't go to Key

West. I'm so despondent, Lucretia, I'm taking my life. I know in the eyes of my church that is as wicked a sin as murder, but you know the old saying, In for a penny, in for a dollar. I'm writing a separate suicide note for the police and one for my husband, but this I'll give to the clerk at the desk to mail for me, which I know he'll do in good faith. I know you'll understand and forgive me for what I am about to do. I shall overdose on these pills I've had for a long time and am sure have kept their strength.

Lucretia, I want to thank you for everything. I know you did your best to save me, but let's face it: I guess the minute I fell for Albert, I was doomed. In some way, try to warn your other millions of faithful readers against what you called the Alberts of this terrible world. Goodbye, Lucretia. Think of me from time to time. To know that you are doing this will be very comforting to me wherever I am, especially if I am in Hell. I am signing this

No Longer Baffled in the Bronx

"Lucretia?"

"Mother, is that you?"

"This connection is *awful!*"

"Well, darling, the Greeks were never famous for their connections. Are you really coming home this weekend?"

"I certainly am. I'm bored with island-hopping and my publisher is screaming for me to resume the column."

"Oh, wonderful! I thought Ronald's sordid murder would mark finish to your career."

"Not at all, darling, not at all. Tell It to Lucretia will be back in print by the beginning of the week after next. I understand thousands of letters are pouring in. Frankly, I'm itching to get back to work."

"Lucretia—"

"What is it, darling? You sound terribly grave."

"It's been on my mind for weeks and I just have to ask you—did you know Ronald was having this affair with this girl?"

"I suspected he was."

"Yes, I suppose you did. You're so strong and so intelligent. And, of course, so wise. Now, Lucretia—"

"Yes, dear. You're sounding terribly solemn."

"What did you do with Ronald's ashes?"

"Well, if you must know, darling, I had them sprinkled over the lawn of that motel."

"Oh, Lucretia! What a wicked thing to do!"

Dear Lucretia:

I never wrote nobody like you befor and I do not rede your column, I only rede comic books as you know. I am the sailor whose wife kilt your husbin with the nife. I do not say he did not deserve this, but I miss my wife even if she was a tramp. Now I wish to go to Key West to open a bar and grill (as I have an idea you no) but I need money for this. So I have found these here ledders you right to my wife. You want them back? Okay. How much? I sine myseff

Broke in the Bronx

Shaun Usher
Bygone Wars

Taut with nerves and embarrassment, Mrs. Howard Anglin alighted from the Southern Region stopping train and peered over the platform fence.

Rupley Station squats on an embankment dominating the downtrodden anonymous London suburb it serves. Scanning the neighborhood laid out like a street map twenty feet below, Mrs. Anglin felt mingled relief and disquiet on spotting Nisbett's shop.

The weight of the suitcase made her elderly arm ache, so it was a blessing to see the place so near, in an alley beside the railway line. Nothing else was heartening. She could tell that the place had been a dairy in its Victorian youth. Makeshift quarters for a business surely more in need of money than likely to offer much.

Chump, Anona Anglin scolded herself, believing that classified ad and obeying a faceless stranger's voice on the phone. Yet having trekked here from Sussex, investing hours of time and quite a lot of pension pounds for the fare, retreat was unthinkable.

Her depression increased as she toiled along Albert Lane and saw *E. Nisbett—Militaria* amateurishly scrolled over the single window. But widows on fixed incomes must bear humiliation, of course. Mouth tightening, she pushed the street door open and plunged inside, setting a bell jingling on its coil spring.

No counter, just a large desk. On every wall, Waterloo-era prints and Nineteenth Century officers' mess group photographs hid most of the wallpaper. Discreet rosettes of white price-labels dotted their corners like daisies on a field of monochrome grass. Mrs. Anglin studied a few, her eyebrows climbing. The prices were absurdly high and so was the tariff on a display case of very ordinary British infantry cap badges.

A door stood ajar behind the desk, disclosing a slice of cooking stove. She could smell fresh coffee. Ghostly silent, a girl prowled past the open door—a sluttish creature, cheaply sexy in spike heels and fishnet tights.

That finished Mrs. Anglin. Sordid, she thought angrily, picking up the case and positively welcoming its cutting pressure against her palm, the renewed dull ache from wrist to shoulder.

Then Ed Nisbett came out, heeling the door shut, beaming. Tall, shabbily elegant, with guileless eyes in a scrubbed face. The fuzzy ginger moustache didn't contradict his boyish air, looking more like something from a toy counter stuck on for a joke.

"You must be Mrs. Anglin! Sorry for the wait there, please sit down." His accent puzzled her. Not English, yet not wholly alien—a burr rather than a drawl, with an odd questioning inflection.

"I don't think—" she began confusedly, mildly startled to find herself

36

in a chair as Ed hefted the suitcase, set it on the desk, and silently asked permission to open it.

Unsnapping the catches, he set its contents out in different piles according to their nature: papers, printed documents, a fat wad of elderly snapshots secured by a rubber band, and finally a grubby cigar box which he weighed thoughtfully, frowning.

Mrs. Anglin started again, bitterly, "I realize I've made a mistake coming here—"

Ed Nisbett said, "No, This looks very promising." He swung the empty case down beside his desk. Flipping open the lid of the cigar box, he smiled crookedly. "All but this, Mrs. Anglin. Baby Mauser. Lady's purse pistol from the Thirties and a definite no-no. Illegal as can be."

"My husband would never have done anything against the law!"

He nodded easily, as if she had agreed with a previous statement. "Major Anglin wouldn't have been a soldier if he came home in 'forty-five without souvenirs. This little pistol's been tucked away in his den ever since, I guess. I *can* surrender it to the police for you—they'll understand." Twinkling, he discussed the matter. "I'd like to ask a very personal question. How d'you like your coffee? Sugar? Cream?"

Anona Anglin giggled helplessly, sighed, and said, "Milk and no sugar, and I'm famished."

"For the famished," Ed assured her solemnly, "we have cookies as well. Melanie!"

"I 'eard. I'm listening, ain't I?" came sulky acknowledgment from behind the door.

The sluttish girl soon appeared with steaming mugs and a plate of digestive biscuits. Ed Nisbett, with a slow wink at Mrs. Anglin, thanked her and added, "Now go listen someplace else, like at home."

Half an hour later, the mugs empty and the plate showing nothing but crumbs, he told Anona, "This is quite a collection. Notice that the photographs seem to feature three different sets of people. And there are two Wermacht paybooks here, vintage '44."

Mrs. Anglin, more relaxed now, made no response. "Spoils of war," Ed mused under his breath.

"He wasn't a thief," she said sharply, color rising abruptly. But then she shrugged and conceded, "Stealing by finding? Howard never talked about this stuff. I nagged him to throw it away every time we moved house. He never *looked* at them, but he wanted them."

"Major Anglin didn't tell war stories, eh? But my guess is his tank got the better of a German one and he collected belongings from the dead crew or from prisoners, like an Injun taking scal—" He coughed and looked away. "Well, it's a tradition you can read about in Homer. And Kipling and James Jones *and* Caputo—"

The literary allusions were wasted, but Major Anglin's widow responded to the sympathetic tone. "I think Howard may have done that. It's fanciful, but I'm sure he came to dislike those—souvenirs. But he balked at throwing them away because that would have insulted the men who—well, provided them."

"His modesty lost us some good memoirs, maybe." Ed didn't sound regretful. If anything, he was relieved, approving. "Mrs. Anglin, I'll buy your collection. Cash on the barrel. How does one thousand pounds sound?"

Oh, Howard, she thought, still looking after me. Clearing her throat, Mrs. Anglin said, "It sounds perfectly lovely."

The little store had a phone but its owner let Mrs. Howard Anglin cloud-walk back to Rupley Station before using the public kiosk at the corner of Albert Lane. There was a meaningless word signifying that the message was low priority and need not reach Langley before the day was out. Then he added, "We have a live one at last. I'll be needing The Magician."

Melanie Carver, flushed from scrubbing the ex-dairy's green glazed tile frontage, rubbed her chilly hands, black-leather jacket creaking. "What are you really up to? You can't make enough out of this dump to keep you in bread and cheese, let alone Savile Row suits."

It took Ed Nisbett aback. He didn't know that she was a bespoke tailor's daughter and niece to another, so that she knew about such things. Almost immediately, he corrected her. "A suit, in the singular. I treated myself out of the accident compensation. Four years ago."

The prettiest thing about Melanie, long fishnet legs apart, was her name. She'd been unemployed for months. He hadn't hired her, she had appointed herself.

"Up to?" he repeated. "I rent this place, apartment and all, for less than a cheap hotel room on Cromwell Road. I don't got to be up to anything."

"You still have to find the rent," she pointed out. "Well, just as long as you're not dealing drugs."

"You're not into recreational substances, eh?"

"I got more sense," Melanie snapped. "I don't care, mind—only you're too soft to make a good villain. If you are up to strokes, you'll get caught."

Going off at a tangent, Ed murmured, "Ever hear of Hans Ulrich Rudel?"

Melaine pulled a face. "Kraut, is he?"

"Superkraut in his day, which was War Two. Flew two and a half thousand combat missions, knocked out more than five hundred Russki tanks, they say."

Eyes glazing, Melanie whined, "There you go, droning about that bloody war of yours."

Ed was patient. "Rudel was awarded the Knight's Cross of the Iron Cross. Last month a London strip-club owner paid twenty thousand pounds for that one medal. There's money in that war. And it isn't mine—I was unborn when it ended."

"Always got an answer. Typical Yank," she jeered.

"I happen to be Canadian," Ed told her.

"Well, you won't get many Knight's thingies in a dump like this," Melanie nagged. "There ain't no passing trade, and the way you sky the prices up for the junk you *have* got nobody's going to come here special for the bargains."

Daft to worry over him like this, she reflected. All right, he was a decent bloke. Gave her a few quid every so often, and coffee till further orders, bless him. Ed Nisbett, coffee apart, wasn't at all her idea of a Yank—Canadians being much the same, she presumed. He didn't brag, didn't make passes. He had slipped into Rupley's modest, blue-collar social life without a ripple. Played darts well enough to join the Railway Tavern's team. But there was something funny about him. You wouldn't say oily or dodgy, but he was bloody elusive in his innocent way—ducking and weaving without moving a muscle, somehow.

Accident compensation, he'd let slip just now. Which tied in with his limp—more a fractional hesitation in stride when tired these days. Ask what accident, or how, or where, but don't hold your breath waiting for a straight answer.

Gesturing her to sit down, he opened a drawer and arranged photographs on the desk top. There were a lot of them, faded, some cracked or torn, others blotched with what might be iron-mold or simple decay. Each was neatly mounted on heavy card, protected by kitchen film, transparent stuff that could be peeled away without damage. Black-and-white, a few with shades of brown or grey, a number with fancy deckle edging she'd not encountered before. Blokes in tanks, on tanks, or beside the things. Germans. War-movie stuff. Melanie's mind shut off.

"Pay attention here," Ed chided gently. "You'll learn something. Take this picture—what does it tell you?"

Melanie's grannie reckoned she was "bright enough to read by" and she wanted to display her gifts. "Three blokes and a tank. Huns, right? Bloke with his head sticking out that hole, he's the driver."

"Very good. Loader in back of him on the engine deck, watching for enemy fighter planes. By nineteen forty-four they were paranoiac about the sky."

Melanie admired him, but she had a keen eye and ear for bull. "Leave off, you can't tell the flaming year just from that."

"The tank," said Ed, "isn't a Mark IV like the one in several of those other photos. It might be a Tiger, but it happens to be a Panther—best battle tank the Krauts fielded in the closing years. Panthers first saw service in Operation Zitadelle. That was Kursk—biggest armored go-round in history, mid-'forty-three. But that scrap of farm building in the background has to be French. Making the period D-Day or after, nineteen forty-four."

"Fancy telling so much from an old snap."

"There's more," he chanted, and she sensed his excitement. "What else d'you see?" he asked her.

"Numbers on the top thing—um, turret, where the gun sticks out."

"Right," Ed affirmed gleefully. "Three digits: company, platoon, individual tank number. Here, it's good ol' six-one-four—that comes out as the fourth tank in the first *Zug* of the sixth *Kompanie*. Clear?"

"As mud," Melanie sighed. "Oh. It's like a car number-plate, you mean?"

"Sort of. In theory. Didn't always hold up, especially when the Krauts started coming apart at the seams." Ed Nisbett brightened again. "But that plus the definite dating—jackpot!"

Melanie pushed back from the desk. "Give over. This the stuff you bought off that snooty old hag? Look, when we was at school they took us to that Imperial War Museum over by the cricket ground. They've got loads of snaps like this over there, and the teacher reckoned there'd be hundreds more for every one up on the wall. You've been had, mate."

Ed refused to be ruffled. Patting her shoulder, he said, "Check out the driver, use this magnifying glass. Would you know him again?"

As the long-ago face jumped up at her in larger scale, Melanie grimaced and looked away. "Bloody hell!"

"Gliding crash in 1937," Ed explained. "No cosmetic surgery to speak of back then. They couldn't get the jaw right, nor his left cheek."

"Don't," Melanie groaned. "Poor bloke. I'd hate to meet him on a dark night."

Ed grunted thoughtfully. "Still, there's no doubt who he is. Not another face like that in the world. Herr Smith, we'll call him, who always swore he was invalided out of the fighting in 'forty-two and was right there in the action two years later."

Unwittingly acting as devil's advocate, Melanie said, "Maybe he just sat up there for the picture."

"Hardly. Same guy appears in four more of these pictures, taken days apart. Anyway, he was supposed to have been recuperating at home in the Rhineland from October nineteen forty-two until the war ended. The interesting part is, the unit this tank belonged to was involved in the massacre of civilians in Normandy in nineteen forty-four, just about the time this photo was taken."

Disappointed in him, torn between derision and compassion, she sputtered, "How corny can you get? Tracking down war criminals—I've seen it on telly a million times. Unless you're thinking of putting the black on him, getting money to keep quiet— You'll be lucky, mate, he's probably in his long box by now."

"Oh, he died ten years back, this guy," Ed admitted cheerfully. "It's kind of intriguing is all. I might write it up, generate some interest for these pictures."

In fact, he wrote a big essay for a little magazine—a duplicated pamphlet circulating to military-history buffs—and a little one for a big glossy periodical specializing in World War Two.

"Big deal," Melanie sneered when he gave her the manuscripts to post. "They might pay enough for you to buy a round at the Railway. Bloody idiot, Ed, letting that old frump take you to the cleaners just to get your name in print."

Julian Boordale's nickname around Fleet Street was Union Jack, a witty taunting of his fleshly color scheme of red, white, and blue—florid, with broken blue veins on his face and the whites of his boozer's eyes generally spiked with red. He seemed to have put *on* Ed Nisbett's little shop rather than entered it, for he was massive in all directions, with the growling, damn-your-eyes-sir joviality of a Hessian colonel.

"Sure, I've heard of you," Ed said respectfully. "All those great beats on Third Reich stuff. I was reading the overseas edition of the *London Clarion* in college—you're the one got me hooked on the period."

"Good show," Julian Boordale shouted. "Too kind, trust a Yank to flatter one, do call me Jack!" The chair creaked when he flung himself into it, his piggy eyes cooler than his manner.

"I can't believe it, *you* reading *me*, picking up on that item in *Militaria Monthly*."

"And *Bygone Wars*, current issue," the journalist smirked. "I read everything, old chum. Keeps me ahead of the pack, always has, always will."

He smacked his lips and rubbed his hands. "I'd be much obliged for a sight of this photographic evidence you snapped up. *Bygone Wars* carried just the old smudgy little repro—could have been a black cat in a coal mine at midnight."

Obligingly, Ed unlocked a steel cabinet and gave Boordale the photographs. The big man needed no tutorial, poring over them raptly in a cloud of attention and Scotch. "These couldn't be fakes by any chance?"

Ed gaped at him. "Why—no. I don't see how. The seller didn't know what she had, and neither did her husband, who was sitting on them from nineteen forty-five. I'm sure they're genuine."

Boordale guffawed. "Just pulling your leg, laddie. Quite a story, you know. I could start earth tremors in Bonn with these."

"Okay, have your fun, Jack. I still won't sell these cheap."

"My dear fellow." Boordale, his face comically grave, wagged a sausage finger. "The joking's over. Upon my word, I'm serious." The sausage tapped the nearest photograph. "Know who this chappie was?"

"Udo Hoffrich," Ed replied promptly. "He made the news in the early sixties, but he's dead and gone. Almost died in nineteen forty-two, he claimed, and was an invalid for years. Inherited money, made more, got to be one of the richest of West Berlin's new-rich. Tried to score in politics."

"And came unstuck," Julian Boordale roared. "Commies started shoutin' Hoffrich was a war criminal, served in the armored column that razed a French village. 'Pack of lies,' Udo said, but his discharge records and paybook were missing, ditto the documentation on the massacre lads he always denied serving with. Lots of smoke, no real fire—but enough to roast his political debut to a crisp."

"It was his word against his accusers, the eastern side of the Berlin Wall. They claim he re-enlisted around nineteen forty-three under a cover name, but his disfigurement gave him away to witnesses of the massacre they couldn't produce. A classic smear. —Only I've proved it was true." Ed shrugged. "So what? It's history, not headlines."

Boordale fanned the photographs like a poker hand and grinned sharkishly. "Hoffrich is dead, *but his son's very much alive and kickin'*."

Ed was listening.

"Udo Junior surmounted the sixties scandal by sheer ability and drive. A born administration man, a power behind the scenes in Bonn. Now there's talk of him quitting the civil service, trying politics, launching a fresh Party. He could pull it off—if the scandal isn't revived." Smirking again, Boordale said softly, "Not that I'd want to do that—but the public has a right to know."

Out of his depth, Ed confessed, "I never knew he had a son. But so long after—would the old scandal matter?"

"Enough to make this story a valuable property. I'll level with you, chum. I came here on my own—the *Clarion's* good for one's prestige but the salary's laughable." He leaned forward. "I'm thinking of going into business for myself. This tale wouldn't raise the roof in England, but West Germany, France, Europe at large is a different kettle of fish." He guffawed. "Stinking fish! Anyway, I'll take a flier, buy these personally, write the story, syndicate the thing as a package."

Ed Nisbett wasn't totally ingenuous. "Fine. They're yours for five thousand."

"Have a heart! Good lord above, *I* might not make that much! The golden egg's all very well, old lad, but don't addle the blasted thing before it hatches."

"Four thousand pounds, then, or forget it." Ed gulped and twined his fingers.

Boordale rocked to and fro, growling thoughtfully. "Three, in cash. I can be back with it this afternoon. Got to—got to raid my piggy bank." He raised a warning sausage. "Ironclad contract, mark you. No more little articles—you keep your trap firmly shut. It might take me months to get syndication off the ground. A leak would ruin me. I want all the photographs. And while we're about it, I must know the seller's name and address—check the provenance for my own protection. Yours, too," he suggested unconvincingly.

"Done." Ed rummaged in a desk drawer. "She was a Mrs. Anglin. She replied to a classified ad I placed in some southwestern weeklies. I have the letter somewhere . . ."

Her gaze moistly bright, Melanie faltered. "You 'n me, theater, French grub and all that? A likely tale—pull the other one, mate."

Ed Nisbett tapped his inside pocket. "I struck it rich, as promised. Work together, celebrate together." He slapped a plump envelope into her hand. "Find a pretty dress, shoes, the works. Get your hair fixed, have a manicure. Bring back a cent of change and I'll break your neck."

Overwhelmed, frightened by her vulnerability, she felt obliged to be offensive, insulting. "You are a bloody Yank, after all. Think you can buy me."

"I'm Canadian," he reminded her. He attempted a leer. "Nothing I bought could be as good as anything you care to give me."

Melanie blushed fetchingly. "Get you!"

"All in good time you may. I'll meet you at the Ritz on Piccadilly, the lobby, seven sharp tonight. Now scat—I must meet with a guy first. More business."

Until opening his mouth, Captain Hobart Willard Porter, U.S.N. (Retd.), might have been mistaken for a Home Counties squire up in Town for the day. He was a Bostonian, which helped, and enjoyed masquerading in tweeds and Mayfair-lasted brogues.

They sat in Regents Park, not all that far from the embassy on Grosvenor Square—it had given Captain Porter his excuse for being in London—with a mosque showing incongruously in the middle distance. Tilting his square face up at the sunlight, Porter said: "You look chipper, son. I told you this would hardly be work at all. More like therapy. Better than moping around in a military hospital waiting on that leg to mend."

Ed waited for more, absently rubbing his moustache.

"No problem over your cover?" Captain Porter's tone anticipated the answer.

Smiling diffidently, Ed observed, "It's funny about Brits, sir. Americans stir them up—either pro or anti, they take notice of us. But for some reason they find Canadians very ho-hum."

"And it helps that there's a real Ed Nisbett around your age who's Canadian and in a Thai jail," Captain Porter added dryly, "under another name, to protect his family reputation, handing us your cover on a platter." The older man nodded briskly. "You did just fine, Ed. Julian Boordale's a stooge for the Soviets but you must have worked that out for yourself. Two hours after he bought those photographs, they were at the Czech embassy. The Czechos do a lot of disinformation stuff on behalf of the KGB."

Glossily sure of itself, a pompous London pigeon strutted over to inspect his brogues. Captain Porter spoke sourly. "All the Iron Curtain embassies, consulates, and trade delegations in London could run an Indy 500 on their own, the amount of drivers they carry on their books. One of those drivers admires England so much he pretends to be a Brit now and then. He visited with Major Anglin's widow recently, posing as a member of the ex-service organization here, Royal British Legion. They had a nice visit, lots of talk of old times."

"And," Ed guessed aloud, "Mrs. Anglin confirmed that she sold me the photographs her husband collected and kept safe and untouched for forty years."

"Right. Truth, with a tad of deception, makes the best lie."

"The Wizard sure does good work," Ed mused. "By the time he got through I couldn't tell Major Anglin's original pictures from the new fakes."

Captain Porter, sunning himself, was benign. "Langley has the facilities, son. Even came up with German photographic paper matching the period stuff. And The Magician says it's easier to rig convincing prints than negatives."

Sensing that Ed wanted to know what the operation had been about, Porter turned dismissive. "You can return to duty soon. We were lucky to find you. Spending time in Canada as a kid meant you could pass for a Canuck. And you were into War Two history—"

Need to know, thought Captain Porter. Ed Nisbett was discreet. It had been drummed into him that what amounted to a long recuperative furlough in London had never happened and must not be discussed. It would be easier yet for the young fellow knowing less than half the story.

Julian Boordale had not lied about Udo Hoffrich's son being a born administrator. But the tale of young Hoffrich running for office was bushwah, Boordale's excuse for showing interest in the dangled bait.

Hoffrich had more power than some elected politicians as it was, and could well rise to gain more. In democracies, permanent officials need not woo the voters to achieve clout. Certain of Captain Porter's friends in Bonn were alarmed over secret information indicating an outside-edge chance that Udo Hoffrich, Jr., was working for East Germany— meaning that the Kremlin might be pulling his strings. But Hoffrich couldn't be challenged directly. There had been too many such scandals in the past decade. In any case, Bonn would rather be aware of a traitor than expose him—and worry over the successor.

The situation had stimulated Porter, appealing to his game-playing side. The Soviets were always eager to discredit the Bonn regime, preferably through anti-Nazi scandals. If Hoffrich was exactly what he seemed, and not in their power, then spectacular evidence against his stormy-petrel father would be too much to resist. On the other hand, if Hoffrich was their man the Easterners would do their utmost to protect him by securing that same evidence, and destroying or burying it. Porter had handed them a dagger, perilously sharp. Revival of the war-crime slur against his father would not only sideline Hoffrich's career but might cause an already shaky government to fall. Things were that volatile in West Germany at the moment.

Yes, Captain Porter gloated inwardly, a dagger: and whether its new owners sheathed the weapon or unleashed it would answer Bonn's question about Udo Hoffrich.

An extreme test of loyalty on the surface, with Hoffrich suffering, whatever the decision.

Surfaces,brooded Captain Porter, were highly deceptive. Should the Soviets and their Liepzig clients launch the Hoffrich scandal, it would boomerang on them. Because four years after Udo Hoffrich's death, his wartime hospital records had surfaced among captured documents in a Washington archive. A U.S. military team had confiscated personal letters from Field Marshal Rommel, "The Desert Fox," to his beloved wife in 1945. Time had passed, the family protested, attitudes and enmities changed. Washington had been genuinely willing to return the letters. But they'd vanished. Only to be found by chance—not hidden, simply wrongly filed under E-for-Erwin, Rommel's first name and the signature on the letters, instead of under R, where they had been searched for in vain.

Well, no matter. Udo Hoffrich, Sr.'s hospital dossier, complete with weekly notes on therapy, medication, and progress, proved beyond doubt that the man had been a genuine invalid for the latter half of the war and never been near France in a wheelchair, far less a tank.

But the dossier's discovery had never been made public and not even Hoffrich's son knew it still existed. Experts, Porter among them, had advised against releasing the material. Why, they argued, disprove an ancient smear—and give West Germany's enemies a fresh chance to revive the scandal? The response was obvious: Sure, one old soldier has been cleared, but how many more are still flourishing undetected?

"No," Captain Porter snapped, puzzling Ed.

If the faked phototgraphs were used against Hoffrich, then the crucial hospital file would be released. The Magician hadn't just rigged the photographs but booby-trapped them with tiny clues to their falsity, which could be pointed out if need be.

And the KGB would be caught out, the world had a right to assume, in yet another clumsy bid to embarrass the West.

The old man rose stiffly. "Sorry, son, but you'd better stay in place, running that store, for another few weeks. It would look suspicious if you decamp as soon as Boordale buys that stuff for his bosses. But a month from now, if you vanish, they'll believe you're quitting while you're ahead, before you can go bust from lack of business."

Surfaces can be deceptive. As far as Captain Porter could make out, his agent was resigned but not especially thrilled at staying in place. Which figured.

Ed, thinking about his date with Melanie and wondering how her Iron Curtain-financed transformation would turn out, echoed neutrally, "Another few weeks." He squared his shoulders and nodded dutifully. "I guess I can handle that, sir."

Robert P. Mills
Jack Hughes

The forecast had been for only a little snow, maybe two or three inches, but as Chief of Police David Bain looked out on his fair village of Bickenton he wondered. The temperature was just over twenty degrees and the snow was coming down so thickly that he could just barely make out Baird's General Store across the green. And the wind, while not exactly howling, was whistling. It could mean work for him, he thought—cars tended to skid and bump into things under these conditions.

As he watched, a heavily bundled-up figure carrying a sack came out of Baird's door and, head lowered against the wind, began walking toward the chief's headquarters. Now "headquarters" was perhaps a tad grandiose as a description of his small office, he admitted to himself, not the sort of police headquarters one saw on television. In fact, he didn't even have a jail cell. When he nabbed a felon, he called the State Police and they sent a trooper in a cruiser to pick up his prisoner.

As the figure drew closer, the chief recognized Paul Richards, the new cook, or chef as he called himself, at The Corner—and a pretty good cook he was, the chief thought. Maybe not exactly the French cuisine Paul described it as being, though—Paul put on airs, but he'd left his native country as a boy and his French consisted mainly of familiar words and phrases such as *merveilleux, c'est vrai, formidable*, and the occasional *merde!*, and his boeuf bourguignon tasted suspiciously more like goulash than the French dish. But he was a nice fellow, and it was pretty good goulash, too. Paul was obviously on his way to work now, and just maybe there'd be some of that good goulash tonight.

The ringing phone took the chief away from the window. It turned out to be Fred Hicks on the desk at State Police headquarters, which was about twenty miles away, calling to say that snow was on the way.

"Already got it, Fred," the chief said. "Think it will last long?"

"They say not, but the way it's coming down now you could have some problems on the road. I thought you ought to know."

"Anything important happens you'll be the first to know, Fred, and I thank you for calling."

Nice to have those guys there, the chief thought, even if he didn't have to call on them often.

When the phone rang again right away, it was Max Charlton, calling to ask if the chief thought it was safe to drive up to Laketown. "Probably is, Max, if you go slow," the chief advised. "That's only fifteen miles, and this snow is supposed to stop pretty soon. But put on your headlights."

Since there wasn't much he could do out there right now, the chief

47

put his feet up on the desk and picked up a new John D. MacDonald.
The man had some pretty good gimmicks in his books, stuff that might
come in handy one day.

Half an hour later the phone rang again, and once more it was Max.

"I'm calling from The Corner, Chief. There's been an accident—Paul
Richards got hit by a car on his way to work. He seems to be hurt pretty
bad—the ambulance is on the way. Bill Crosby found him and brought
him here. I've suggested he wait here until you come over. All right?"

The chief was immediately his efficient self. "I'll be right there," he
said crisply.

Crosby seemed badly shaken when the chief arrived. "It was terrible,
finding Paul on the side of the road all twisted and almost unconscious.
The ambulance guy said there are some broken bones, but he couldn't
tell for sure what else might be wrong."

"Well now, Bill, why don't you just tell me what you know?"

"He was just on the other side of the bridge, almost here. When I
stopped, he was just barely conscious. All he said was a name, Hughes.
Jack Hughes, I think—or maybe Zack Hughes. And then he passed out.
So I hefted him up as carefully as I could and brought him here."

"You're sure it was Hughes he said?"

"It was Hughes all right. Zack or Jack Hughes. But I never heard of
anyone by that name around here."

"A stranger to me, too," the chief said, puzzled. "Think I'll call Fred
Hicks, see if the State Police know him."

He came back from the phone a few minutes later and said, "They're
checking on it. I think I'll go up to the Bridge Cafe, see if Bertha or Dusty
know that name. Those two know some people around here I never
heard of."

If there was one place in the village of Bickenton where crime took
place on a regular basis, Chief Bain thought, it was surely the Bridge
Cafe. On the other hand, it was a warm and pleasant place to be, and he
didn't remember ever having made an arrest there.

The door from the street led directly to the bar.

"Chief!" Dusty Cram's voice was loud enough to be heard on the
other side of the partition dividing the bar from the dining area where
the pool table was, which was a good thing because there might well be
criminal activity going on at that very moment and the chief didn't want
to know about it. In his opinion it was perfectly natural for high-spirited
young men, and older ones for that matter, to wager a beer on the outcome of a game of eight ball or nine ball, and he surely didn't want to
take action against that kind of illegal activity.

"Mighty good to be here," the chief said in an equally loud voice.
"It's kicking up a storm out there and that wind is *cold*. Can you spare
me a cup of coffee so I can warm up these figures enough for a quick
game of eight ball before I have to go back out?"

Dusty was a sort of all-around right hand to Bertha, the owner—waiter, part-time bartender, potato slicer, you name it. And a nice young fellow, in the chief's opinion, even if his hair did stick up at all angles.

"No problem at all, Chief. I'll bring it to you out back."

"I thank you. Oh, one thing. Do you know a fellow around here by the name of Hughes? Jack Hughes—or maybe Zack Huhges?"

"I've never heard the name—but I'll ask Bertha when I get your coffee."

The chief nodded gratefully and went off around the partition to see what was happening. To his surprise, Tony Charlton was there, starting a game of eight ball with Jim, from Duke's Hardware.

"Tony. I didn't know you were an athlete."

Tony looked a touch abashed. "I'm not, really, but Jim is trying to teach me."

"Well, now, if he should happen to beat you, maybe he'd play me a game, give me some pointers."

It was Jim's turn to be surprised. "I didn't know you played, Chief. But now I think about it, you've got the look of a hustler."

Dusty brought the chief his coffee and said, "Bertha never heard of that Hughes guy, either, Chief."

"Thanks for asking her, Dusty." He turned to Tony and Jim. "Did either of you fellows ever hear of a Zack or Jack Hughes?" He noticed a tall, lean older man leaning against a pillar, sipping on a beer. "How about you, Professor—know anybody named that at the university?" The professor taught at a nearby branch of the state university.

The professor shook his head. "A stranger to me," he said, adding, "I must say I agree with Jim—you could be a hustler. I base that on your appearance, which is gratuitously honest-looking. A good hustler is a man who in no way resembles the sort of person who might be suspected of hiding his skills to the end of bilking his opponents. On the other hand, knowing you as I do, I tend to doubt that you could find it in you to embark on a course of deliberate deception for purposes of self-enrichment. I might add though, that I have erred in such judgments."

"A hustler? Me? I'm a man of the law, and we lawmen don't hustle."

"I begin to wonder, Chief," the professor said thoughtfully. "What you should have said, of course, is 'A hustler! I?' Your deliberate violation of the rules of grammar, with which a man of your education is surely familiar, strikes me as suspicious."

"Are you hiding the fact that you're good with words, Chief?" Tony sounded genuinely impressed. "I wouldn't be surprised. I read a detective story the other day where the detective solved the case because he knew words so well—and you've been a pretty good solver around here, you've got to admit."

"Just done my job is all," the chief said. "How did your detective solve his case?"

"A rich man was murdered on his Long Island estate and he had two nephews, one of whom had certainly done it. They were both short and blondish, looked a lot alike, but they were very different. One read books, was shy with girls, and liked opera. The other read only stuff with pictures of girls, and loved girls and dancing and musical comedies. There was some evidence that it was probably the second guy and a witness who casually knew both nephews said he'd seen one of them in a restaurant in the New York theater area the night of the murder and later assumed he had to be guilty of the murder because the other nephew had been in Boston.

"The detective asked the witness exactly what he had observed in the restaurant. The man said he'd overheard the young man say to his date, both apparently having come from a Broadway show, 'Ah, her "Londonderry Air"—*c'était magnifique!*' A police sergeant said that it must have been the first fellow because the second fellow would never appreciate the 'Londonerry Air.' But the detective disagreed: the first nephew probably would not have been in a restaurant with a girl in the first place, he said, and in the second, a new show *Montmartre Girls*, had just opened that night, starring Vanessa Lovejoy, a marvelously built British siren. What the witness had probably overheard was the second nephew speaking of the glorious Vanessa's magnificent London *derrière.* Probably making an intentional pun."

The professor looked at Tony clinically. "That's rather ingenious, I'd say. The two would sound very much alike, I should think. Though I teach English, not French."

"But you do teach your students French writers, Professor," the chief said. "You've told me a lot about Emile Zola, and how he got involved in the Dreyfus case."

"That's true, but I read him in translation. Chief, I heard you say you couldn't stay long. Why don't you and I play a quick game of nine ball? Tony and Jim haven't started their game yet and I'll put up a quarter for them to play when we're done."

Tony and Jim agreed to that, and the professor won the lag and broke the balls. He sank nothing, but he left the chief in a bad spot. The #1 ball was right in front of a pocket, but the cue ball was at the other end of the table and there were a couple of other balls in between. "I thought this was going to be a friendly game," the chief said plaintively.

"What he has to do," Jim explained to Tony, "is hit the one ball before he hits any other ball. Any ball that goes in after that lets him go on shooting, always hitting the lowest-number ball on the table first. If his misses the one ball, or doesn't sink a ball, the professor gets his turn. Whoever sinks the nine ball wins."

"He doesn't have much of a chance, does he?" Tony asked.

"Thank you for pointing that out, Tony," the chief said. "But maybe if I just sort of close my eyes something good may happen." He squinted down at the one ball and stroked deftly, jumping the cue ball over the intervening balls and hitting the one ball, sinking it in a corner pocket. The cue ball bounced off the one onto the cushioin and caromed off the cushion into the nine ball, pushing it into another corner pocket, ending the game with the first shot.

"How did he do that!" Tony exclaimed.

"Well now," the chief said, "it was all set up so that all I had to do was hit the one ball and everything just sort of fell in place after that."

"Pretty louche, if you ask me," the professor said.

"Loosh? How much of that beer have you had, Professor?" The chief was obviously worried about the professor driving home in his condition.

"Chief, I said louche, which is spelled *l-o-u-c-h-e*. It's a word, originally French, which means of suspicious or disreputable character.'

"Well now, I never said I hadn't played the game before, and furthermore I wasn't betting. And now I've got to get back to headquarters—I'm expecting an important call."

Unfortunately, when he did get his call from Fred it gave him no help. There was no Jack or Zack Hughes known by the State Police in any of the surrounding towns.

As the chief sat low in his chair with his feet up on the desk—a position he figured helped the blood get to his brain—Max Charlton came in. "Working late, Chief? I stopped by to let you know I called the hospital and it looks like Paul's going to make it okay, though he's still unconscious."

"I'm mighty glad to hear that, Max—and thank you for coming by. I been sitting here thinking on whether it was an accident or deliberate. It could easily have been a car that skidded after hitting a bump or a pothole and Paul just happened to be in the wrong place. But why did he say a name then, as though he knew who had hit him and maybe thought it was on purpose?" The chief shook his head. "It's louche, as the professor would say."

"Loosh? Lush? You're not putting me on, are you, Chief?"

"Nope. Don't have time for games. Come to think of it, though, it's a little like a story your son Tony told me, about a detective who solved a case because he realized that what a witness overheard could be interpreted two ways. Just goes to show it's a good idea to have an open mind, think about all the possibilities." He pulled his feet off his desk and stood up. As he reached for his coat he said, "I think I've go me an idea, Max. I'll see you around."

Oh his way home that night, Chief Bain stopped off at the Charlton place. It turned out Tony and Andy had stopped there, too, to get a bite to eat before they went to their own place. The chief had thought more than once that Nancy Charlton spoiled her two kids rotten. Having food around for them all the time gave them no incentive to find nice girls of their own, girls of the sort they could marry and who could give them kitchens of their own to come home to. Not, however, business of the law, he reminded himself.

"Hi, there," Andy said. "I hear you've got a mystery on your hands."

"Well, I did have, but it's all solved now. And seeing as how your father was around when it happened, I thought I'd stop by to tell him about it."

"Nancy," Max said in that comfortable way of his, "why don't we offer this man a drink on a cold night? It's a little louche that he would stop by like this if he didn't have something for himself in mind."

"Max, have you been drinking behind my back?" Nancy asked sharply.

"Not behind your back, dear," Max told her. "And I'll explain that funny-sounding word later. Why don't you get the chief a beer while he tells us what's been going on?"

"A small one, Nancy, if it's no trouble," the chief said. "Though why *you* should get it when you have all these able-bodied males around I don't understand." He hesitated. "I keep being surprised by all the things I don't understand. Like tonight—it took Tony to tell his detective story and the professor to confuse me with a new word to make me suddenly remember what the professor once told me about Emile Zola, which is what solved this case."

"*My* story helped you?" Tony asked, glowing some.

"It contributed, it contributed." The chief was always a courteous man. "The point is, I was thinking about how easy it was to misinterpret words we hear and I suddenly remembered what the professor had told me about the Dreyfus case and the book Emile Zola wrote about it. It was called *J'accuse*, and the way the professor pronounced it, when I thought about it back in my office, sort of sounded like 'Jack Hughes.' And I had it. What Bill thought he heard Paul say was really '*J'accuse*,' and what Paul was doing was accusing Bill of hitting him. When I went to see Bill and put it to him, he admitted that was what had happened."

"Bill!" Nancy was unbelieving. "But he wouldn't hurt a fly!"

"Well now, he couldn't help it. He said his car hit a bump and slid just far enough to hit Paul. He got right out and did everything he could to help Paul, but he couldn't help wanting to stay out of trouble. When I pointed out there were going to be medical expenses which his insurance should cover, he agreed he'd done a dumb thing without thinking, which is a kind of human behavior I run into quite a lot. In fact, Andy, I seem to remember a time with George Banks when *you* were a little slow about accepting responsibility."

"Well, maybe I did kid around a little too much."

"That you did, my boy. And while you're up, maybe you'd like to save your mother a little trouble and get me the rest of this beer."

"I think maybe you're getting to be a women's libber, Chief," Nancy said happily. "Jack Hughes!"

And thus justice once more was done in the fair village of Bickenton.

Ernest Savage
Tillie, the Ex-Con

She sat down at my table in Sheldon's Restaurant and announced in a wall reaching voice, "I'm Tillie Emerson." I'd never seen her before, nor heard the name.

Sheldon's serves the best Irish stew in the city of San Francisco. But Irish stew is a common man's dish and this stiff-backed uncommon old doll jarred the smoky blue-collar air. Spoons paused in midair, heads swiveled.

I was miffed. I hate being disturbed at the trough, even by a friend.

"And you," she added, "are Sam Train."

I neither denied nor affirmed. I buttered a slab of warm, fresh-that-morning sourdough bread and edged it into the littoral of the bowl. You take Sheldon's stew at a just-so heat. Pause and the moment's lost. Ask any gourmet, or gourmand, most particularly: eating alone, undisturbed by talk, is the essence of the art.

"Your ad in the Yellow Pages," she thundered on, "your *minimal* ad in the Yellow Pages, offers only an answering-service number. No personal phone or address."

I said nothing, the moment fleeting. Then I took time to say, "Have some stew—on me if you don't talk."

"Talk," she said, "is the *sine qua non* of human intercourse," and then blushed at the echo of the word she'd used.

Tillie Emerson. I looked up at her from behind the edge of my bowl. She carried 65 years if a day. On top of her coiled white hair was a Buster Keaton type hat made of black straw. She had large, blue-violet, heavy-lidded eyes and those Garboesque cheekbones that carry beauty unimpeached to the very depths of the grave.

"And, I might add, an *incompetent* answering-service. Seven times I phoned, seven times nothing happened. What do they do, advise you once a month of your calls? Or is the incompetence yours?"

"Yes, mine." I hoped she'd go away.

"I doubt that," she said, somewhat less stiffly. "You were highly recommended to me."

"By whom?"

"May Phelps. You recall the name?"

I did, clearly, and looked up again. "She's in the women's jug at Corona. She has been for three or four years and will be for three or four more."

"We don't call it the women's jug, Mr. Train. We call it the Women's Facility."

"We?"

"Its resident population."

"Of which—?"

"Yes. Of which I was one until five days ago. I am presently on parole, a condition I resent almost as much as honest incarceration."

I smiled. "Whatever it was that you did," I said, "you really didn't do, right?"

"Awkwardly expressed," she snapped, "but correct. I was accused of embezzling one hundred and twenty-seven thousand dollars. I didn't do it. I want you to—"

"May Phelps did," I said, mopping up gravy with a slab of bread. "Only a lot more than a hundred and twenty-seven grand."

"I know. And she admired your tenacity and wit in proving that she did. She's a good loser. I'm not. I want you to help me prove my case."

No. I'm on a case now. That's why I don't respond to calls. Maybe next week, Miss Emerson. It is Miss, isn't it?"

She nodded brusquely. "I can't wait that long, Mr. Train."

"There are dozens of private investigators in the phonebook. I can recommend at least—"

"No! I want you!" Her wide-spaced eyes were dark with fury. This was a familiar syndrome: jailhouse ideas—and hopes—are carved in stone. To tamper with them breaks their perfect whole, kills them dead.

Eddie Conners, the waiter, appeared at my side. Eddie has had a dime-size gravy stain in the same place on his white shirt for five years. I think his laundry puts it there for him. Eddie is also an ex-con and the impulse to make introductions was hard to quell. He asked me if I wanted more stew and I told him no, but to bring a couple of coffees.

It's possible she hadn't been aware of Eddie's intrusion. She leaned far forward across the table and delivered a sotto voce message: "I can pay you very, very well, Mr. Train. In *cash*."

"That has no significance, Tillie. I pay my taxes."

"I will *triple* your usual fee!" She snatched out of her purse a fat roll of bills in a rubber band and dropped it in the middle of the table. My big hairy hand covered it with the speed of light, but not fast enough. What is it about money? Heads had swiveled again, cutlery stopped in midflight.

"That," I growled, "was a damn fool thing to do, and you still warm from stir." I shoved the roll back across the table and she returned it to her purse, chin stiff with angry hauteur. "Never expose more than a buck at a time in a joint like this, Tillie. In a *town* like this. It will surely fetch you a knock on the head."

She stood up with a rattle of her chair and I said, "Where you going?"

"Home!"

"Take a cab. I'll have Eddie call one."

"I'll walk, thank you."

"Oh, hell!" I put money on the table and followed her out the door to Van Ness. She turned north and I caught her by the arm. "Where's home?"

"I have a room on Kearny near Broadway."

"That's a dozen blocks, for God's sake." A cab cruised by and I hailed it but missed.

"Never mind," she said. "I enjoy walking."

She was past arguing with and I wondered how long she'd been in the Corona "facility" and how erratic her behavior would be. Getting out is as big a trauma as getting in. "How'd you find me?" I said. "I mean tonight."

"I discovered where you lived. May told me what you looked like and when you came out of your apartment building this evening, I followed you. *Your* sort of thing, Mr. Train, when you deign to work."

"How long were you in?"

"Four years, ten months, and seven days."

They always answer with precision, sometimes with pride. "For something you didn't do."

"Exactly. For something Arnold Farnhorst did."

"Who?"

"Arnold Farnhorst, of Farnhorst and Gray, the importers."

"You recite that name as though you expect me to know it."

She stopped in her tracks. "You mean you don't?"

"Should I?"

"On Sutter Street a half block up from Powell. Oriental objets d'art. Since 1853."

"Sorry," I said. "Not my line of country. But if you know who did it, how come you need me?"

"To help me persuade him to confess, to clear my name."

"Break his arm, you mean."

"May said you were clever and inventive. That seems neither to me." She'd resumed her long-strided pace. We had crossed Washington Street and turned right on Jackson.

"But it has," I suggested, "its appeal."

"No, not at all. Arnold and I were lovers for twenty-seven years, Mr. Train."

"Huh?" She stopped and looked at me. "I'm sorry. You surprised me."

"You think I'm incapable of—"

"No, no way! I think you're a dish— but, Lord God, what happened?"

She resumed our walk. "Arnold, who is the third Farnhorst to bear that name, was—and no doubt still is—a desperately hag-ridden man, the hag being his mother. She's still alive, so I've learned."

Two darkling types eyed us as we passed a shadowed door—but decided against. The old frisson scurried up my back, but Miss Tillie Emerson, free at last, and walking, remained oblivious. "Arnold," she went on, "is precisely my age, which shall remain our shared secret. He's a scholar, an expert in Oriental culture and art. He's an innocent—and I mean that in its least pejorative sense. He—'' She fell silent for a quarter of a block.

"He what?"

"He wanted to marry me. *We* wanted to marry from the first. But Cecile, his mother, was adamantly against it. I was at that time a clerk in the store. I became good at that and ultimately good at the business end, but I had the wrong antecedents, to conjoin the Emerson line with the Farnhorst. Disgusting rot, of course. The first Arnold Farnhorst pirated most of the wares he and Gray opened the store with, and I've yet to hear of anyone named Ralph Waldo Farnhorst."

I laughed.

She stopped again. "You don't take me seriously."

"No, I do. Please carry on." I took her arm and we strode through another cunning stretch of street.

"Five years ago," she said, "Arnold took one hundred and twenty-seven thousand dollars from the business account, went to Reno, and lost it all in three days."

"Wow!"

"Wow indeed. It was a breakdown, Mr. Train, a morale collapse. He is generally honest to a fault, but I had issued an ultimatum a few days before—either marry me now, this week, or we're through. Arnold couldn't handle it. He went to his mother, but she merely bludgeoned him in her usual way. And—well, that was it. Arnold broke like a reed. After Reno he went into a rest home somewhere up in the hills, and not much later I went to jail. Arranged, of course."

"How arranged?"

"Oh, so simply. I was by this time office manager, well enough paid—it's a very lucrative business—but nevertheless clearly living over my head in a deluxe apartment secretly subsidized by Arnold. The rent statement was presented in court. Moreover, I made a bad mistake—"

"What?"

"In my innocence, I defended myself and opted for a non-jury trial. I thought that any fair-minded judge would dismiss the whole crazy thing in a minute. But—need I go on?"

"No."

"But," she said, going on anyway, "he was part of the old-boy circuit, his progenitors Forty-niners, too. And I did a very poor job of defending myself, merely proclaiming my innocence over and over again."

"And maybe," I suggested, "laying off Arnold?"

A quarter block later she said, "Yes, laying off Arnold."

"Do you still love him, Tillie?"

Through my arm, now linked with hers, I could feel the shudder. "No—my God, no."

"But twenty-seven years—"

"No, no, no! He's a weakling! He's a—" Words failed her as we turned left onto Kearny.

She lived in a dive. At the scabrous street-door of the building, I said, "Here?"

"I've taken it only by the week, Mr. Train. And it's furnished."

Kearny was alive and noisy at this early evening hour, people on the move. A half block away, Broadway—"Sex Street West"— was gearing up for its nightly pickpocket trade. A long dreary whore of a street. I've been there often, worked there often, found people there who didn't want to be found—and a few who desperately did. It could be that the seventeen-year-old girl I sought now—my present case—was there, hoping to be taken home and loved again. Or hoping to die, maybe, and be done with it. You never know.

"You have a fiery look in your eye," Tillie told me.

I'd been staring north at the cascading lights, bemused by our hunger for the mud, the need to sell ourselves cheap, the persistence of that gaudy, fleshly marketplace in every town in every land. "With my cosmic eraser," I said, "I would expunge the whole flaming thing—but it would resurrect itself tomorrow somewhere else."

She smiled at my glum fervor. She was wearing an ancient tweed suit, too long in the skirt, lumpy around the shoulders, plus that Buster Keaton hat. She had no sense of style, but she had enough innate class to put me and the town to shame.

"How come," I grumbled, "you picked this dump to live in? And don't give me that 'furnished' bit."

"It's near to where the Farnhorsts live. On Telegraph Hill. I can walk there in fifteen minutes."

"You've called on them, have you?"

"Not yet. I had thought to recruit your aid first."

"I'm presently hired—as I told you. Next week maybe. What's your hurry?"

"Because Cecile Farnhorst might die at any moment. She's eighty-eight as of last month."

"I don't understand."

"I want them *both* to clear my name. I want them *both* to confess."

"And then what, Tillie?"

She hadn't thought past that. In the buttoned-up jailhouse world, that was all she wanted, to clear her name, to get this awkward monkey off her back. An end, not a beginning.

"Why bother?" I said. "Forget it. Your time in the can is gone. It was unjust, so what? So are most parking tickets" Her face looked set. "How much money in that obscene roll of yours?" I snapped.

"Two thousand dollars. Why?"

"Where'd you get it?"

"From my savings account. It's been running all the time."

"Forget the Farnhorsts, Tillie. Get a job—get on with your life!"

"You're angry," she said, "at something other than me. I won't ask what." She touched my arm lightly. "But thanks for seeing me home, Mr. Train. I quite clearly understand that if you hadn't I could now be in some gutter with a broken head and no purse. Surely I owe you something."

"Yes, two things. Two promises. First thing in the morning put that money back in the bank. And second, find a new place to live."

She looked solemn. "I promise."

The girl's name was Evangeline, and she hated it. She hated the "angel" part in the middle—this isn't an age for angels, she said. Her maternal grandparents were retired missionaries. They'd chosen the name seventeen years ago, and they were footing the bill for me to find her now and return her to home, hearth, and redemption. At home was an alcholic mother and a disabled father who beat them both with his crutch now and again.

I found her the Wednesday following the Thursday I'd met Tillie Emerson. That afternoon she'd bought a new Datsun four-wheel-drive pickup truck, an off-the-road vehicle. The salesman told me she paid cash and where she lived. The salesman thought I was a cop because I was one for nineteen years and still look like one. It's a useful wound sometimes.

I had a Polaroid color shot of Evangeline given me by her grandfather nine days ago. Her grandfather had spent most of his missionary years in Central America and it had worn the flesh off his bones. He didn't wear his clerical collar at our meeting, but he didn't need to. He looked like a cleric the way I look like a cop. He was full of holy fire and lusted to snatch his granddaughter back from the clutch of the Devil—who resides in San Francisco. I began to understand the alcoholic daughter, about whom he'd spoken almost with pleasure—an in-house case to redeem.

The family lived in a small town in one of the counties north of the Bay where cannabis sativa is the richest cash crop. He didn't mention that, but he probably realized I would know—it's wide-spread news.

Her picture was good enough so that when I showed it to the right people they usually said, "Oh, yeah, that's Vangy." No last name. In the subculture of the desperate nomadic young, nobody has, needs, or wants a last name. She'd been missing from home for nine weeks and Gramps knew that time was running out. He'd tried the usual channels to no avail. He was a hunched-over, crabbed sort of man and took my fee, one thumbed bill at a time, from a leather snaptop purse that was surely as old as the shiny black alpaca suit he wore.

It surprised me. No crash-pad, this, but a clean, bright four-to-five-hundred-buck-a-month apartment out Sunset way, the Datsun tucked into the garage underneath.

I said "Vangy" at the door and she opened it, restrained by a chain. She'd expected somebody else and when she saw my face, the door started shut again but ran into my bricklike shoe. "Let me in," I said, "or we'll have to run down to the hardware store and get you a new chain."

She did, sighing, but not partcularly alarmed. The Polaroid hadn't done her justice. She was tall and slender. She had long dark-brown hair, intense brown eyes, and an oval face with the same high precious cheekbones Tillie had. She wore a smart new yellow pantsuit and a pale-green blouse. She looked at least five years older than her given age. Now she folded her arms and said, not really shaken, "Who are you? What do you want?"

"I could tell you," I said, "that I'm an IRS man and I'd like to see your latest income-tax statement. I could ask you where the nearly ten grand cash came from that you just bought the Datsun with, *and* those clothes, *and* this classy pad, but I won't because I think I know. Mary Jane."

She went and sat down on a folding chair alongside a card table, the only two items of furniture in the room. She still seemed composed, but there was fatigue in her eyes and an old established harried look.

"When did you rent this place, Evangeline?"

She shrugged. "Yesterday. What does it matter? Listen, Mister, in less than two months I'll be eighteen and you won't be able to touch me. You send me home today, I'll just come back tomorrow. Why bother?"

I'd trailed her through some of the dicier parts of town. Before her recent affluence she'd been on the bricks, a runaway, crashing here and there, but moving on fast, possibly untouched—I hoped, somehow, untouched. Which is the way she looked now—a worldly wise young woman, not an emotionally shredded kid. Yes, why bother? Except that now she was dealing dope.

"Humboldt County," I said, "where Mary Jane lives and prospers and makes a certain few rich. You wouldn't have a lid or two of pot around the place, would you, Vangy? I mean—just a sample?

"No."

"Not a user yourself, huh? I gathered as much over the past several days. Just a dealer, a middleman. So you made a deal. Some pals of yours back home grow the stuff and you find the buyers down here. A nice wholesome business for a high school kid, Evangeline."

"Please," she said, and turned her head aside.

"Oh, yes—you don't like your name, do you? Gramps told me. Gramps wants me to take you home, Vangy."

She closed her eyes. "I'd just come back again."

"To the pot business, Vangy? Dope?"

She drew her fingers across the long dark lashes of her eyes. They came away damp. She was tired. She'd been on a spending high. She was coming down now, she was living with herself again.

I said, "Was it a one-shot deal or are you committed down the line? Are you in the business, Evangeline, or not?"

"Not," she said.

"What about your buyer?"

"I'll never see him again. He scared me. I just want to get away from home." She was losing years and poise.

"What about your suppliers up north?"

"No." Her eyes glistened. "They're too scared to ever do it again. Like me."

"Yeah, I'm sure. So instead of buying a modest little Fiesta, or something suitable for, say, a future secretary, you buy this rugged off-the-road truck, suitable for pot-farming and other backwoods work. Come on, Vangy."

"I always wanted one," she whimpered, and cupped her face in her hands and cried like the kid she was.

What I wished then was that Gramps wasn't such a rod of steel.

At four-thirty I was back home. Normally at this hour on Wednesday, I meet Bill Grady at Nandino's and we liquefy our troubles in a small sea of gin, expertly served up by Marty, the world's number-one liquefaction man. But the stuff on my mind was beyond even his ever-expanding reach. At five to five, after a brisk mostly downhill walk, I opened a sculpted teakwood door and entered the arcane and expensive world of Farnhorst and Gray. A hint of jasmine, subtle as the first whiff of spring, met my nose. It set the tone: a man seriously shopping in this place should have his own private Brink's truck parked at the curb. Tillie had warned me.

A man approached through austere patches of light, tinted in Chinese tones, vermillion, green, ivory. "Sir," he said, neither a question nor a greeting. It was closing time and a big, lower-class hulk had intruded upon the moment. He put manicured fingers on a display case between us and summoned up a tardy smile. "Sir? May I help you?" Two questions.

"I would like to speak with Mr. Arnold Farnhorst," I said. "The Third, as I understand it."

His reaction surprised me. One of his hands flew up and rubbed his brow. "Ah—" he said, and stared at me for an uncommon length of time. In his eyes was fear. Always I am finding fear in people's eyes. "He—ah—" he blurted. "Isn't, ah, hasn't—"

"You mean he's not here."

"Ah—! Yes—yes."

"And hasn't been for a while. And you don't know why."

The two positive declarations steadied him. His world here amongst the treasures, I thought, was closed and serene. "How long," I asked soothingly, "since he's been here?"

"Since closing time last Friday," he said firmly, and it crossed my mind to ask if the office till had been hit again, but I didn't. "Sir—may I ask who you are?"

"You may." That established cop effect. "Have you tried his home?" I asked him.

"Yes, of course."

"And?"

"Well, sir, no answer."

"None at all?"

"None."

"Did you go there?"

It shocked him. "Oh, no, sir! Mr. Farnhorst made it perfectly clear years ago that none of the employees—"

"Mr. Farnhorst or his mother made it perfectly clear? They live together, don't they?"

"Well, yes, sir. His mother, actually, laid down the, ah, rule."

"What's their address?"

He recited a street name and a two-digit number. "On the Hill, sir. Telegraph Hill. A very old and lovely place."

"Then you *have* been there?"

"Yes, I have." He looked wistful. "When the old gentleman was still alive. A Christmas party for the staff."

I wondered where he went when he went home and who was waiting there. He had the air of a genteel servitor, a household slave, but he was an expert, no doubt, in this long slender room full of splendors— some possibly still of pirate provenance. If I'd had the odd thousand bucks at hand, I'd've bought one of the carved ivory trinkets displayed in the case between us. It would have made the last ten minutes of his day.

"Thank you," I said with respect.

It did nothing for him.

If you lived there, you drove into the three-car garage carved into the sheer face of the cliff that rose from the edge of the street. And then no doubt took an elevator to the level of the house proper. But if you merely wanted to visit, you walked an array of sixty or seventy redwood steps that doubled back on themselves twice to the front porch and door. There, you knocked on the door or rang the bell. I stopped on a landing halfway up and sank onto a bench that had probably prevented countless heart attacks.

After leaving Farnhorst and Gray's, I'd taken a cab to Tillie Emerson's Kearny Street address and been told by the Pakistani manager of the place that she'd checked out the Saturday before. As advised. Then I went to Nandino's and, late but willing, entered into that two or three Boodles martinis prelim, followed by the steak, baked potato, salad, and bottle of Napa Valley red main event that are the standard bouts on my Wednesday-night card with Bill Brady. Heavy cop food.

Bill is the only friend I've retained from my days on the force. He and I rode a squad car together for ten of my nineteen years and we know each other's heartbeats.

I discussed the runaway girl with him—what to do with her. A great deal of cop time these days is devoted to runaway girls and boys. He said mournfully, "Believe her when she says she'll only run away again if you turn her in. Gramps sounds like Jeremiah himself, and how many times would you put up with your old man whacking you with a crutch?''

"Once."

He reached for his glass of red, his face without expression.

"You're telling me what she needs," I said, "is a leg up and a friend."

"Isn't that what you wanted me to tell you?"

A few strenuous moments after regaining my breath on the Farn-horsts' halfway-house bench I was peering through the big, dimly-lit front window off the porch, your true private-eye. It looked like a mate to the Post Street store, a museum of Oriental art, but nothing stirred within the room and I stepped a few paces to my left and knocked hard on the massive front door.

It opened, and there before me stood Miss Tillie Emerson, in the same lumpy tweed suit she'd worn six days before. "Was that," I said, "issued you at Corona or have you had it in storage for the last thrity years?''

"Twenty years," she said. "Arnold bought it for me at I. Magnin twenty years ago. The clerk said it would last a lifetime."

I sighed. "Where's Arnold, Tillie?"

"Downstairs. You've come to help me, haven't you?" She was delighted. "Let me show you."

The elevator seemed to take twenty minutes to go from A to B, or possibly C. I didn't know it until then, but I'm painfully claustrophobic when encased in a small snail-paced room deep within the earth. When it finally clanked, wheezed, and whimpered to a halt and the accordion door shuddered open, I would have bought anything offered at any price to get out of there.

"This is the garage level," Tillie said. "Relax, Mr. Train. It is also the wine-cellar level, and the level where Arnold's father built his hideaway."

"Hideaway?"

"Den. Retreat. Sanctum sanctorum."

"A harried man, you said." I wiped my brow.

"Unbelievably harried. But he built a very cozy—fortress, you might say, behind that door there." She pointed at a metal-skinned firedoor set into a poured concrete wall with ten inches or so of space at the bottom. With righteous pride she said, "I have Arnold in there."

"Imprisoned?" I said. "In his own house? For God's sake, Tillie!"

She was impatient with me. "I told you," she said, "that I intended to have this out with Arnold and his mother. Last Friday morning I came here prepared to do just that—without your aid. I was let in by a day nurse hired to take care of Cecile, who is now senile. I dismissed the woman, who was as happy to leave here as I was to leave Corona. Even senile, Cecile is not easy to deal with."

"She knows you?"

"No. She's completely out of touch. Anyway, I had brought with me that combination lock you see on the door there and I waited down here for Arnold to get home. when he did, he went in there for his usual bottle of wine and I shut the door after him and snapped on the lock. He's been in there ever since, and when he signs the confession I slid under the door he can come out."

"*Tillie*, you simply cannot do—"

"Don't worry about him, Mr. Train. He has a comfortable bed in there and a full bath. He has one of the truly great San Francisco wine-cellars and a more than adequate library—his father was a great reader. As you can see, there's enough space under the door for me to slide him trays of food and the daily paper."

She was standing as straight as a West Point plebe, her eyes aflame. She had been wronged, and this was the way to right that wrong. Direct action. To hell with the devious course of the law, with its delays and treacherous traps.

I sighed, still damp and shaken from that endless elevator ride. "One of my obligations as a licensed PI," I said, "is to report any crime I happen to see in progress, and this is a crime in progress if ever there was one. Before this goes any further, Tillie, what's the combination to that lock?"

"You'll know when he signs the confession."

"What if he doesn't?"

"Then you'll never know." She was a rumpled pillar of moral indignation. And she was a beauty in that moment, this old concubine.

"Who's out there?" The question warped out from under the fortress door. "Tillie, who's out there? I hear a man's voice."

Tillie bent down and shouted, as over old-time long-distance, "Mr. Sam Train is out here. He knows all about what you did, Arnold. Sign the confession and I'll be very pleased to make the introductions. I think you'd like one another."

There was silence.

"Arnold," Tillie said, "*you* know you did it, *I* know you did it, and *Mr. Train* knows you did it. Make your peace with the Lord, the law, me, and him, Arnold. *Please.*"

There had been the affectionate worry in her voice of a mother pleading with a wayward son. She straightened up and I looked into her big violet eyes. The imprisoned man and she had been lovers for longer than most marriages last. "You love him," I said. "Isn't that the bottom line?"

She stared at me blankly.

"Tillie," I said, "listen. There's one tidy way to end all this. Marry him. I mean, that's what you wanted before he went astray, so—"

"My Lord!" she said, stiff-backed and stern-voiced again. "What in the world makes you think I'd marry a *common thief*?"

"And what makes *you* think," we heard from under the door, "that I'd marry an *ex-con*? Think about *that*, lady!"

A full minute's silence fell. Tillie's eyes widened as though this was fresh and pivotal news. "That's what I am, isn't it?" she said finally, and there was a touch of pride in her voice, as at a hard nut swallowed. "I mean, no matter how or why—that's what I am?"

"Willy nilly," I said, "that's what you are—and one of the finest."

And then we heard from under the door, "Tillie? Tillie, darling, listen. I really didn't mean to—I mean, mother—oh, pshaw!"

Darling? She hadn't been called that for years, and she beamed. "At least," she said, "he seems to know how to hold his wine, doesn't he, Mr. Train? Under the circumstances, that's something."

"Under the circumstances," I said, a natural winebibber myself, "it certainly is. He's been in there for what—four full days?"

"Five," she said, proud of him.

They were married on the Friday of the following week in the big front room. Arnold's mother had been placed in a home for the aged and I was denied the pleasure of meeting her. But I was conscripted as best man, at Tillie's insistence, and Arnold didn't cavil.

I took no fee from Tillie for my two or three hours' work on her behalf, but I brought Gramps' granddaughter to the wedding. There were a dozen other people in the room at the ceremony, but Tillie and the girl found an affinity almost at once. Well, who knows? Now and again you put people together the way chemists mix things in their labs. And then you stand back and see what happens.

Anthea Cohen
Dead of Night

The man still felt muddled in the head, strange, light, as if he were not lying on the bed, but suspended about a foot above it. Memory came flooding back to him from the drugged sleep. The outline of the doctor's face above him became less fuzzy as his eyes focused, but then it began to recede, then came back again. The man shook his head sharply as if to clear it. The doctor spoke. "Headache?"

The man heard his own voice answer. "No." Then, belatedly, "No, thank you."

Time seemed to be peculiarly mixed up. Either the doctor was taking a long time between questions or his memory was working in flashes. He felt confused, and heard again the crash, the splintering of glass. His new car had slewed on ice? Gravel? He didn't know, but it hit the tree, askew, bashing in the passenger-side door, flattening his wife on the seat beside him, turned half toward him, half leaning back— Oh, God! The top of the door seemed to have bashed into her head. He saw again her poor, blood-soaked face.

The sirens as the ambulance approached. The man in the green car who'd stood there, gesticulating—he must have stopped, seen the crash. The arrival in Emergency, the trolley with his wife's mutilated figure under a red blanket. He had seen the crushed arm, the gashed head, the eyes rolled up—showing no pupil, just the whites. She had been breathing, though, surely. But then her head, her poor head—her lovely hair. He remembered watching them wheel the trolley away. He himself had walked into Emergency—the ambulance driver had tried to stop him, tried to make him get into a wheelchair. But why? There was nothing wrong with him. He remembered, too, the mound of her body, the mound of her abdomen, full of their child, their first child, as they had wheeled her away. "Oh, God!" He turned his head away, then he was summoned back by the doctor's voice.

"I'm afraid I've got to tell you." The doctor signaled to a nurse. She came and pulled the curtains 'round them, leaving them in a little isolated space. The man sensed the urgency and pulled himself up in the bed, trying to clear his head. No, he didn't have a headache, he felt better—stiff and peculiar, but not ill. He turned eagerly toward the doctor.

"Yes, what's happened? How's my wife?"

The doctor shook his head. "You signed a form last night for us to operate. Do you remember?" The man nodded. Yes, he remembered—they had said they must operate. Of course he'd signed, they knew best, she was in good hands, it was a good hospital.

"Yes," he said anxiously. "What happened?" But the doctor's face told him before he spoke, at least part of it.

"Your wife had brain injuries, very bad ones. We decided that we must try and save the baby."

The man looked at the doctor incredulously. "Baby!" What, his mind screamed, did the baby matter now? It wasn't the baby, it was Marilyn—it was her! What had they done? The baby was only seven months, seven and a half—what had they done? He thought he was asking the doctor, and yet no words came. The doctor went on.

"We brought in the gynecologist, did a cesarean section. The baby is alive. It's a little boy. He's in the Children's Ward, in the Intensive Care Unit. You'll be able to see him."

The bloody fool, he thought he was bringing him comfort, telling him that Marilyn's child, their child, was— He didn't want the bloody baby, he wanted Marilyn! He swung his legs over the side of the bed before the doctor could say anything. "Marilyn. I want to see her."

"She's not—I'm afraid she's dead."

Blame spread over him like a blinding heat. "You've killed her," he said quietly, coldly. But the doctor shook his head.

"No, we didn't kill her. She was so badly damaged around the head there was no hope for her at all. So we had to take the decision. You were—you did sign the form."

Sign the form, sign the form, the words went through his head. Was it his fault they'd done this to Marilyn—cut her open, got the baby out? He began to calm a little. Were they right? Would she have wanted this? Maybe.

The nurse came in and looked at the doctor inquiringly.

"Yes, Nurse." He turned back to the man. "Nurse will bring you some breakfast. You seem to have no injuries—we examined you carefully yesterday and your X-rays are all clear. You were on the right side of the car, you see—"

"On the wrong side of the car," said the man, "on the wrong side of the car," and the nurse and the doctor exchanged a glance. The doctor nodded, went out, and the nurse pulled the sheets tidily 'round the man, plumped up his pillows, and said, "Would you like coffee or tea? Are you hungry?"

"Hungry?" The man looked at her. They were all mad in this hospital: they thought that life would go on. Suddenly he heard a man's voice.

"Nurse, nurse—please, I want to go out to the lavatory. You said I wasn't to go alone. Will you take me?"

The nurse put her hand on the man's shoulder, pressed him back against the pillow, and said, "I won't be long. We're rather short staffed." And she disappeared, leaving the curtains partially open. The man realized life was going on, and that there were people who didn't know about that terrible, splintering crash. Didn't know about Marilyn, their lives together, the love they had for one another. Nobody knew except him, behind these curtains, suffering. Well, everybody suffered, he argued with himself, everybody had tragedies. Was this worse than most?

They kept him in hospital and said tomorrow maybe, perhaps tomorrow he could go home—they'd see. Home? What did they mean?

During the afternoon a different nurse came and asked if he felt well enough to go down and see his son. His son! Yes, he felt well enough, he supposed. It was just that he felt so detached, so different. He supposed it was shock. He got into the wheelchair.

In the Children's Ward the nurse wheeled him along a row of glass cubicles and pointed toward one. Enclosed in glass, in the middle, was a small cagelike cot. Inside that was a glass box with a child in it, if you could call it that—a wizened little creature, a tube in its nose, a bandage 'round its middle. You could see just a small bubble coming from the other nostril as he breathed rapidly in and out. The body was completely uncovered save for the bandage. It was brick-red, mottled. It looked dreadful.

"He's holding his own," said the nurse brightly and turned to the Sister beside her. The Sister nodded, smiling, and the man thought, Perhaps she doesn't know. Perhaps they haven't told her that—And yet, why should I come down here in a dressing gown? It was such a muddle, here in a hospital, in this dressing gown, looking at my child.

Placing a hand on his arm, the Sister said kindly, "You'll get over it—life must go on. You've got a little son to think about now." She looked at the nurse and another strange look passed between them which he couldn't interpret. He let himself be wheeled back to the Men's Ward and wordlessly got into bed.

What was he getting into bed for? He looked at the nurse and asked her.

"Just observation. You'll probably be able to go home soon." Home—that word again. Their little bungalow, so carefully bought, so carefully furnished. They had done well. The new car—Blast the new car! Suddenly he leaned forward in the bed and supported himself on the bed table, beating it with his hands, then put his head forward and started to cry. The nurse put her arms 'round him.

"That's better, you'll feel better after you've cried. I'll leave the curtains 'round you." She comforted him, she did her best, then someone called for her again and she disappeared.

All day he sat in the bed quietly. Once he took a visit to the lavatory, where he met a shambling old man who was querulous and said, "Hold the door for me. It's too heavy. I can't open it."

In the evening they turned on the television. Some of them had little plastic earphones plugged in their ears. The curtains were drawn back again and he could see the whole ward. So many men, what had happened to them all? There was one heavily bandaged—he could have been in a car accident, too.

He lay, eyes closed. Crying had made his eyelids prick and irritate, and now and again he put his hand up and rubbed them. Lunch had come. He'd ignored it, taking no notice of the woman in the white coat who'd taken away the still-loaded tray. Then he was given a cup of tea—it must be teatime. He had drunk that avidly and asked for another, but they had forgotten to give it to him. He was now becoming part of the routine of the ward. After all, he wasn't injured, just shocked.

A doctor came by in the evening, and said gently, "You can't go home tomorrow. All the X-rays are okay, but you're still under observation. We want to keep an eye on you for a little longer." It was a young doctor, different—he hadn't seen him before. The man looked at him with a spark of interest. He was so young, this doctor. Quite suddenly, the nurse again did this drawing of the curtain and the doctor pulled the chair up to the side of the bed and sat down.

"I want to talk to you about the baby," he said. He had a sheaf of notes in his hand and he riffled through them as he spoke, as if he didn't want to meet the man's eyes.

"Yes. I've seen the baby."

"It won't be going home yet—we shall probably have to keep it for some weeks. It was premature, you see."

"I know that." The man's voice was irritable and the young doctor looked up quickly.

Then, as if he was trying to apologize, he said, "There's a slight difficulty with the baby. I felt you should know about it. On top of everything else, it's certainly a double blow, but I felt you must know."

"Know what? Won't it live?" There was a note of hope in the man's voice, but it was dispelled.

"Oh, yes, yes, he'll live. He's doing quite well, Sister tells me, but— Have you heard of the condition called spina bifida?"

The man shook his head, his eyes never leaving the young doctor's face. In spite of the head shake he answered, "Isn't it a sort of deformity? Don't they—?" Isn't there a charity—?"

"Yes, that's right. It's a sort of deformity. Your child has—well, his spinal cord is exposed in the back. It's difficult to know just how far it will affect the child, but the outlook is not very good." The young man dropped his eyes to the notes again, as if reading them helped.

"Why in God's name did they rescue it? Why didn't they let it die with her? Why didn't they give it—?"

"They didn't know, and anyway our job is to save life, isn't it?"

The man felt dulled. This thing on top of the other was too much. You forget what it was like to feel.

"Yes, I suppose so. You did what you thought was right." He felt an infinite weariness. After a few moments the doctor got up and left and the man was suddenly filled with panic. What have I got? A deformed child, one who will be in a chair all its life? Or mentally deficient? The nurse came and drew back the curtains. Her face was dripping with sympathy. She held a small glass and a little cup containing two pills.

"I think you should take these, then you'll get a good night."

The man looked at her. "Yes," he said. He swallowed the pills, and he slept the night through.

Next morning it was obvious that they weren't quite happy about him. Another doctor came and flashed a light in his eyes, asked him if he had a headache. He didn't know if he had a headache or not. His head felt strange, cold, and he still had this feeling he was suspended a little above the bed. He didn't tell anybody this—he didn't think it mattered.

All that day and the next they asked him again and again if he wanted to see the baby. Each time he shook his head no. If it was a nurse she looked sad, if it was a doctor he shrugged his shoulders. But they continued to ask. Did he want to see the baby? Did he want to see the baby? Did he want to see the baby?

He slept nearly all day. On his fourth day in the hospital he suddenly felt more alert, and when the doctor came he asked, "Where is my wife? Where have they taken her?"

The doctor paused before he answered. "They've taken her to the Chapel of Rest at the cemetery. Her mother and father are here, they—" He paused again and then resumed, embarrassed. "The funeral is to-morrow. They've made the arrangements. They came to see you, don't you remember?"

The man shook his head and said, "No," and yet there was a vague feeling that two figures had appeared beside his bed sometime during a day. He must have been half asleep. He looked at the doctor. "Why don't I remember?"

"You're still a bit concussed and shocked—that's why we're keeping you in. Don't worry. I don't think you'll be able to go to the—I'm sorry, old chap." The doctor was trying to be matey. It almost made it worse. It would have been better if he had stuck to his calm, professional detachment.

The man nodded. "I see. The funeral is tomorrow then. And I can't—"

"I wouldn't, honestly I wouldn't, old chap." The doctor went on, "I think it would be better if you rested here. After all, her mother and father will be there and—"

"But not me." He started to cry.

That night he was given two more sleeping pills. He took them, but this time he didn't sleep. After two hours he was wide awake and thinking. His head seemed clearer. He knew what he had to do.

He waited until the ward clock said half past three. Everything was quiet, the nurses in the kitchen. He got out of bed, slipped on his dressing gown, tied the belt firmly 'round his waist, scrabbled silently in his locker for his slippers, and slipped them onto his cold feet. He noticed with disgust that his feet were sweaty and smelled. He made his way toward the ward door. If anyone noticed him he would just say he was going to the lavatory. Then he stopped. No, the lavatories were the other way, weren't they? He glanced up the ward, past the many beds with the soft blue lights shining above them. An old man coughed, groaned, and shifted in his bed. Yes, the lavatories were at the other end, but that didn't matter. If anyone saw him they'd think he was fuddled in his head. But he wasn't now.

He pushed open the swing doors and looked out. To the right was the brightly lighted kitchen, the door almost pushed to. He could hear the nurses inside. One was saying, "Oh, bugger that. Let's make a cup of tea and risk it. She usually has a z around now, you know."

He padded softly along the corridor, stopped, put one foot up, inserted his forefinger into the back of the slipper, and drew it more firmly onto his sweaty foot. He had a long way to go, a lot of things to do, and must not be seen or heard.

The large iron cemetery gates squeaked slightly as the man pushed them open. He looked around with apprehension, but nothing stirred, save the trees rustling slightly in the early-morning breeze.

The sky was streaked with grey, the day just beginning. A bird twittered sleepily here and there and the man cocked his head to listen, then walked on, his slippers making hardly any sound on the gravel path. In his arms he carried a small bundle wrapped in a white blanket. At the door of the Chapel of Rest he lay the bundle down on the grass beside the step and tried the handle. Locked. He had thought of that. He took from his pocket a credit card—his head was clearing all right, he had anticipated what to do. Gently he inserted the card. It wouldn't work. Then he took a second card from his pocket and tried the two together. The latch slipped back. He opened the door, peered inside, bent down, and picked up the white-wrapped bundle. He entered the chapel, then pushed the door behind him.

Once inside the chapel, he waited, his back to the door, looking 'round him. There was room for three coffins. One, two, three stands, but only one coffin there. The man put the bundle down on one of the vacant coffin stands and looked 'round him, shivering slightly. It was colder in the chapel than outside. The smell that came to him was of death.

He looked at the closed coffin and tried to lift the lid but it was sealed. He looked around and breathed a sigh of relief. *There*, the one thing whose absence would have balked him, it was underneath the stand. He picked up the large ratchet screwdriver. It made a rasping noise in the silent chapel and he looked apprehensively 'round him as he worked, but soon all the screws had been removed. He set the screwdriver back where he'd found it, raised the lid of the coffin, and looked down at Marilyn.

Her body was covered up to the chin, her dear face bruised, her dark hair pulled forward to hide as much of the bruising as possible. The top of her head was covered by a cap of bandage. The man stood looking at her for some seconds, his face twisted in grief. He put one hand in and gently touched the face. It was ice cold and he withdrew his hand hastily. He gently raised the sheet covering the white-robed body and grasped one arm, the right arm—he knew the condition of the left. He placed it across the middle of the body and then pulled the sheet up as best he could under it, almost to the chin again, leaving the shoulder exposed.

The man turned and picked up the bundle, pushing the blanket away from the face of the baby. It looked old, wizened, like a little old man, the face whiter now than it had been when he'd seen it three days ago. He carried the baby over to the coffin and placed it gently in the crook of the woman's arm, curling her fingers 'round the child's tiny feet that protruded from the bottom of the blanket. He looked closely at the baby. There, visible on the top of the head, was a pulse, faint but regular, beating through the open fontanel in the infant's skull. He parted the blanket a little and looked at the small chest. It was rising and falling in shallow breaths. The man sighed.

A pink glow coming through the window of the chapel bathed the two occupants of the coffin. The day was getting stronger. He took one last look, placed one last gentle touch of the fingers on the child's face, and the woman's, and replaced the coffin lid, gently and accurately, so that the screw holes were in alignment. He replaced the screws carefully, one by one. When he had finished, he looked 'round him. There were flowers on a small altarlike table at the end of the room and he nodded at them, pleased.

He replaced the screwdriver again, stood for a while with his arm across the coffin, then started for the door.

As he came up the stairs to the Men's Ward, a nurse greeted him, startled. "Where have you been? We've been looking everywhere for you! Where did you go? Have you been out in the grounds? You're cold." He looked at her and said yes he was cold, he was cold. She led him to his bed, speaking the strange way nurses sometimes do to patients, as if they're all children. Indeed he felt rather like a child as he sat down on the side of the bed, intensely weary. She helped him take off his dressing gown and slippers, swung his legs up on the bed as if he were helpless, and covered him up. The bed seemed especially warm, as if they'd had an electric warmer in it, ready to welcome him back.

"I'm going to get you a hot drink," she said, bustling off.

He lay quietly, his eyes closed, a tremendous feeling of satisfaction enveloping him. They were together now, there was no more need to worry. Whatever was the matter with the baby, she had it in her arms, and would have it in her arms forever. He almost fell asleep, but was roused by the nurse bringing a cup of hot milk.

"Come along, drink this and you'll feel better." He opened his eyes and looked at her. There were noises in the corridor, people were up and about. "I've told Night Sister we've found you," she told him.

"What time is it?" he asked.

She looked at her watch. "Twenty past five."

That was all?

"What's all that outside?" he asked without any real interest. Then he thought of the baby. Of course they must have discovered it gone.

A nurse shouldn't be telling things to patients, but she was young and inexperienced—and excited, horrified, scandalized with the drama of it. "A baby has disappeared from the Children's Ward. All of a sudden it was gone, just like that. Such a thing has never happened before."

The man looked at her warily. "A little boy?" he asked.

She looked at him. "No, a little girl—a premature baby girl from the Children's Intensive Care Unit. She's gone, just gone."

A feeling of horror spread over the man, like the cold morning light that was stealing through the ward. There was a wild clanging in his ears that shut out all other sounds—then a complete silence, a blankness, a lack of awareness of what was happening around him that would last until the day he died.

Ron Goulart
Keep It Clean

He took another walk around the dead man.

Outside the green-shuttered windows of his ground-floor office cottage, a Mercedes 220S came purring to life in the executive-guest parking lot and went humming away across the hazy afternoon studio grounds.

"Nitwits," murmured Leo Madrid, alluding to no one in particular just yet.

He was a middle-sized, pudgy man of thirty-seven, sixteen pounds overweight and wearing the faded denim slacks, checkered workshirt, and bedraggled boat shoes he always wore when he came in to write at the studio.

The corpse was taller and trimmer than Leo, about six years younger, and not more than an hour or two dead. He was slumped in Leo's chair behind Leo's desk and there were two bullet holes in him. Both in the chest, causing bloody splotches on his blue shirt.

Leo knew him.

"I can't figure why the devil you came in here to get murdered, Sid," he said, pausing next to his typewriter to see what was printed on the sheet of yellow copy paper that'd been rolled into the machine since he was here, late last night.

People frequently, too damn frequently, used Leo's cottage for meetings of various kinds. They knew he only came onto the Wheelan lot maybe twice a week and always fairly late in the day.

"C'mon," said Leo, scanning the page, "not a halfwit dying message."

Typed in a single line midway down the sheet were the words *Trina killed me because*

"Sounds like a contest. Complete this sentence in twenty-five words or less." He pulled the sheet free of the typewriter.

Two lines further down was typed *earp*.

Leo took hold of his nose between his thumb and forefinger and gave it a thoughtful squeeze. Then he folded the dying message in four and deposited it in his hip pocket.

The .22 target pistol on the rug next to his desk he picked up with a pencil through the trigger guard. He'd written several scenes where this was done, but never actually tried it before. The maneuver went a little awkwardly—the gun came sliding down the pencil to bonk into his hand.

"Forty-five minutes to turn in a revised scene and they murder Sid Mellon in my damn office." He yanked a drawer open, dropped the weapon in with his collection of spare shorts, socks, and old *X-Men* comic books.

Frowning, Leo squatted again. All around the leg of his chair were tiny specks of white.

He straightened up, remembering he'd noticed similar whitish flakes scattered atop his desk blotter. Not Liquid Paper. There was none in sight and he didn't use it.

"Please, Allah, don't mix me up in a drug-deal murder," he requested at the high, soundproofed ceiling.

He poked a fingertip into the trace of white powder on the rug. He brought the finger up and smelled it. It had a thin perfumy smell. It was powdered detergent.

Leo turned to study the body of the deceased portrait photographer.

Clutched in Sid Mellon's dead hand was a torn piece of a glossy photo. The picture had originally been about four inches by six and the fragment was a shade less than three by four.

"Trina again," remarked Leo, after prying the torn photo free and scanning it. "Not your traditional publicity photo, though. At least not for the young lady who's currently portraying *Betty Button, Girl Detective* for a family television audience. No, indeed." The fragment showed Trina Danish from the waist up. She was naked, sitting on what looked to be a bed in a tacky motel, smiling nervously into the camera. Her hair was a more flamboyant shade of red than it was nowadays and she looked to be no more than seventeen or so. Meaning the picture had been taken four or five years ago.

Leo added the photo to the contents of his hip pocket.

Stepping back, he studied the room and then scrutinized the body again.

"I want to remember you just as you are, Sid," he said.

Then he took hold of the corpse under the armpits.

By the time he got the body out of the chair, across his office, and into the closet, he was panting and wheezing.

"Exercise," he gasped. "I'm going to have to commence a sensible exercise program no later than tomorrow."

He bent, inspected his chair, then sat down. After blowing and brushing the soap powder off his desk, Leo inserted a fresh sheet of paper into his typewriter.

Leo came striding into Mo Beeker's outer office with several pages of revised script held out in front of him. "Afternoon, Joline. I have here—"

"He says you're to give it to me, quick," said the blonde young woman behind the white desk. "I'm to retype it and take it rapidly over to Rodlow Kupples in the Guest Conference Room—"

"You've done something new to your hair," Leo said.

"Oh, this isn't my hair. Mr. Beeker insists I wear a wig so I match the furnit—"

"Well, it's a handsome wig."

"Left over from the *Isn't It a Drag?* show."

"Very fetching." Leo walked on by her, aiming for Beeker's door.

"He doesn't want to be disturbed."

"My advent is always soothing and not disturbing." Leo pushed on in. "Usually, anyway."

Mo Beeker was a small tan man of thirty-one, clad in a pale-blue denim suit. He was sprawled out on the thick cream rug, flat on his back.

"Not another one!" Leo hurried over to the producer. *"Mo?"*

"In a minute, Leo." Grunting, straining, Beeker sat up and managed to touch his white-shoed toes. "Ninety-six."

Leo wandered over to the big white desk and dropped the revised pages of the *Betty Button, Girl Detective* script on it. "She doesn't kiss Butch now. Not even on the cheek."

"Good," panted the little producer. "Those damn Kupples & Leon people don't want even a hint of sex on their damn show. Keep it clean is their motto."

"Good motto for the largest soap-and-detergent manufacturer in the Western world," said Leo. "Anyway, in the new scene, instead of kissing Butch, she fondles him in an intimate location, to show her appreciation for his having saved her from death in the haunted mansion on Huckleberry Hill. All below camera range, to be sure."

"Very funny." Beeker was flat on his back again. "Didn't Joline tell you she has to retype that stuff and rush over to the conference room? Old Kupples and that ad-agency banana, Oscar Jopp, are waiting to glower over it."

"We have an additional problem." Leo settled into a blonde chair.

"Ninety-eight." Beeker groaned through another situp. "Which is?"

"Why was Sid Mellon on the lot?"

"Who knows? He does publicity shots for some of our Tip Top Productions shows now and then. Why?"

"How many of those situps are you intending to do?"

"One hundred. I don't want to end up looking like a watermelon smuggler the way you do."

"Extra weight is no handicap if you're personable."

"Ninety-nine. What about Sid?"

"Somebody murdered him, left the body in my office."

Beeker remained sitting up. "This isn't one of your whimsical remarks?"

"Nope. They shot him twice, with a .22."

"Damn, I hate to have the police trampling all over everything while one of the damn sponsors is visiting."

"We're not going to call the cops yet."

"We aren't?"

"See, Mo, somebody tried to rig this so the cops'll think Trina Danish did it. But—"

"Trina?" Beeker struggled to his feet. "The star of *Betty Button, Girl Detective*? How the hell is that going to look to old Kupples?"

He commenced pacing the rug. "He objects, the old coot, to kissing on the damn show, to hand-holding, to foul language such as heck and darn. He really bitched once when Trina wasn't wearing a bra. How the hell is he going to react when he finds out she's gone and shot some goon? And it's just about time for KidSuds to renew for next season—"

"Trina didn't kill anybody."

Beeker stopped, hunched, scowled over at the pudgy writer. "What makes you say that?"

"Trust me," Leo said. "I just know."

"Maybe you can operate on hunches and feelings in the gut—" Beeker resumed his pacing "—but the police aren't creative people. If they see evidence pointing at Trina, they'll—"

"There's no evidence."

"I thought you just told me things made it look like—"

"What I said was the situation had been arranged to make it seem Trina'd done the deed," explained Leo. "I cleaned all that up."

"You aren't supposed to do that," said Beeker. "That's against the law. Remember when we were doing *Murder Squad*? Don't touch anything! That was what Sergeant Weber always said whenever—"

"Sergeant Webster."

"What?"

"Our hero. Name was Webster, not Weber," said Leo. "Played by Randy Zeal, who now plays Betty's handsome secret-agent father."

"I never liked that guy. He gets good ratings, but he's too tall and too handsome."

"And not a pound overweight."

Beeker paced for a few silent seconds.

"You shouldn't have tidied up the clues," he said finally. "But at least the body's there for the cops. We'll phone them—I'll have Joline do it—"

"I put the body in my closet, out of sight."

Beeker stopped still.

"That's going to make them mad as hell," he said. "Touching the damn evidence is bad enough, but when you tell them you stuffed poor Sid Mellon into your—"

"Look, we aren't going to call the cops until we can give them the killer. A package deal."

"How do we do that? Do you know who really killed him?"

"Not yet."

"You only wrote *Murder Squad*," reminded the producer, "you didn't live it. You can't solve murders."

"I want to try this one." Leo glanced at his watch. "Give me until six this evening, then we'll phone the law. Okay?"

"Why until six?"

"I've got a business appointment at seven. I'll need time to drive to my place in Malibu, shower, change my—"

"Is there any chance, Leo, you can really do this? Solve it?"

"Sure."

"Suppose it really is Trina? What's that going to do to us? I've only got two damn shows on the network this season. *Betty Button, Girl Detective* and *Isn't It a Drag*? If my girl detective is indicted for murder, I—"

"Trust me," Leo repeated as he moved for the door. "That new scene I just whipped up is, by the way, terrific."

The Wheelan lot had been constructed originally in the late 1930s and some of the old outdoor sets were still standing. Leo cut through a Cairo street and by a mosque. Then he hurried along the dusty falsefront street that had represented Tombstone, Arizona, in several long-ago westerns.

He located the huge glittering trailer that served as Trina Danish's dressing room, moored near the outdoor set representing the haunted mansion on Huckleberry Hill.

Sticking out of the open doorway into the smudged afternoon were two very handsome bare legs.

"Ah, like mother like daughter," Leo said, stopping beside the legs. "You still have a handsome set of pins, Mrs. Danberg."

"Why shouldn't I? Being barely forty."

Trina's mother was an attractive woman, her red hair the exact shade of her daughter's.

"Who's that mooching around out there?" inquired a pleasant voice from within the trailer.

"Leo Madrid, my child," he called through cupped hands.

"Ugh," replied Trina.

"Pet, don't address your senior scriptwriter like that," advised her mother.

"One of the few things I haven't lost in this town," said Trina, appearing in the doorway, "is my honesty." She looked Leo up and down. "Ugh."

Gazing up at her, he pressed his hand to his heart. "An ugh from you, Trina, is like a caress from a lesser mortal. Your fresh loveliness is like unto—"

"And quit calling me 'child,' Madrid. I'm twenty-two."

"No, you aren't," said her mother. "How could you be? If you were, I'd be forty-six."

Trina was dressed for her Betty Button part in a simple print dress and had her auburn hair in braids. She climbed gracefully down out of the trailer. "*You* wrote this claptrap we're shooting today, didn't you, Madrid?"

"Every shimmering word."

"It's godawful."

"Nope, it's actually brilliant," he corrected. "And the way you deliver the lines, in such dulcet tones, turns it into poetry."

"You really are mostly a schmuck," Trina decided.

Shrugging in a dismissive way, she walked away toward the haunted house.

"Trina's fond of you," Mrs. Danberg assured him. "But she adopts this flippant demeanor to hide a sensitive—"

"Sure, so do I." Leo grinned up at her. "Listen, can I come in and talk about Sid Mellon and how he was blackmailing you folks?"

Leo had his feet up on the battered sheriff's desk and was holding a strip of negatives up toward the dusty window. "Ah, there's a lively shot," he muttered.

"Madrid?"

Lowering his feet, Leo swept all the negatives back into the manila envelop he'd found taped under the desk. "Howdy, Oscar."

Oscar Jopp hesitated on the threshold. "I thought I saw you heading this way," he said. "I wanted to talk to you."

"Set," invited Leo.

Jopp was tall and wide, wearing a dark-blue suit and a thin grey tie. "I left Kupples reading the revisions," he said, sitting on the edge of a wooden chair that faced the prop desk. "Went over to watch them shooting in front of the haunted mansion. It looked great."

"Did the old gentleman approve of my changes?"

"Kupples thinks you did a fine job of cleaning the script up," replied the advertising man. "That's what I came to tell you."

Unbuttoning his shirt, Leo slipped the fat envelope away. "You don't have dandruff, do you?"

"Huh?"

"White powder all over your shoulders and sleeves."

Frowning, Jopp brushed at his suit. "Naw, that's KidSuds," he said. "I even get it in my shoes. Old man Kupples insists I tour the plant down there in Hawthorne every time I pick him up."

"What time did you arrive here with him today?"

"A little shy of noon. Why are—"

"You two stay together?"

"No, I had to go see a few people around the studio." Jopp was still brushing at his sleeve. "Kupples was going to dodder over to the commissary to meet with Beeker or somebody."

"Trina continues to do a splendid job on the show." Leo stood up. "Projecting innocence, yet not losing her feminine charm. A perfect character to be co-sponsored by KidSuds."

"Yeah, and it's a shame he isn't going to— Well, I just wanted to tell you what a nice job you're doing."

"Kupples isn't going to what?"

Jopp glanced away, looking at the empty gun rack on the wall, at the faded wanted posters, and at the dented spittoon beside the desk. "Well, Leo," he said, "the old man isn't going to renew. Sorry. I wasn't going to tell anyone until it was officially announced, but I'm sure you guys will get a new sponsor to take over our share of—"

"Ah!" Leo snapped his fingers. "That explains it all. Where's Kupples now?"

"Waiting in the limo. I'm going to drive him back down to Hawthorne soon as I finish up—"

"Bring him over to Beeker's office right away." Leo eased to the doorway.

Jopp shook his head.

"He can't be persuaded to change his mind about the show. He's going to put our KidSuds spots on the *Hubba Hubba-Purple Monster Saturday Cartoon Hour* next season."

"Just tell the old gent I found the negatives."

"The what?"

"Negatives. He'll comprehend."

"Leo, Kupples is a powerful man," said Jopp in a lowered voice. "I don't think you better try pressuring him into any—"

"Ten minutes." Leo stepped out into the streets of Tombstone.

Rodlow Kupples was seventy-two, lean, and suntanned. He walked briskly into Beeker's office. "Did you authorize this idiot to—"

"It's his idea, Mr. Kupples," explained Beeker from behind his desk.

Leo was slouched in a canvas chair, the manila envelope resting on his knee. "That's a handsome grey suit you're wearing, sir," he said amiably. "One really has to squint to notice the soap flakes it's dappled with."

"Detergent flakes," said the old man. "And what do my clothes have to do with—"

"Sid Mellon got murdered in my office," said Leo, "roughly between noon and two today."

"Sid Mellon?" Kupples glowered from Beeker to Jopp.

"A photographer," said Jopp. "You've probably seen him around here."

"The person who shot Sid in my office," continued Leo, "attempted to arrange things to look as though Trina Danish had done him in."

"Trina Danish?" Kupples lowered himself into a chair. "Good heavens, if word of this gets out, it'll smirch the reputation of *Betty Button, Girl Detective* and, most assuredly, that of KidSuds as well."

"You're dropping your share of the sponsorship in a couple of weeks," said Leo, smiling. "So it wouldn't affect you that much. In fact, you could make a nice gesture of publicly washing your hands of our tainted show."

"KidSuds is dropping us?" Beeker asked. "How come you didn't fill me in on that before?"

"That's what I'm doing now," Leo said. "Okay, the murderer wanted us to believe Trina had a rendezvous with Sid, then had a quarrel over some incriminating photos he'd taken of her in her youth."

Jopp inquired, "Isn't that maybe what really happened?"

"Nope. Trina wasn't anywhere near my office," said Leo. "She has an iron-clad alibi."

"How do you know?" asked Kupples.

"Trust me," answered Leo, making a dismissing wave with his right hand. "The killer, though, thought she was alone in her trailer while her sweet mother was lunching in the commissary." He cleared his throat. "Sid actually *was* blackmailing Mrs. Danberg and Trina with those pictures. But he was only asking a thousand a month, which they could afford. Mrs. Danberg tells me she hired a private detective a few months ago to try to locate Sid Mellon's negatives and destroy them. This gent poked around at Sid's house in Santa Monica and his studio in Beverly Hills, but he couldn't find a damn thing. Meaning the pictures and all were stashed elsewhere."

Kupples was watching him.

"*Were* hidden?"

"Right," said Leo, grinning and holding up the envelope. "I found them. See, Mr. Kupples, after you shot Sid and typed that fake message on my typewriter— A dying man, by the way, probably wouldn't take the time to use a capital letter for Trina's name, a point I'll make more clearly in a moment. Anyway, you'd set up a meeting with Sid to supposedly make a payment on your own blackmail. You knew I never came to work until two or three and that my office was usually open and had been used for all sorts of meetings and assignations. You—"

"Hey, now," said Jopp. "You're accusing Mr. Kupples of murder."

"You left my office too soon," Leo told Kupples. "Sid wasn't quite dead and he managed, possibly getting the idea from you, a message of his own. It read 'earp.' No caps."

"Urp?" Beeker blinked. "What the hell kind of dying message is—"

"E-a-r-p," amplified Leo. "Wyatt Earp and his brothers cleaned up Tombstone. Sid was nasty to the end, and he wanted his cache of blackmail material found and made use of. Revenge."

"You found the photos?" the old man asked quietly.

"Under the sheriff's desk, right here on the lot. That office was supposed to have been Earp's," said Leo. "That's where Sid kept the stuff stashed away."

"You've looked at all of them?"

"Every blessed one," answered Leo. "You really ought to follow your own advice, sir, and keep it clean." He shook his head reproachfully. "And if you must carry on so with ladies who aren't even of age, don't do it in a room with one-way mirrors, especially when there's a black-mailing photographer behind one of them, snapping away."

"Well, what ought we to do?" said Kupples. "I'd be willing to start paying you what I was Mellon."

Leo said, "Nope, that's not the way I work. What we do now is phone the cops."

"Hey, now," said Jopp smoothy, "you ought to be able to work out a—"

"Too late, anyway." Leo stood. "I phoned the police before I popped in here. Laid the case out for them. They weren't even especially angry about my having moved Sid." He returned the envelope to his hip pocket. "I'll meet them at the gates with this stuff."

"This," said Beeker, "has been a day of surprises."

Leo checked his watch.

"Fifteen of six," he said, heading for the door. "It didn't take quite as long as I thought."

"Where'd he get that photo of me that Sid was clutching in his hand?" asked Trina Danish.

"I imagine," replied Leo, "that Sid sold him a set."

"Then that old coot knew about it and didn't—"

"Kupples didn't want to make waves initially," Leo said. "But when he decided to drop *Betty Button, Girl Detective*, he no longer cared about bad publicity for the show. So he used one of the pictures to point the finger of blame at you, my child."

Picking up her brandy glass, Trina crossed to the long wide window of his beach house. "You just can't account for fate sometimes," she said.

"True," he agreed, joining her at the window. The Pacific was a misty black down below.

"If you and I hadn't had a clandestine meeting on the lot today," Trina said, "and spent two wonderful hours together hidden in the old Hotel International set, why, I wouldn't have had an alibi."

"Even without an alibi, I could've cleared you."

"You're pretty vain sometimes, Leo."

"I am, yes, and with good reason."

"I still think we ought to come out in the open with our relationship," she said, leaning against him. "Then we wouldn't have to sneak around and meet on old sets and such."

"Eventually, maybe."

"I hardly ever get to visit you here at your own place," Trina complained.

"That's because my wife doesn't go out of town that often."

She sighed. "You know what I'd like to do tonight?"

"Keep it clean," Leo advised.

Randye Lordon
Nobody's Fool

Will Parsons died on a balmy Tuesday afternoon in midwinter. It was recorded as an accident. His third wife, Ceal, had had to identify the body. Two men had stood on either side of her in the morgue as they pulled out the vault with Will's cold body laid out on a slab equally as cold. Her stomach pitched and her knees felt weak, but she held her own. No one had to assist her from the room. She drove herself home.

Ceal cried alone that night. Hard as others tried, they just couldn't find the tears for Will Parsons. Not his children, who relocated out of his reach years earlier, nor his first wife. (His second wife had died in '78.) His few friends had an extra drink and acquaintances shook their heads, hoping to feel bad, but only Ceal cried.

She went through the funeral arrangements alone, surprised to find it was so easy. She was a young woman, never having had to handle this sort of thing before, and the simplicity of the routine cheered her. Late on Wednesday night, the night after Will's death, when all the arrangements were completed and she had made all the requisite phonecalls explaining to the interested few of his unfortunate accident, she sat out in the back yard by the pool, a snifter of cognac clasped in her right hand. There was one call left to make, but it could wait. If she didn't hear from him first, she would call in the morning.

The phone rang. Eleven-fifteen—right on time. She answered before the ring subsided.

"Hello." Her voice was calculated with exhaustion and pain. It needn't have been. She relaxed her shoulders and slid down in her chair. The purr in her voice returned as she invited him over.

"Will out of town?" She could hear his anticipation.

"In a way. Come over." She replaced the receiver in its cradle without waiting for a response and padded barefoot into the bedroom, where she sat before the vanity and stared at her reflection and sipped her drink.

They were in one another's arms by midnight. His initial tension, unaccustomed as he was to being in Will's house, was quickly forgotten as she led him into the bedroom.

"God, Ceal, I wish it could always be like this." He pulled her closer to his chest and shut his eyes.

"It can." She ran a finger along his beard.

His response was a sigh. They'd been over this four dozen times in the last eight months. She was married, he was married with three kids—any change would be too costly. It was impossible.

"Will's dead." He could hear her lips move into a smile. "You hear

me? I said Will's dead. Now we can have it all, Sugar. Just you and me."
She tightened her grasp around him.

He pulled himself up against the bedboard and reached for a cigarette. The flame from the match brought her face out of the darkness and
he saw a familiar expression of hers—a woman expecting confirmation
He pinched the filter between his thumb and middle finger as he inhaled
deeply.

"How'd he die, Ceal?" He finally spoke.

"An accident." She shrugged her bare shoulders. "Him and that
stupid bicycle. I told him over and over again he was too old for that sort
of thing."

"You encouraged him to ride," he reminded her. He kept his tone
easy, knowing how quickly she took offense.

She flattened her body against his side. "None of that matters. What
matters is that I love you. Now it can be just the two of us." Silence filled
the darkened room. Her breathing was labored, his steady as he finished the last of the cigarette. "You know it can't be, Ceal."

"Do I?" She sounded far away, as though she was only half listening
to him.

"Come on, Ceal. We've never lied to each other. You know I'd never
leave Carol or the kids." It didn't strike him that this was an odd thing
to say as he encircled her waist with his left arm.

"You mean you don't want me."

"Want you? I love you. But I've got responsibilities, Ceal. I can't walk
away from them." He watched her as she pulled away the sheets and
walked wordlessly into the bathroom and closed the door between
them. He proceeded to dress.

She found him in the living room, a glass of scotch in his hand,
glancing at his watch. A robe was pulled tightly around her small waist.
She leaned against the archway and stared at him.

Her silence unnerved him. He laughed. "You're mighty beautiful
woman, Ceal.—Want a drink?"

She twitched her head to the side as though she was listening for
something and then answered, "Club soda." She sauntered into the
room and seated herself on the arm of the sofa. She waited for him to
face her. Too many times in the past she'd addressed his back. "What
are we going to do?" She watched his face carefully.

"About us?" He handed her the glass and settled himself in Will's old
chair. "I don't know." He took a long drink. "I just don't know."

"I don't like being alone." She leaned forward and rested her elbows
on her knees. "I cried myself to sleep last night because I was alone."
She started flexing her toes—opened, closed, opened, closed. "I
thought Will's death would bring us together." Her face remained
expressionless.

"How could that be, Ceal? I told you from the start I'd never leave my family. Christ, you're making me feel like I've done something wrong, made a promise I didn't mean to keep. But, honey, that just isn't so." He looked around the room as though he'd lost something, then rose and returned to the bar.

"Making you feel like you've done something wrong." She spoke softly, as though she was talking to herself. "You think Will never should have died?"

"What?"

"I said, are you telling me Will never should have died?"

"I don't know what you mean." His hand trembled as he poured.

"He was a bastard and you know it." She placed her glass on the back of the sofa. "Are you a bastard, too, sweetheart?" She smiled sweetly. "That *would* take me by surprise. A woman can only take so much. Why don't you sit down?" The suggestion was an order. He took a moment and then complied. She pulled herself up from the sofa, her hands dug deep into the pockets of her robe.

"Now, I'm not a stupid woman. I know well enough that calling you at home or telling dear Carol would only push you further away from me, wouldn't it, honey?" She stood directly in front of him and glared down. "I went to a great deal of trouble to insure our happiness. Probably all they have to do is examine what's left of the bicycle.

"Would you like the details? When I first decided I couldn't take any more of that abusive old man acting like a four-year-old? When I discovered that the possibility could exist for the two of us to be together? Or perhaps you're more interested in how I learned about simple mechanics. Or which bolts I loosened. Was it the brakes or the handlebars, or both?" She took a deep breath and moved away from him. "No, I'll bet you're more interested in where it happened." She leaned against the bar. "We both knew his routine, didn't we? Every morning at seven o'clock the same route, the same four miles. Only this time it wasn't the same. I always warned him that hairpin turn would be the death of him." She replaced the scotch bottle in its appointed place on the bar. "But that doesn't matter to you, does it? My guess is you'd be more curious about whether his neck was broken by his own fall or by a passing car. Personally, I'm fascinated by my new-found theories regarding fate and luck."

He pressed his fingertips against his brow and shook his head slowly back and forth. The dull ache of grief was beginning inside him.

She paced the room. "Do you think no one knows about us?"

He swallowed hard and cleared his throat. "Why don't you just tell me what you want from me, Ceal?"

"Want from you? What I want it seems as though I can't have." She continued pacing. "We have a big problem here. You see, you know about Will's death. You also don't want me any more, do you? You walk out of here and I run the risk of you going to the police and telling them everything you know. Everything I did for us is backfiring on me. As I see it, that puts me somewhere between a rock and a hard place."

He twisted in the chair, recrossed his legs, and squinted toward her. "I wouldn't go to the police, Ceal. I love you. I don't see why we can't go on the way things have been." He pinched a patch of his beard between his index finger and his thumb.

"We can't because I want more than this." She leaned against the glass door dividing the living room from the patio. "It's crazy. Here I am, a very wealthy woman now, free as a bird, and all I want is you—the one thing I can't have. What do you suggest I do?"

"You planning on killing me, too, Ceal?"

"It's an option," she admitted, smiling. "Enough people know about us to conclude that you couldn't take having to share me, so you rigged a bicycle accident, then tonight you came to me and told me what you had done, I became enraged, we fought, and in selfdefense I shot you. No witnesses, only enough people who knew about our affair and your possessiveness."

"I'm not possessive."

She clicked her tongue against her teeth. "Damn, I knew there was something I forgot to tell my friends. They all seem to think you love me more than life itself."

"Ceal, I do love you." He let out a deep sigh and finished his drink. "There's no way I can prove to you I wouldn't go to the police—only my word and, like it or not, you know I'm good for it. But I don't want to die, either." He motioned to the bar and lifted his empty glass. "May I?" She nodded and watched him as he went and poured the scotch, took a sip, and turned back toward her. "This is crazy. I have responsibilities to Carol, but I love you. *And* my kids. I love my kids. I don't know, Ceal, maybe you're right. Maybe I would be happiest with you."

"That's the scary thing about commitment, isn't it? One never knows up front if things are going to work out."

"Hold me?"

She opened her arms to him and they clung to one another. She could tell by his breathing that he was crying. She pulled him closer to her, cooing gently in his ear. Their lips touched and they pulled gently away from one another. "I'll tell Carol I'm moving out tonight." He cupped her face in his hands and kissed her brow. "I love you, Ceal."

"Me you, too." She held his hand in hers and and pressed her lips to his palm. "You're going now?"

"Just to pack a few things. I'll be back within the hour." He downed his drink. "You want to come with me? You can wait in the car."

She shook her head. "I want to clean up." She walked hand in hand with him through the living room, into the dining room, and out to the foyer. She stopped by the mirror there and glanced at her reflection as he continued toward the door. When his hand was on the doorknob, she called out to him. As he turned, he saw the .38 in her hand and heard the shot, and his own scream. Blood poured from his chest.

As he lay slumped on the floor, unable to speak, barely able to breathe, he felt her kneel beside him and wrap her arms around him. "I love you," she whispered. "But I'm nobody's fool."

Shizuko Natsuki
It's Best Not To Listen

"Strictly between you and me—"

I'm sure that at some time or another one of your friends must have let you in on a secret and by so doing forced an unwanted burden on you. However, whatever they might say, they will probably have told the same thing to others, so even if you should accidentally let the confidence slip out, you will not be betraying them very much.

My situation with Hideko Saiki was a little different. We had been best friends since college, and in the eleven years since we graduated our relationship hadn't changed. Of course, during that interval we both married, had two children each, and for the last five years had lived in the same condominium, but basically we hadn't changed in the least. Hideko lost her mother when she was still quite young, and as she didn't have any sisters to discuss things with, she shared all her secrets with me. It didn't matter whether it was something important or just a little thing, when she said, "Between you and me," she meant just that and I always had a feeling of responsibility when I listened to her.

It was early one afternoon toward the end of June of this year when the rainy season was at its peak that Hideko came to see me. Her husband was at work in the foreign insurance company where he was employed and her two sons, one ten and the other eight, were both at school. My husband was also at work, and with my two daughters at school it was a perfect time for us to get together for a chat—although Hideko seemed to be upset about something and didn't bring any cakes as she usually did. She hadn't been quite herself since the beginning of the school term, but I had not paid it much attention.

I poured us some tea and we went into the living room. She was thirty-three now, but didn't look much different from when she was in university. She sat in silence and I was about to ask if there was something wrong when she suddenly looked up.

"As you know, I am not good at keeping things to myself," she said.

I knew from experience that she was leading up to a secret, but what she said next was most unexpected.

"Did you read about the airline hostess who was murdered the other day?"

"You mean the one in the apartment on the other side of the station? That was last Friday, wasn't it?"

Hideko nodded and gave a deep sigh. The murder she referred to had taken place in a medium-priced apartment on the second floor of a condominium about half a mile from where we lived. The victim had been strangled to death on Thursday night. When she failed to turn up for work on Friday, her boss became worried and rang the caretaker of her building and asked him to check her apartment. The caretaker found her door open and discovered her body on the bed. That was only last Friday, just three days ago.

"The newspaper said that her room had not been in disarray and that she was usually very careful about whom she opened the door to, so the murderer was likely to have been an acquaintance," I said. "Why—what about it?"

"She was twenty-three and lived in apartment two-oh-three." Hideko spoke in a flat, husky whisper. "This is strictly between you and me. I think Saiki was seeing her."

Saiki is Hideko's husband. I was at a loss for words.

"They say that the police are checking her acuaintances. They haven't come to see Saiki yet, but I keep expecting them at any minute. I can't sleep properly at night."

"What makes you think Saiki was seeing her?"

Hideko frowned. "He started coming home late last fall. Sometimes he didn't get in until early morning, and although he said it was because he was busy at work it seemed very odd. One day—it was the end of March, I think—I happened to see him at the station, but before I could call out to him he left by the exit leading to the other side. I followed him. He went into the building where the murder victim lived and rang the bell of an apartment on an upper floor. I heard a woman's voice answer him through the intercom before she let him in. Then he went inside and got on the elevator."

Tears filled her eyes, and she bit her lip in an effort not to cry.

"Are you certain it was the same building where the murder was committed?"

She nodded, wiping her eyes. "Not only that. The night of the murder Saiki didn't come home until almost two o'clock. He was as white as a sheet and would not talk to me—he just went straight to bed."

My pulse raced. "Have you talked to him about it?"

Hideko shook her head. "I've been too frightened. What would I do if he admitted everything? What about the children?" Hideko gave a sob and buried her face in her hands.

I thought about her thirty-eight-year-old husband, Saiki, and their two children. Hideko had been very popular with the young men at the university and all our group were surprised when she announced she was going to marry the man her parents had chosen for her. They were married the March after she graduated and their first son wsa born that December. Their second son was born two years later. Saiki's career seemed to be progressing steadily and they had appeared to be a happy family.

"So you mean you're going to behave as if nothing has happened."

"Yes. It's probably only a matter of time before the police catch up with him, but I want to give him the benefit of the doubt. I want to keep my family together." She looked at me imploringly. "I couldn't keep it to myself any longer—it is so painful. That's why I had to tell you. I know I can trust you—you never give away any secrets."

"Of course," I assured her. "I wouldn't dream of it." But I found myself in the grip of a horrible premonition.

Unfortunately, my premonition became fact—but in a way I never even guessed.

Next morning, just after I had seen my husband and children off for the day, I had a phone call from Harue Takehara. Harue, Hideko, another friend, and I had formed a close-knit group during our university days, and although the other two had drifted away from Hideko and me, now that Harue's children had started school and she had more free time, she would sometimes give me a ring and chat for a while.

"I was reading in the newspaper this morning," she said, "about the murder near your apartment."

"Have they caught who did it?" I asked.

"No, not yet, but apparently the police had a tip about a man who lived about half a mile from there who had been having an affair with the victim and they've called him in to interrogate. He's an executive with a foreign insurance company and is married with children."

The pulse started to pound in my head.

"I know it's an awful thing to say, but the man couldn't be Hideko's husband, could it? I mean, the description fits him perfectly. Hideko hasn't been behaving strangely, has she?"

Even as I realized that the worst had happened, I felt an almost overpowering desire to tell Harue everything Hideko had told me the day before, but of course I didn't. "I haven't noticed anything in particular," I said. "How did you say the police found out about the man?"

"Someone who knew about them tipped them off."

"I see."

"Anyway, why don't you pop down to see Hideko. If it is Saiki, she might be all alone and need someone to talk to."

Although Harue sounded outwardly worried, she seemed to be suppressing a strange excitement.

After I hung up, I decided to go and see Hideko. But even as I started to get ready, the doorbell rang. It was Hideko. I had only to glance at her almost deranged face to see that my worst fears had come true. "Come inside," I said, putting my arms around her. She followed me into the living room and stood staring at me darkly.

"I thought you were my friend." She spoke in a cold, disdainful voice I had never heard her use before. I had no idea what she meant.

"I trusted you. I have always told you everything, even things I would never tell my parents or my husband."

"I know that, Hideko. And I would never dream of—"

"How can you lie to me like that?" She was so angry she was trembling. "I want to know why you told the police about Saiki and that woman."

"What?"

"Yesterday I told you an important secret—you are the only one I told! And then last night a little after ten, two detectives came to our apartment. I answered the door and they told me they had learned that my husband had been a regular visitor at the victim's apartment. Saiki came to see what was wrong and they started to question him. It woke the children, so he suggested he go with them to the police station.

"He didn't come home until after one in the morning. From what he could gather, the police had received an anonymous phone call at about nine o'clock from a woman who gave my husband's name and address and suggested they look into it. Saiki told them he had never even met the victim and that he had nothing to do with her murder. But he doesn't have an alibi for the night of the crime and they are suspicious. What made you phone them? What have you got against us?" She was almost hysterical.

"It wasn't me, Hideko!"

"Don't lie to me! Who else could it be but you? No sooner did I tell you than you phoned the police and told them the whole story. Are you jealous of us because we're such a happy family? Is that why you've spent all these years pretending to be my friend? To get me to tell you my secrets so you could betray me?"

I reached out to her. "Wait a minute, please, Hideko. Stop and think. Why would I—"

She pushed me away. "My husband has been called down to the police station again this morning! This time they might arrest him! His life is ruined and so is mine—and it is all your fault!"

Again I tried to calm her down, but she brushed me aside as if I were diseased and ran out of the apartment, still cursing me. A neighbor looked out to see what the commotion was about and I decided it would be best not to follow Hideko for the moment.

The more I thought about it, the more I realized how difficult it would be to explain away Hideko's misunderstanding. It was a hideous coincidence that an anonymous caller should happen to phone the police on the very same day that Hideko had told me her suspicions about Saiki. I could only suppose it had been someone who lived in the same building as the victim or someone who knew her and knew about her affair with Saiki, but there was no way of telling who it was.

If Saiki was arrested for murder, Hideko would never forgive me for as long as she lived. I pressed my head against the soft pillow and groaned. I wished she had never shared her secret with me. Secrets are lethal. They are almost always sure to leak out and bring suspicion on everyone who knows about them.

When the evening paper was delivered, I found the story Harue had seen in the morning edition. Although Saiki's identity was not exposed, anyone who knew him would soon guess he was the suspect, as Harue had.

I also watched the television news, but they did not say there had been an arrest, so I supposed that Saiki's interrogation was still under way.

Next morning, there was still no news. I had to go to shopping in the afternoon and at about four o'clock I set out for the local supermarket. On my way, I ran into three other women from my building. Our condominium is quite small, so the residents all know each other. Hideko, three other housewives, and I who have children of approximately the same age were especially friendly and we often met at the supermarket at that time of day. However, their reaction that day was chilling. I smiled as usual when I saw them, but although two of them automatically returned my smile, they looked embarrassed and would not meet my eyes and the third gave me a look of disdain. After exchanging a few words, they turned their backs on me and hurried away.

There were several older housewives standing on the corner. One of them was my next-door neighbor, and although we weren't close we always exchanged greetings when we met. This time, however, she looked through me as if I were not there. I dropped my eyes and walked on, and as I did she said in a loud voice, "You can't judge a person by their looks, I see. You have to be very careful what you say to some people, even if they do live next door."

Realizing now why everyone was behaving so strangely, and not wanting to meet anyone else, I hurried back to my apartment. It was a hot, humid day and I was drenched with perspiration. I was just about to enter the elevator when I noticed the plump figure of the caretaker's wife. She was a friendly woman of about forty-five who loved to chat, but you had to watch what you said to her as you could be sure that the next day it would be all over the building. Still, I made up my mind to speak to her.

"Excuse me, but I wonder if you can tell me something?"

I must have looked desperate, but she just watched me in silence.

"Have you had any news about Mrs. Saiki's husband?" I asked.

A look of confusion appeared on her small round face, but I knew she must know.

"I noticed something about him in the newspaper yesterday and I couldn't help but worry," I said, fixing her with a hard stare.

"You mean about him helping the police with their inquiries? Apparently some sneak phoned the police and told them he'd been a regular visitor to that murdered woman's apartment," she said in an offensive, sarcastic voice.

"But was it true? I mean, is he still being investigated?"

"No, it was all cleared up yesterday. The police cross-examined him the night before last and all day yesterday, but he finally managed to prove his innocence. I heard the whole story from his wife."

"From Hideko?"

"That's right. She came down to see me. She was very angry, very hurt."

"Well, at least he was able to prove his innocence."

"Yes—apparently it was true that he was a regular visitor to the victim's building, but it was not her apartment he went to. It was the one above. It belonged to the female proprietor of a bar he frequented and they had been very close since last autumn. Mr. Saiki tried to keep it a secret, but yesterday afternoon when he saw that he had no alternative he told them everything. The woman's statement backed him up, and when they realized he had nothing to do with the victim the police let him go. In other words, the woman who tipped off the police made a mistake."

"The important thing is that he isn't a suspect any more."

"Not necessarily. Put yourself in his wife's place. Not only did her husband admit that he was having an affair, but she also had another shock. As a matter of fact, she had known that her husband frequented that building for some time, but when she read about the murder she didn't have the nerve to ask him about it. Instead, she talked it over with an old school friend—and would you believe that same friend went and informed on him? The person Hideko trusted most told the police! What kind of person could do a thing like that?"

I walked away in silence. It went without saying that she was referring to me and that the reason that Hideko had gone to the caretaker's wife was to ensure that everyone in the building heard about my betrayal. She was so angry she didn't care that she was spreading the word about her husband's affair as long as she could make everyone despise me for my faithlessness.

It was so unfair. I wanted to run through the building and tell everyone I wasn't guilty of betraying Hideko. But I forced myself to calm down and go back to my apartment. I knew it would be best ignore it. In time the neighbors would find something else to occupy their curiosity and Hideko would probably realize her mistake eventually.

Two days later, it was announced in the papers and on television that the woman's murderer had been arrested—a young man who had once been her lover had tried to renew the relationship and when she refused he had killed her in a fit of anger. I thought this would make Hideko feel a bit more charitable toward me, but the hostility around me did not subside in the least. The group I had been friendly with before still ignored me when we met and even the older housewives who had not heard the rumors initially now looked at me coolly. My guess was that Hideko continued to bring up the subject in conversation to make sure they would not forget what she thought I had done. I led a lonely existence.

In July, almost a month later, we held a class runion. Hideko and I had attended a private university and thanks to the hard work of a dedicated few, eleven years after graduation most of our classmates were still making the effort to appear at the annual reunions.

I arrived at the restaurant about fifteen minutes late. It was filled with over twenty classmates and our favorite old professor. I saw Hideko at the end of the long table, but she would not meet my eyes so I went to an empty seat and sat down as if nothing was wrong.

We spent the meal listening to the reminiscences of the professor, and when we had finished eating we moved into the lounge where old friends could sit together and chat. I sat in a group with Harue Takehara and other old classmates and started to talk with them but I soon realized there was something strange in their behavior. They would be in mid-sentence and see Hideko looking at them, and they would break off, make an excuse, and move away.

"Please stay with me for a little while when this is over," I whispered to Harue, who was still close by. "I need to talk to you."

After the reunion broke up, she and I went to a small coffee bar nearby and sat at a rear table, out of sight. "You didn't by chance hear anything bad about me from Hideko, did you?" I asked her.

"Yes," Harue replied with a nod. "Before the meal started. Did you really tell the police about her husband?"

"Of course I didn't." Tears came to my eyes. "It's a terrible misunderstanding. Someone did telephone the police right after Hideko told me her fears about her husband, so she refuses to believe it was not me. But I never told a soul, much less the police—I swear to you I didn't, Harue."

Moved by my fervor, she said, "I'll tell this to Hideko if she gives me the chance. All the same, it's best not to listen to people's secrets. It's only natural to want to talk about them and they're sure to slip out sooner or later."

After Harue and I parted, I found myself growing angry with Hideko. I could understand her wanting to spite me after her husband was arrested, but she was carrying things too far. If it really had been me who phoned the police, it might have been my just due, but I hadn't—it was the fabrication of a suspicious mind. And possibly, it occurred to me, a guilty one. She could be feeling disloyal about suspecting Saiki of murder and of going so far as to voice her suspicions to me.

Until that moment, I had merely felt confused and hoped that Hideko would soon get over it, but now I found and angry resentment growing within me. I began to wish she would move away or get psychiatric help—anything to stop her from ruining my life.

It was the beginning of August, about ten days after the class reunion, and Hideko was walking from the station at about ten-thirty at
night after a visit with her parents. The main road was much brighter
and there were more people around, but she was in a hurry and chose
the shorter route through the back streets. She had just passed a
crossroads when she was suddenly hit about the head and shoulders
with a stick. She cried out and collapsed and her assailant disappeared
into the night, but not before Hideko got a view of the retreating figure.
She managed to make her way to a nearby police box, where she
reported that the attacker had been a woman wearing slacks. From the
woman's hairstyle and figure, Hideko recognized her as a resident of
her condominium. When asked who, the name she gave was mine.

It was a little before eleven o'clock when the local police sergeant
came to see me. My husband was away on business, my two children
were in bed asleep, and I had just got out of the bath when he arrived.

He told me what had happened and asked me everything I had done
that evening and the contents of all the programs I had watched on TV
after putting the children to bed. After interviewing me for about an
hour, he went away.

Next morning the detective in charge of the case came to see me with
a young assistant. With regard to my motive for attacking her, Hideko
had told them I had informed on her husband and that the subsequent
disintegration of our friendship had so incensed me that I had lain in
wait for her the night before. I told them it had not been I who had
tipped them off about Saiki and that Hideko was laboring under a
horrible misunderstanding. And I would never dream of attacking her
—it was an appalling and false accusation.

"I am the officer who received the tip about Saiki," the younger
detective said thoughtfully. "And I must say that the voice on the phone
did not sound like yours."

The questioning took another hour of my time, but in the end they
went away empty-handed, unable to find enough evidence to support
Hideko's charge . . .

I spent the next two days in a kind of vacuum. The rainy season was
over and the searing heat of summer had begun. I don't like air con-
ditioning and after two days of the relentless heat I found my anger
toward Hideko accelerating. She was ruining my reputation and I
didn't want her to get away with it.

The police were no help. I hadn't heard a word from them since their
second visit and I didn't know if they still considered me a suspect or if
they had caught Hideko's assailant. I decided that if they did charge me,
I would sue Hideko for defamation of character.

Finally I telephoned the police station and asked to be put through
to the detective in charge of the inquiry. After a short wait I was put
through to a voice I recognized as belonging to the younger detective.

"Am I still suspected of the attack?" I asked him. "If that is the case, I would like to confront Hideko at the police station and see if she still accuses me of it."

There was a short silence and then he said, "The detective in charge of the case is at Mrs. Saiki's apartment at the moment. We are trying to get at the truth."

"How do you mean?"

"We did a door-to-door inquiry around the scene of the crime and came across a student who heard Mrs. Saiki scream. He looked out from his third-floor window and saw a woman lying in the street. He was about to go help her, but she suddenly stood up and ran off."

"What about her attacker?"

"He saw no sign of anyone else."

He told me that he would get in touch again as soon as they knew anything definite, and with that the young detective rang off.

Trying to get at the truth, he had said. Did that mean they suspected Hideko of lying? I started to tremble uncontrollably.

Was it possible that Hideko had beaten herself around the head and shoulders and then made up a fictitious account of an attack, putting me in the role of assailant? That the whole thing had been planned in an effort to incriminate me? This led to another shocking thought. Perhaps this was not her first lie in connection with me. Perhaps the anonymous phone call to the police had been part of a plan. Hideko had come to me three days after the discovery of the murder of the stewardess and told me that her husband had been a regular visitor to the victim's apartment. Later that day the police had received an anonymous call suggesting that Hideko's husband might be the murderer. The timing being what it was, Hideko had accused me of being the informer. However, it could just as easily have been Hideko herself.

She must have known that her husband was having an affair with a woman on the floor above the victim's apartment. Using this knowledge she gave the police a false tip, then blamed it on me. Now that I came to think of it, her husband would not suffer very much—he had only to admit to his affair and have the woman in question provide him with an alibi. Since he worked for a foreign company, his career was not likely to suffer any serious damage. Foreign companies do not interfere with their employees' private lives the way Japanese companies do. It would be the ideal revenge for Hideko to take on him for having an affair in the first place.

I felt as if a fog had been lifted from my eyes. I was sure I was right. But why did Hideko try to blame it on me? What had I done to deserve her enmity? Ever since we had been students together, Hideko had told me countless secrets she would never dream of telling anyone else. It was a sign of how much she had trusted me, and I had never betrayed that trust. Or had I? I sat down on the sofa and thought back over all the secrets she had told me through the years. And one in particular stood out in my mind.

It was the year after we had graduated from college, just before she was due to marry Saiki. On the evening three days before the wedding she had phoned and asked me to come to her house. When I arrived, she took me up to her room and showed me a photograph she had hidden in the drawer of her bureau. It was a picture of a handsome young man wearing mountaineering clothes. I recognized him as Toshiro Isomura from our class in university.

"I've been seeing him since we graduated," she told me, "and although he likes me he hasn't offered to marry me. That is why I'm going to marry Saiki—to spite him. But I really love Toshiro," she had added, breaking into tears.

Contrary to my fears, Hideko's marriage had seemed to be a very happy one. Her first child had come so fast, I don't think she had time to think about her earlier love.

I heard later that Toshiro Isomura had gotten married—but a year ago he died at the age of thirty-two. He had been on a mountaineering trip with some colleagues and they were caught in an avalanche. I had attended the funeral with Harue. As fate would have it, Hideko happened to be on a trip abroad at the time and did not know about his death.

The funeral had taken place on a cold drizzly day and when it was over, Harue had remarked sadly, "Think of it. He died almost exactly ten years after graduation."

Ten years—somehow it had sounded to me as if the statute of limitations had run out.

I sat on the sofa, gripped with a terrible memory. Then I reached for the phone and dialed Harue's number.

"Harue," I said when she picked up, "do you remember what I told you after Toshiro Isomura's funeral?"

It was obvious Harue didn't know what I was talking about.

"Don't you remember—I told you that he and Hideko used to be lovers and that as ten years had passed I thought it was all right to tell you?"

"Yes. I remember now."

"Did you tell anyone else about it?"

There was a pause, then Harue said vaguely, "I think I might have mentioned it to my sister."

"Your sister? She works at the same company as Saiki, doesn't she?"

"Yes. I asked Hideko to help me find a job for her."

"You don't suppose she could have told anyone at work, do you?"

There was a longer pause than before and when Harue did finally speak, she sounded a little nervous. "Now that you mention it, I do remember her saying she told the other girls in her section and one of them suggested that, being a honeymoon child, Saiki's first child might have been fathered by Toshiro. They weren't serious, of course ..."

Her voice seemed to fade away and I felt suddenly faint. It was quite possible that Saiki had heard the rumor and confronted Hideko with it, and that it had spoiled their relationship. If so, Hideko was sure to have blamed me, for I was the only one she ever told about her first love. She never said anything to me about it, but she may instead have waited, consciously or unconsciously, for a chance to prove that I was a woman who was capable of betraying a friend's secrets.

I put the receiver down and walked to the window. The sun was shining brightly, but the buildings and trees seemed to be surrounded by a strange black shadow. I remembered Harue's words: "It's best not to listen to people's secrets. It's only natural to want to talk about them and they're sure to slip out sooner or later."

I realize now that there is no time limit on secrets.

Kozo Igarashi
The Visitor

The pale-mauve cosmos in the flowerbeds bowed gently in the autumn breeze, making the garden, framed by an elegant two-story building, a mass of color and movement. The same breeze blew in through the open windows, bringing with it a slight chill that hinted of approaching winter.

Only one thing spoiled the harmony and beauty of this scene—the ugly iron bars set into the window frame, which spoke eloquently, if cruelly, of the fact that this was the visitors' room in a mental hospital. The bars separated sanity from insanity—but who was to tell which was which? We all assume we are sane, but by what standard do we judge ourselves? Do we really know which side of the bars we are on?

Yoji Fukuda was waiting for his wife, Kanako, to be brought to the visitors' room to meet him, but the thought of having to see her in a place like this was enough to make his heart break.

The door behind him opened and a member of the staff, wearing a white coat, came in with two cups of tea. "Your wife should be with you in a moment. Please be patient," he said politely, placing one cup on the table in front of Yoji and another in front of the chair that his wife would use, before going out again.

Having nothing else to do, Yoji picked up his cup and was surprised to find that what he had assumed was thin porcelain was actually a carefully made imitation in polystyrene. He guessed, however, that this was to protect the patients from themselves rather than an effort to economize. This hospital, about thirty miles southeast of Tokyo on the Shonan Coast, catered solely to rich patients and no expense had been spared in its construction and equipment. Not even the rich or powerful can be guaranteed a life free from mental illness and this facility was for the unlucky ones who had succumbed.

"Oh, poor Kanako," Yoji moaned against the desolation that had risen in his throat and threatened to choke him. He still loved his wife with all his heart and had never wanted to see her in a place like this. In fact, he had absolutely no recollection of ever having agreed to have her committed. He could only guess that when Kanako's behavior started to become abnormal, his parents and so-called friends had all joined together and forced her to enter the hospital.

Today was to be no ordinary visit to his wife. Today, Yoji had made a terrible decision.

"How much longer are they going to keep me waiting?" He peered out the window at the quiet hospital building, half of him waiting irritably for Kanako to be brought through, the other half dreading the moment she would appear before him.

98

The leather-covered armchair he sat in was very plush and seemed to be trying to suck him into its warm embrace. He had spent sleepless nights worrying over his plan, and although his anguish should have made it impossible he felt himself becoming drowsy.

His mind became cluttered with images from his past, and the years he had spent with Kanako especially. He still remembered the impact when he first set eyes on her. It had been during his last year at university before he went on to join his father's company. He had felt irresistibly drawn to her amber-flecked eyes and her graceful, slim body and decided at once that this was the woman he would have for his wife.

This first impression was reinforced during the captivating conversations they had, the pride he took in escorting her to various social events, the excitement of the trip they took around the world together, and, finally, their wedding.

Up to that point, everything had gone very smoothly. When exactly had it been that Kanako's behavior had started to change? She was not at all the delicate type. If anything, she was almost too robust in both mind and body. Of the two of them, he was the one who had devoted himself to the fast life. Being the son of the president of the company where he worked, his nominal superiors had not been able to say a word against him and he had taken as much time off from work as he wanted. He had attended wild parties and in the end had even turned his hand to opium, which he had had sent to him from Hong Kong.

Her disease could have been hereditary, but he doubted it. His father had had her family scrutinized very carefully before the wedding and mental illness in the family would not have gone unnoticed. If anything, it was his family that was more prone to mental illness—so it was unfair that Kanako had to be the one to suffer.

He remembered now—it was the summer before last when he began to notice that there was something strange about her behaveior. She took to running around their large garden clad only in a flowing white robe. One time after they had made passionate love, he woke to find her no longer at his side. Going to the window, he saw her flitting through the trees like a huge white butterfly.

That was not all. She developed a strange sixth sense and was able to see through all his deceits. She knew about the geisha girl he used to visit at Kagurazaka and the whereabouts of the smoking instruments he used for the opium he was supposed to have given up. He could tell by the way she looked at him that she knew everything.

When they were first married, she had been very quiet and reserved, but as time passed she started to complain about everything he did. He tended to behave somewhat arrogantly in company and when she started to criticize him in front of others it was too much.

At last he looked up to see Kanako being led in by one of the hospital orderlies. She was not wearing hospital clothes, but an ivory-color suit with a spray of lily of the valley on her lapel. She walked with her head bowed and then slowly raised it to look, with just a trace of fear, at Yoji. He gave her a long look, trying to divine how far her disease had progressed. Their eyes met and they were filled with a sympathy stemming from ten years of marriage.

"How are you?" Yoji asked.

"I've been very well recently—how about you?"

"Me? I'm fine, the same as always."

"Please take your time," said the orderly who had brought Kanako in, and disappeared the way he had come.

Looking at Kanako, Yoji could not help but think that she looked more beautiful every time they met. Her mind had been stricken by a terrible disease and she should be deteriorating rapidly, but her appearance only improved, as if she possessed some kind of magic.

"I'm sorry I can't be with you all the time, but you have everything you need, do you?" he asked.

"Of course, and I am looking forward to the time when you and I will be together again."

Together again—Yoji knew that that would never be and he struggled to force down the lump that rose in his throat.

"I have knitted you a sweater," she said with a bright smile and held up a polar-neck sweater for him to see.

"It looks nice and warm."

"Yes, it will be getting colder soon—I thought you might need it."

Kanako had always been fond of knitting. Even though her sensibilities and feelings were slowly being destroyed, it would appear that the basic skills and motor functions of the brain remain stable to the end.

The sweater was perfect in both size and shape and had obviously been a labor of love on her part. He hugged it to himself and thought, I will keep this next to my skin from now on in Kanako's place.

As he sat fondling the sweater lovingly, Kanako started to chat animatedly but Yoji had no ears for her. Since her illness had begun, their enforced separation only served to make him want her all the more. However, he had learned what happened to schizophrenics in the end. Their fantasies and delusions became worse and finally they had to be locked up in a cage like the beasts in the zoo. They could live on for years, wallowing in their illusions.

Kanako was chatting away gaily and Yoji dragged himself back to the present. "I drove up to Karuizawa yesterday in my B.M.W. I drove the whole way myself!"

"Oh, really?" Yoji said weakly.

"I have suddenly become an excellent driver. I wish you could have seen me, Yoji. Yesterday I drove up to Karuizawa and back and it was like a bird soaring through a clear blue sky."

She was carried away with herself, but he was not listening any more.

He was waiting for a chance to slip the white powder he had hidden in his pocket into the cup on the table in front of her.

He thought she must be able to hear his pulse, it thundered so loudly in his ears, but even if she did not she might realize something was wrong through that strange sixth sense of hers. However, he need not have worried—he managed to slip the powder into her tea without her noticing while she was still caught up in her nervous narrative.

He picked up his own cup and made a show of drinking his tea. Seeing this, Kanako paused in her account of what Yoji could only assume were hallucinations of everyday life and drank thirstily from her cup.

It is over, Yoji thought to himself in relief. The powder he had slipped into her drink was something he had kept hidden for some time in the false bottom of a writing box he kept in his room. When it entered the bloodstream about ten minutes after ingestion, it would paralyze the lungs and cause certain death. He would not have to watch his beloved Kanako decline. She would die now, while her beauty surpassed even that of when she was sane. By saving her from her terrible fate, he had done the last thing he could as a loving husband—he believed this without any slightest doubt.

"You must go back now," Yoji said. He could not bear to hear her relate her fantasies of normal life any longer.

"Oh, but there is so much I wanted to talk to you about."

Yoji ignored her and pressed the button beside him to call the orderly.

The door opened and the orderly looked in. "My wife would like to go back now."

"Certainly." He gave Yoji a quick glance, then said to Kanako, "You will be able to see him again very soon."

Yoji felt the tears build up in his eyes. Only he knew that he would never see Kanako again.

Kanako seemed frightened of his sudden show of emotion and, giving him a quick hug, she followed the orderly out the way she had come. Yoji remained in the visitors' room, leaning back in the chair as still as a statue.

A white B.M.W. drove past the row of trees outside the Hachiman Shrine of Kamakura and was halfway down the hill to the town when it suddenly swerved and smashed into a telephone pole killing the driver. The police identified the body as being one Kanako Fukuda, age 39, who was on her way home after visiting her husband at a psychiatric hospital on the coast at Katase.

Lawrence Treat
The Cremona Varnish

But for the absence of power tools and for the presence of the kind of materials lying around, the workshop might have been that of any cabinet maker. But the violins and cellos and antique lutes, half of them dismantled and in pieces, plus the grand piano at the far end of the room, told you otherwise.

"A piece of wood?" I said, looking around. "Worth fifty thousand?"

"Two time. Four time. He is priceless. Maybe millions. He is shape like a violin and his tap tone is—" The short, stocky violin maker was at a loss for words, and all he could do was put his hand to his lips, make a kissing sound, and send it up to the angels, where money no longer counted.

I frowned. "Tap tone?"

"You tap the plate to the note E, like the piano. See?"

"No, I don't see. You tap it. With what?"

"With knuckles. The top plate, that is the belly. Then you tap the bottom, and you tune that They must be apart, maybe a half note. You tune to the piano."

"And then what?"

"Then you know he is right. The Stradivari note, only you never do."

"Let's go back to what I'm here for. You say you lost a part of a violin."

"Please—I do not lose."

"Then you claim it was stolen."

"I do not claim. I tell you."

"Okay. Who stole it?"

"I do not know, so I call you."

"Would it be easy to get into your shop?"

"It is not only impossible, it did not be. I have a ring-a-bell alarm, it scares even the police."

"Did it ring at any time?"

"No."

"Was it disconnected?"

"No."

"Then someone came into your shop during the day. Maybe while you were here."

"No."

"When did you last see this piece of wood? The belly, I mean."

"Yesterday in the breakfast time, on my work bench."

"I can see several pieces shaped like the one you described. How do you know which is which, and which was taken?"

The little violin maker puffed up like a balloon pumped to capacity.

"Sir," he said, "Jackomondo Erasmus Mussasky know. He never mistake."

"Let's get this straight. Nobody can come in here without pushing the buzzer, and after that you let them in. The only ones with a key are the Potters, who work for you, and you love them like a brother and sister."

"I do not love my brother and I have no sister, but I love Joseph and Gina Potter, and they do not steal."

"But they could have come in and then let somebody else come in."

"No."

"Why not?"

"Because they do not. Never."

"Besides them, Oakley was here with his wife. You say you were with them every single moment they were in the shop and that it's Oakley's instrument and you think he'll pay me twenty thousand dollars if I find that piece of wood."

"Wood? Please—you speak of a Cremona belly. It is spruce, with a modulus as soft as a baby behind, only drier."

"Modulus?"

"A measure of the softness of the wood. It must be soft across the grain and strong along the length."

"And it belongs to Oakley and he's going to pay me. What are you doing with his violin? Repairing it?"

"His cello. And I change it into a violin."

"How do you do that?"

"I carve. He has a great cello, a Cremona cello, but he is not worthy of it, so he think he is worthy of a violin. I think not, but for money I make his cello into a violin. I ask the police to find the belly and they laugh. I ask the insurance and they do nothing. So I ask you. With Mr. Oakley to pay."

So I went to see Oakley.

First, however, I tried Mussasky's living quarters, which were next door to his workshop. Gina Potter, who cooked and cleaned for Mussasky, opened the door and practically dared me to speak, move, or breathe. I did all three with difficulty under the fear that she might fall down and crush me to death. I suppose a crane could have lifted her, and I wondered how she got in and out of bed. And why.

She must have known that Mussasky had called me in because her first words were, "No. I have nothing to say. I did not. What would I do with half a violin? Tell me that."

"What would anybody do with half a violin?" I said. "Play 'The Unfinished Symphony'?"

"Don't you dare accuse me!" she shouted and slammed the door shut. I was inclined to absolve her.

I found her husband weeding in the rose garden. He was a wisp of a man and it seemed to me that he made love to every rose bush. He forgave it its thorns and sprayed it delicately, as if each flower was a precious gem.

He turned and stood up as I came along the path. "You're Mr. Potter?" I said.

He nodded meekly. "And you're the investigator?"

"That's right. I'm trying to get information and I was hoping you'd help me."

"Whatever I can do—"

"First of all, what do you think happened? Who would take the belly of a violin?"

"I don't know, but I keep wondering how they got in."

"By using your key. How else?"

"Spirits," he said in a confidential whisper. "The ghosts of the old Cremona violin makers. I've seen them. Stradivari, Amati—they're jealous of each other, they're trying to make trouble and throw the blame on each other. Just the other night I heard them arguing. Stradivari thinks that Amati made love to his young wife. That would be Niccolo Amati, who was almost fify years older than Stradivari, so you can see why there was trouble. They had a real row and I was afraid they'd kill each other, but luckily Guarneri stopped them. He hates violence."

"And what did they want to do with the belly of one of their own violins?"

"They wanted to examine it and see what the years had done. They will examine the bottom next, and then the other pieces, but it will take time. Did you know that there are seventy separate pieces to a violin?"

"And you think they're going to steal the other sixty-nine pieces, one by one?"

"Wait and see," Potter said. And that was all I could get out of him.

I phoned the insurance company next and spoke to a man by the name of Reilly.

"Something phony about it," he said. "We're holding off payment."

"Why? What's phony about it?"

"The whole thing. Any more questions?"

So there I was. A piece of a violin had vanished out of a locked workshop and nobody could or would give me any facts beyond stating that it was impossible.

I figured, however, that I'd done enough work without getting a firm commitment for a fee, which meant it was time to see the Oakleys.

They lived in a kind of small, private hotel filled with antiques, and the lobby was furnished with ornate chairs and tables and cabinets that the kings of France had ordered for a few of their favorite palaces. Jonathan Oakley himself, however, was a simple guy with light-brown, curly hair and a smile that, like his millions, he'd inherited. Brains had skipped a generation, but what he lacked, his wife Evelyn had. And she had enough for both of them.

I spoke to them in what I suppose was called the Turkish Room. It had low divans and heavy drapes and arabesque screens and intricately carved furniture. They were quite certain of everything they told me. Whatever he said, she backed up, and vice versa.

"Mussasky is as honest as they come," he said.

"Besides," she said, "what good would the belly of a cello do him? He can't sell it. He can't use it."

"What makes it so important?" I asked. "Why can't he carve a duplicate?"

"Varnish," Jonathan said, and Evelyn explained.

"Nobody knows why those Sixteenth and Seventeenth Century instruments are so superior to anything we can produce today, but everybody agrees that the varnish is an important part of the answer. It has to be able to stretch, and to vibrate with the pores of the wood. It's all very complicated, and the Stradivaris and the Amatis and all the rest of them kept their formulas secret."

"But why change a cello into a violin? What for?"

Evelyn answered. "The cello was all wrong for Jonathan, and it's a nuisance to carry around, so we decided to switch to a violin. Since the varnish can't be duplicated, Mussasky said he'd use the wood with its original Cremona varnish and carve it into a violin."

"He liked the challenge," Jonathan said.

"And you'll pay me fifty thousand to find that belly?" I said hopefully.

Jonathan nodded. "Willingly." And Evelyn smiled and said, "Of course."

The butler who let me out of the place grabbed my sleeve and held me back. He was the shortest butler I've ever seen and he spoke in a low, conspiratorial voice.

"I listened in," he said. "I heard every word of it. You're a detective?"

"So?" I said.

"Mister, if I had the money I'd pay you a hundred thousand not to find it."

"Why? What's your interest?"

"Sleep," he said. "That guy Oakley thinks he's a musician and he's not. He gets up in the middle of the night and plays and it wakes me up. I hadn't had a decent night's sleep for years until he got rid of that thing. And now he wants a fiddle!"

"You give me an idea," I said. "Do you know the Potters? The couple who work for Mussasky?"

"That pair!" he said, and for the time being I dropped the subject.

"What's your name?" I asked.

"Fido."

"Like a dog?"

"I lead a dog's life here, so why not call me Fido?"

"But what's your real name?"

"Fido."

"Fido," I said, "when do you have a night off?"

"Anytime. Tonight, for instance. Why? What's up?"

"I think if you and I work together, we have a pretty fair chance of earning fifty thousand. I'd give you a nice cut. So how about meeting me tonight?"

"Where?"

"I noticed a rather attractive little restaurant and bar on my way here. The Golden Ark. How about meeting me there around six?"

I was careful not to promise him a full half of that fifty grand. But even if I had made such a fool offer, he'd have no right to collect, because it was pretty obvious to me that the Potters, who could get into the violin shop anytime they wanted to, must have let Fido in. So Fido had the opportunity and, as he'd admitted, he had the motive. All I had to do was get him drunk and persuade him to confess. *In vino veritas* is the Latin expression. The truth comes out when you're in your cups. Since it's well known that the smaller you are, the less your capacity for alcohol; all I had to do was put the right questions at the right time, which would be at some period before Fido passed out.

He was a nice little guy, I'll say that for him. He was friendly. He stood a little in awe of a detective and he withheld nothing. I started him off with a double scotch, and he lapped it up and asked for more. On the second round, he got confidential. He told me he always fell in love with tall women and that they held his height against him. I told him my first wife had been tall and that she cut me down to size practically every morning. Fido laughed. I was helping him face his difficulties.

I woke up the next morning with a vicious hangover and found a note on my dresser: Harry—You passed out cold and weren't fit to drive, so I brought you home and put you in bed. I took your car. Phone me so we can arrange about your getting it back. Fido.

So much for little men who can't drink.

He came over to my room promptly enough, and he was as cheerful as I was sour. After talking it over, we decided to return to the Oakley estate, where he said he could fix me up. "Every good butler has a pick-me-up for a hangover," he said. "I'll give you a sample of mine."

In the large pantry off the kitchen, he unlocked a cabinet and took out some unlabeled bottles and containers. He turned his back to me as he mixed the ingredients. "Can't let anybody find out my secret formula," he said. "There's a valet who wants my job and he's tall, so I have to watch my step. Butlering jobs are getting scarcer all the time." He poured his concoction into a glass and said, "Here, try this."

It made my eyes pop and my ears ring like a carillon, and I had tingles in my feet and almost jumped out of my shoes, but my brain dazzled me with its sheer brilliance. In no time at all, I ironed out all the complex

problems of the world and incorporated them into a single clear statement. I can't remember it right now, but I assure you it was noteworthy.

After that, the problem of the Cremona belly was simple, and thanks
to Fido I had my answer in a few seconds. Or at least the theoretical one.
The practical aspects eluded me, however, so I went out into the hall to
think things out.

While I was pacing up and down, considering various possible
courses of action, I heard footsteps and dashed into the nearest room. It
seemed to be the TV room, and it had a closet I ducked into. A moment
or two later, Evelyn Oakley came in. I could tell it was she by her light,
confident step. Besides that, she had a habit of talking to herself and I
recognized her voice. I was even surer when I heard her dial a number
and speak into the phone.

"Paul dear," she said, "I'm afraid Jonathan won't be able to come to
the rehearsal. He's so upset. You know he wanted to play, but I persuaded him he wouldn't be up to his standard with any ordinary instrument, not after being used to a Cremona, and so he's given up his
music until he has a worthy instrument. Now the strangest thing has
happened.

"You know Mussasky, of course. He's been working on the cello.
He's a genius, everybody knows that, and he's one of the few men in
the world who could change a cello into a violin. But he went and lost
the belly! Either that or it got stolen."

Paul, at the other end of the wire, was talking now. Evelyn said yes a
couple of times, then she spoke again. "I know it's quite impossible, but
there it is—the thing simply disappeared into thin air, nobody knows
how . . .

"Oh, the police aren't interested, and the insurance people haven't
gotten anywhere. Jonathan finally hired a private investigator, but he's
as stupid as the rest of them, I don't expect much of him. So what it
comes down to is poor Jonathan isn't playing right now. He may never
play again."

After she hung up, I stepped out of the closet. She gasped and looked
beautiful.

I smiled at her. "I'm not quite that stupid," I said.

"What do you mean?"

"It's pretty obvious," I said. "Your husband used to get up in the
middle of the night and play his cello, didn't he?"

She agreed at once. "Yes," she said.

"It will probably be even worse when he has a violin. It's less of a
nuisance to set up. He might even play it in bed."

"Horrors, no!"

"You'll be losing sleep again. You'll be tired all the time, you'll have
wrinkles under your eyes and that quick mind of yours won't function
the way it does now."

"You paint a very grim picture."

"You foresee a grimmer one. Even the possibility of losing your husband. So you decided that at all costs you had to stop Mussasky from making the violin. Your chance came the other day when you were in the shop and Mussasky and your husband were talking about something. Whatever it was, they were so engrossed they forgot all about you and didn't notice when you picked up the violin belly and hid it under your coat. Or your jacket. Or your cape. I don't know what you were wearing, so I can't be specific."

"It could have been done that way," she admitted.

"And was. And if I tell your husband, if I make a search and bring in the police—that's an unpleasant prospect, isn't it?"

"Very. Just what do you suggest?"

"I was offered fifty thousand to find the belly. I intend to get my money."

"Come upstairs," she said.

I had a confused impression of her bedroom. It was sumptuous—it had a queen-size bed and a chaise longue and a vanity table—and when she slid back the closet door I saw a wardrobe that was ample enough to stock a department store. She reached in between a blue dress and something that seemed to shimmer and fished out the violin belly and handed it to me.

I hated to do it. I had to force myself, but I closed my eyes and smashed the thing over my knee. Then I stamped on the ruin.

She got a shopping bag from the closet and we scooped the splintered pieces into it. Then she sat down and wrote me a check for fifty thousand.

I examined it carefully, and then I kissed it tenderly and leaned down and kissed her, too.

Just as tenderly.

Donald Olson
A Very-Special-Occasion Dress

As McEvery had expected when Joanna called, and as her lost, injured look now implied, it was another Larry crisis, and he had made up his mind to say no and mean it.

"I mean it, Joanna. My patience is limited and so is my bank account. Now I'm sorry, honey, I really do mean that. I can't help you."

Her defenseless blue eyes in a face somewhat too heavy for prettiness regarded him sadly but without reproach. "I love him, Daddy. And I know he's been warned a million times, but we both know it's a kind of sickness. He can't help gambling."

"Oh, I agree. Haven't I a drawer full of canceled checks from Dr. Zeiglitz to remind me how sick he is? Didn't I spend a bundle to prove to all concerned that Larry's a compulsive gambler? Now everybody knows it—and I'm out five thousand dollars."

"I know, Daddy. And I didn't want to come to you again, not when you're not well yourself. I went to three banks and two finance companies before coming here."

He rose from his chair and came to pat her tenderly on the shoulder. "Baby, why must you degrade yourself? No one's going to loan you anything without collateral, and any you might have had has already been thrown away on Larry's habit. Sorry, I mean his *sickness*."

She began sniffling and murmured something about loving Larry enough to die for him, about marriage vows and wifely duty, phrases which only hardened her father's resolve.

"Honey, it pains me to see you like this. It's not just his gambling, you know. If it were *only* that."

Their eyes lightly touched, then slid past, not quite meeting. "What do you mean, Daddy?"

"You know what I mean."

"No, I don't."

"Then maybe it's time you did."

"Tell me. I couldn't be more miserable than I am already."

His natural instinct had always been to protect her, which was why he hadn't before revealed what he had made a point of finding out the last time Joanna had wheedled money out of him to pay Larry's gambling debts. Now the misery in her eyes convinced him the truth could have only a salutary effect.

"Surely you must have had some inkling that Larry is seeing another woman."

Her look of sudden withdrawal told him he was wrong, but it was too late now to retract his words. I'm sorry, honey, but it's true. Oh, he'll deny it. But it's all in the report the investigators I hired showed me."

That her tears stopped eased his mind about having told her. But when she asked who the woman was, he said quite honestly that he didn't know. "Some floozy he met in one of those gambling parlors downtown, I suppose. That's not important. But now you know the truth I'm sure you can appreciate the pointlessness of defending him. My advice to you, honey, is to cut your losses. Leave him. Sooner the better. He's no good. Charming, intelligent, handsome, but no good."

Her expression grew even more inscrutable. She looked hurt, of course, but at the same time resigned. "I love him so," she whispered. "He's the only man I ever loved, or could love."

"Love can turn out to be as bad an investment as any other."

She picked up her bag, rose from the chair, and coolly returned his kiss. He said, "Honey, I am truly sorry. But you'd have found out sooner or later. It's better to hear it from me."

A smile trembled on her lips and vanished. "Yes, Daddy. Thank you. It's late, I must run."

"What are you going to do?" He found her reaction to the news perplexing, her lack of visible emotion more worrisome than tears.

"Do? I don't know. I've no idea."

"Leave him," he urged. "Before he causes you any deeper hurt."

She turned at the door. "That's impossible, Daddy. I can't be hurt any more than I have been."

The memory of that stricken look on her face haunted him throughout the evening. He regretted his lack of adroitness in telling her about Larry's infidelities. Had Joanna's mother been alive she would have known how to handle the matter.

He phoned his daughter as early as he dared the following morning. She sounded neither cheerful nor despondent.

"Lunch? That would be nice, Daddy, but no. I don't feel like getting dressed up."

"It'll do you good. I insist. Daddy knows best. Quasimodo's at twelve-thirty?"

She didn't look her usual drab but well groomed self by any means. Her hair had been hastily combed and she was wearing the wrong jewelry with the wrong dress. And clearly her mind was elsewhere. "I can't linger, Daddy. I've an appointment this afternoon."

"With a lawyer, dare one hope?"

"How did you guess?"

He beamed at her. "You mean you *are* seeing a lawyer? Really?" He tried to conceal his satisfaction. "Did you tell Larry?"

"Tell him what?"

"That you're divorcing him."

She picked at her salad. "Who said anything about divorce?"

His face crumpled. "I thought—why else should you see a lawyer?"

"I'm changing my will. If anything happened to me I wouldn't want

Larry to get the house. And I'll be changing my insurance to make you my beneficiary."

Her attitude perturbed him. That air of decisiveness overlaid with indifference was unlike her. He started to remonstrate but she shut him off with a brittle smile. "Till death do us part, Daddy. I shall do what I must, but no divorce. you see, I love Larry. I couldn't live without him."

He sighed heavily. "Joanna, I simply don't understand you."

At this she reached across and gently stroked his hand. "You will, Daddy. You will." And with this cryptic farewell, she blew him a kiss, got up from the table, and walked away.

Jane met her outside the boutique in the Boulevard Mall the next morning. Jane was tall, slim, and flawless. She lived on alimony and dieted as a hobby. She was Joanna's best friend and confidante, insofar as Joanna ever confided in anyone.

"I needed your advice," Joanna said now. "You're into clothes more than I ever was."

"Some nasty people would say just the opposite. But you never take my advice, so why bother?"

"This is different. I want a very-special-occasion dress, chic but simple. Something that'll wear forever."

"So what's the occasion?"

"You'll find out."

They moved among the racks. Jane tried to be helpful, but all her suggestions were dismissed as too dressy, too drab, too frivolous, or too matronly. Jane despaired. "If you'd only tell me what it's for. Hey, wait a minute—you're looking for something for the cruise."

"That's off."

"Since when?"

"I phoned Aunt Alice this morning. You could say I need something for traveling, but not to the Caribbean."

"Then where?"

Joanna was deliberating over something in midnight-blue with a shawl collar. " 'Somewhither cold and strange.' "

"Come again?"

" 'Let us go hence, somewhither cold and strange.' Tennyson, isn't it?"

"You tell me. You're the bookworm."

"Oh, that reminds me," said Joanna. "You go by the library. I've a couple of books in the car I wish you'd drop off."

She decided to take the midnight-blue, then suggested an early lunch at the Greenhouse—Jane's favorite restaurant, modish and noisy, with stark-white *treillage* so thick with hanging baskets of greenery and potted plants you could scarcely overhear what was being said at the next table.

"You're up to something," declared Jane when they had been served. "I've never seen you like this."

"Like what?"

"So mysterious. And indifferent. You usually study a menu as if you were cramming for an exam."

"So why cram? Didn't you hear? I flunked the course."

Jane was intrigued. "Have you and Larry had a tiff?"

"We never tiff."

"How boring. Stu and I did nothing else. It was the music to our merry-go-round. When the music stopped so did the merry-go-round. And we got off."

"But you keep going."

"Darling, one *must* keep going."

"Maybe *you* must. Not me."

"You're depressing me. Let's get back to important things. I do approve of the dress. It's understated but with flair. Your sapphire pin will be perfect with it."

"Strange you should say that." Joanna reached down for her bag and drew out the very pin, wrapped in tissue. "I brought it along to give you. I want you to have it."

Jane's amber-colored eyes widened. "You what?"

"You heard me."

"But that's your favorite. It was your mother's."

"I'm bequeathing it to you—in advance. Please, no fuss. I'll wear my pearls with the dress."

Jane, constitutionally incapable of declining a gift, thanked Joanna effusively and slipped it into her own bag. "What about shoes?"

Joanna looked down. "They'd never fit you."

"I mean shoes to go with the *dress*. Honey, are you feeling all right?"

"Terrific."

In the parking lot, Joanna reached in her car and handed Jane three library books. Jane glanced at them with only the dimmest curiosity, then frowned. "You getting religion?"

"Oh, that. No, I just wanted to check up on something. Did you know the Church isn't nearly as sticky as it once was about suicide? One's not eternally damned. You can even be buried in consecrated ground."

Jane, to whom only department stores and dance floors were consecrated ground, merely shrugged. "You do come up with the weirdest things." She made no comment about the other two titles, being not precisely sure what the word "toxicology" meant. Nevertheless, she seemed reluctant to part with her friend. "What about stopping off somewhere for a quick drink? I think you need one."

"Not today, Jane. I'm sorry. I must dash."

Jane stared at her. "I think I'm worried about you, girl."

From the house, Spanish style with a red-tiled roof, there was a superb view of the bay from the crest of the hill. Joanna drove through the gates and maneuvered the car around the high white-stucco wall draped in bougainvillea and parked in front of the double garage.

Larry was in the den nursing a drink. He was tall and broad-shouldered, with sexy green eyes and springy dark-red hair. "Jo? Where the hell have you been? What about dinner?"

"I didn't expect you home this early. I had a lot of errands."

"Your father called. Your Aunt Alice told him you've backed out of the cruise. Is it true?"

"Yes, I changed my mind."

"Why?"

"I'm not in the mood, Larry. Why? Does it upset your plans?"

"Speaking of plans, what's *this* all about?" He tossed a letter on the table in front of him.

Joanna glanced at it and shrugged. "They made a mistake," she said. "It was supposed to be sent to me."

"A bill from a monument company? For a cemetery stone?"

She headed towad the kitchen. "I read an article about how it's wise to take care of these things in advance."

"And you complain about my extravagance. A tombstone's the last thing we need!"

"It's my stone and my money. Chicken or Salisbury steak?"

Carrying his drink, he followed her to the kitchen. "And where's Gruffy?"

"I took him to the vet's. To be put away."

He set the glass down sharply on the counter. "You did *what*?"

"He's been acting funny—not that you'd notice. They said it was his kidneys, nothing they could do."

Her air of indifference didn't inspire sympathy. "You're very cool about it, I must say. You adored that pooch!"

She turned on the microwave and started fixing a salad. "If you've nothing to look forward to in life, you're better off dead."

"Jo, what's got into you? You've been acting peculiar for days. That cruise would do you good."

She turned to face him. "You pushed me into that cruise. Obviously you want to get rid of me for a while."

"That's crazy."

"Is it? Who is she, Larry?"

"What the hell are you talking about?"

"Don't pretend. Do you want a divorce? Because you're not getting one."

"Have you gone out of your mind?"

She smiled a brittle, icy smile. "No, you don't want a divorce. Daddy's had two heart attacks. He's old. That's what you're counting on, isn't it? Daddy's money."

He cast his eyes at the ceiling. "I don't know what's got into you. I'm not involved with another woman. You know that."

"You haven't sold a house in months. You've got gambling debts we can't pay. Daddy's finished with it. So am I. Oh, what's the use? It doesn't really matter now."

A week passed. McEvery invited them for dinner. He had sold the big house after his first attack and taken an apartment in a new building. Dinner was uncomfortable. Joanna noticed the occasional furtive glances between her father and Larry, suggesting some sort of truce. Finally, over dessert, McEvery said, "Joanna, I've been hearing some very disturbing things. And now this."

"This?"

As McEvery hesitated, Larry took over. "Jo, I wasn't snooping, but I happened to see that paper on your desk. I had to tell your father."

Joanna looked blank. "What paper?"

"Your—your obituary! Joanna! It gave me an awful feeling in the pit of my stomach! Writing out your *obituary*!"

She giggled. "Oh, that. Daddy, I was telling Larry about this article I read—how everyone ought to take care of these things while they still can. It's only good sense."

Both men appeared temporarily at a loss. McEvery said: "That's not all, Jo. Your friend Jane is worried about you. Now I know you've been upset, honey, and I blame myself partly for that." He dropped his eyes. "You remember what we talked about last week. I may have spoken inadvisedly. Things might not have been as bad as they appeared. There could have been a misunderstanding."

Joanna came close to losing her temper. "What is all this? I cancel plans for a cruise, I have Gruffy put away, I exercise a little sensible foresight in matters most people don't like to think about, and you sit there looking at me as if I've taken leave of my senses."

"You compose your obituary," said Larry relentlessly, "you order a tombstone, you give Jane a pin you've always treasured, you—"

"Oh, yes," Joanna cut in acidly, "why isn't Jane here? Why didn't you invite *her*?"

If the evening had been meant to clear the air, it couldn't have been more of a failure, perhaps because no one quite dared utter the dreadful word hovering in their midst like some ugly black spider.

When they arrived home, Joanna, still with the headache that dinner had only aggravated, went straight up to bed. Larry parked himself in front of the TV in the den. At eleven, still awake, Joanna heard the phone ring downstairs. Presently Larry came into the bedroom.

"Sleeping?"

"No."

"Your father just called. He's very upset."

Her eyes flew open. "Daddy's ill?"

"No, no—just disturbed. He went to take his medicine before retiring and it wasn't there."

"He must have misplaced it. You know Daddy."

Larry turned on the light beside the bed. "You don't understand. The bottle was there, but it was empty. No digitalis. He just renewed the prescription yesterday."

Joanna raised herself on an elbow and stared at him. "Why are you looking at me like that? Daddy forgets things."

"Possibly. Only it was Mrs. Okama who picked up the prescription. This is serious, Jo. Tell me the truth. When you went upstairs to get an aspirin, did you pick up those pills?"

This provoked outrage. '*Me* take Daddy's pills? Why would I do a thing like that?"

"Normally you wouldn't," he said dryly.

"Oh, that's right. I haven't been acting normally, have I?"

He sat down on the bed. "Surely you must realize what anyone would think. All these things you've been doing and saying—we're not imagining them, you know."

"Maybe *you* took them," she shot back. "*You* used the bathroom while we were there. Maybe you're planning to kill me. Or Daddy.'

He sprang up, looking around the room. "Where's your bag?"

He spotted it on the chaise and as he picked it up Joanna tossed back the bedcovers. "Don't you *dare* touch my bag!"

Before she could stop him, he had it open and was pawing through its contents. She snatched it out of his hands. "I've had just about enough of your monstrous insinuations! If I wanted pills, I could get them without stealing them from my own father!"

"Where are they, Jo?"

"You find them if you're so worried about me!"

He picked up the phone and thrust it toward her. "Here. Call your father. I promised him you would."

When she didn't move, he reached down and dialed the number, and pushed the receiver to her ear.

She listened. "Daddy? I can't believe what this man just told me. You actually *asked* him to find out if I'd stolen your pills? Oh, Daddy . . . No! No, I did not! Well, *of course* I know you can easily get a new prescription. The point is that I didn't take them! Ask Mrs. Okama! I *know* she's the most reliable housekeeper in the world but that doesn't mean she couldn't have misplaced them . . . *What*? No, it most certainly is not time I *saw* someone. There is nothing wrong with me, everybody gets a little depressed now and then! *No*, don't you dare make any such appointment! I don't care how good he is or how well you know him . . . Oh, that's absurd. There was nothing surreptitious in the way I did it. Gruffy was fifteen years old and incurably sick. I don't care what Larry says. How would he know? Gruffy was *my* dog . . .

"No, I will not change my mind about the cruise. Daddy, darling, I'm tired and I still have this beastly headache and you're only making it worse. Call the doctor or the drugstore and have them deliver a new prescription right now and we'll talk about it in the morning."

She dropped the phone and flounced back into bed. "There! Are you satisfied?"

"No, I'm not—and I'm sure your father's not! Good God, am I going to have to watch you like a hawk from now on to make sure you don't do something you'll regret?"

"If you mean what I suppose you do, I'd hardly be in condition to regret it!"

"Don't think I don't know what this is all about, Joanna. You're just in a rage because you're not getting enough attention. It's childish. But then you were always spoiled, thanks to *Daddy*. He once told me about the time when you were a little girl and ran away to his hunting lodge and pretended you'd been kidnaped. Tricks like that aren't cute any more—you're a big girl now! It's time you acted like one!"

Joanna snapped off the light. He muttered something under his breath and presently she heard him fumbling about in the guest room.

Larry had no sooner driven off the following morning without a word passing between them when Jane was at the door, babbling some facile tale about a date that had ended on a sour note and imploring a cup of coffee.

"And a couple of those yummy croissants if you've got any," she said, leaning against the kitchen counter.

"Croissants? You?"

"Unless you don't think it's too early in the day for a banana split. I always take off the second Monday in every month to backslide. Fresh incentive, you know."

Joanna served the coffee on the little terrace with its dazzling view of the bay. Fog still obscured the valley while here on the hill the air was piercingly clear.

"You don't have to pretend, Jane dear," Joanna said. "What are you all going to do, take turns watching me?"

"I haven't the foggiest notion what you're talking about."

Joanna proceeded to relate the pill incident. Jane nibbled a croissant. Her luminous eyes reserved judgment even after Joanna had finished.

"Well?" said Joanna pettishly.

"Well what?"

"Isn't it outrageous?"

"What? That they accused you of taking them—or that you did?"

"Oh, thank you very much."

"Honey, this is me, remember? I'm sure it's all nonsense—circumstantial evidence. But you're a smart girl—what would you think if I did all those things? I'm sure you're right about the pills. A simple mix-up. Both your father and Mrs. Okama are at the age when it's easy to think you've done something that you haven't. And if you did snitch the pills I'm sure it was just your way of—of—"

"Getting attention? That's Larry's story. We had a row last night and it was all I could do not to blurt out a few recriminations of my own. Don't think I couldn't"

"Maybe it's time you did have a row. As long as you know enough to make it up at bedtime. Or is bedtime what it's all about?"

"Never mind bedtime."

"If you believe that, you *are* in trouble, girl."

Joanna's tone grew solemn. "You don't understand, do you, Jane? When you and Stu split up, you took it blithely in stride. More than one fish in the sea and all that. Well, look at you. You've got the bait. Larry's been everything to me. Me, the awkward wallflower. The bookworm. Do you imagine I ever dreamed of catching a husband like Larry? Do you know what it's like for me to sit by, utterly helpless, while he drifts away? Money, clothes, cars, this house, they mean nothing to me without Larry. It's happening, Jane, and I can't do a damn thing about it. It's like knowing, if only by instinct, that some terrible process is going on in my body and the fear of it is nothing compared with the pain that lies ahead. I can't face that pain. I don't want to face it. if I lose Larry I won't want to go on living."

The unexpected frankness of this confession obviously shook Jane. "But, Joanna, you're not losing Larry."

"Oh, I am, I am. I'm not blind or insensitive. I sometimes think money's the only thing that's holding him. Not that I have that much left, thanks to his—diversions. But Daddy's old and not well. And rich. Daddy advised me to divorce Larry, which shows how well *he* understands *me*. I'd be left with nothing and Larry would simply latch onto some other woman with more money than sense."

Jane scoffed at this. "Honey, you're doing both you and Larry an injustice. Sure, there are guys like that. I've met more than a few who've found my bank balance more ravishing than my many, many charms."

Joanna shook her head.

"Oh, I know it didn't start out that way. I'm not saying Larry *didn't* love me. But things have changed. He's changed. All this gambling and who knows what else. I've seen the way he looks at other women. Including you."

Jane laughed, not a little smugly. "You can't expect him to be devotedly blind, even if you expect blind devotion. He is a man, after all." She looked at her watch. "It's so pleasant sitting here but we'd better get a move on."

"We?"

"*We* are going shopping. You're going to help me pick out a new bathing suit."

"No, really, Jane—I'd rather be alone today."

"I don't think that's a good idea."

"Oh, *stop*! I'm not that depressed no matter what you all think."

"Then come with me. I insist. Otherwise I'm going to park here all day."

Finding it easier to agree than argue, Joanna started clearing the table. She was upstairs getting ready when the phone rang. Jane answered it, and when Joanna asked her later who it was Jane said, "Some idiot asking if you wanted your carpets cleaned."

In the driveway she said: "Whoever designed this place must have been a lousy architect or thought big cars were permanently passé. How the hell do you back out of the garage? The incline's steep enough but I should think you'd slam into that dumb wall."

"I'm used to it. But let's take your car anyway."

Descending the hill into the city Jane said, "When are you going to get another dog to take Gruffy's place?"

Joanna stared moodily out the window. "No dog could take Gruffy's place. But as I told Larry, sometimes even a dog is better off dead . . ."

Two days later, as Larry was about to leave for his office, Joanna asked him if they could have lunch together. He looked uncertain. "We'll see, love. I expect to be tied up in a meeting into the lunch hour."

"Please try, Larry. I'll call you at eleven."

She watched him drive off and then sat down at the desk and wrote the note:

My darling, I can't face what lies ahead. Forgive me. I love you.

Jo.

She folded the note and placed it in the center of the bar between the living and dining rooms. Then she called her father.

"Joanna, I was just going to call you!" he said. "Come and have lunch with me this noon."

"Sorry, Daddy. I'm meeting Larry for lunch—if he can get away."

"Oh. Then what about dinner?"

"We'll see, Daddy. I just called to tell you that I love you and I'm sorry I've been such a worry to you."

"I love you, too, honey. And things are going to be better. Daddy promises."

"I know they will," she said brightly. "You don't have to worry about me any more. Goodbye, darling. I love you."

She hung up, thought for a moment, then called Jane to tell her that she hadn't slept well the night before and was going back to bed to nap until noon. Jane promised not to ring her.

The next couple of hours she spent tidying the house and then she went to the garage and backed her car out onto the driveway. From different vantage points, she once again made certain that the driveway was hidden from neighbors by the tall screen of eucalyptus trees on one side and the high stucco wall on the other.

Back in the house, she checked the time. It was a few minutes before eleven. She picked up the phone, dialed, and asked for Larry.

"I'm sorry, Mrs. Callison. He's in conference with Mr. Bigby."

"I must speak to him immediately. It's an emergency."

Larry's voice rang sharp with vexation. "Jo, if it's about lunch I'm sorry—"

"Larry! There's no time to talk—something terrible's happened! You must come home at once! Please, darling, *hurry!*"

"What is it? What's happened?"

"There isn't *time*—get here as soon as you can and for God's sake don't say anything to anyone! *Hurry!*" She slammed the phone down and then, after a few seconds, took it off the hook. She hurried back to the car, suddenly overcome by the madness of what until this moment had seemed a clever plan.

Screening her eyes with her hand, she watched until she saw his car swing into Bay Crescent at the foot of the hill, whereupon she opened the car door, depressed the horn, and jammed it with the point of a tiny screwdriver. Then she picked up the brick and stood holding it behind her as Larry swerved into the drive and leaped out of his car.

"Jo! What the hell's wrong?"

"Do something to stop that horn first! It's driving me mad!"

He came around to the driver's side, pulled open the door, and leaned in. He discovered the screwdriver immediately, yanked it free, and as he backed out of the car, ducking his head, Joanna swung the brick. His legs buckled. She hit him again.

Moving quickly now, but no longer in panic, she dragged him behind the car and the additional five feet to the wall. Laboriously, she propped him on his knees with his head where she had struck it resting against the wall. She proceeded now with each step exactly as she had rehearsed it—climbing into the car, driving forward almost to the garage door, shifting into neutral, and allowing the car to roll backward down the incline of the driveway, bracing herself for the impact as the car crushed Larry's body against the wall.

She fought back the nausea that rose in her as she examined the damage to Larry and to the car. To Larry, she quickly determined, the damage was fatal. As for the car, all that mattered was that the exhaust pipe still be functional. Once she had made certain of this, she hastened to procure the length of hose she had hidden in the garage, fastened one end securely to the exhaust pipe and guided the other through the front window on the passenger's side, closed the window just enough to hold the hose firmly in place, and then sealed the remaining narrow aperture with fiber insulation from a roll in the garage.

She left the car running while she went back into the house and dialed the Rescue Unit's number. Muffling the mouthpiece with a dish towel and speaking in the unnaturally deep tone of voice she had practiced, she explained what had happened.

"My wife is locked in the car, she's trying to kill herself! For God's sake, get here fast—2200 Bay Crescent! What? I can't get the hose off. I'll try—'' She dropped the phone, rushed back to the car, climbed in, and locked the doors. As she shut her eyes and slumped forward across the steering wheel, her doubts miraculously vanished. She felt supremely confident. As if by some trick of the mind she was able to believe it *was* the frightful accident she had made it appear to be. And even if *they* had doubts, how could they possibly prove that the car hadn't rolled back on Larry as he had tried frantically and recklessly to rescue his wife?

Jane insisted on driving her home from the cemetery. Once there, Joanna threw off her hat and veil and wandered out onto the terrace. Some moments later Jane followed, carrying a tray holding two tall glasses. "Here, you need this," she said.

Joanna looked at her, so slim and so enviably gorgeous even in her grief. Tears only made Jane's marvelous eyes more luminous. "Honestly, Jane, I'm sure the mourners had a hard time telling which of us was the widow."

"That's a heartless thing to say."

"Yes, well—I had a heart once."

Jane picked up her drink, then set it down untasted. "You knew, didn't you? You've known all along."

Joanna smiled at her. "About you and Larry. Yes, I knew. Instinctively. I told you before, I'm neither blind nor insensitive."

"How stupid of them—pumping your stomach when your father insisted you might have swallowed those pills of his as well as doing all that business with the car."

Joanna shrugged. "I never took those pills. I'm sure Daddy or his housekeeper must have misplaced them or something." She lifted her glass and drank as if the ceremonies had left her with a consuming thirst.

Jane regarded her stonily. "You killed Larry, of course. But they'll never know. I like your father—I wouldn't want him to suffer that knowledge."

Joanna glared at her. "Killed Larry?"

"*Murdered* him. Would you like to know when I first became certain all those hints of suicide you kept dropping were a hoax? That phonecall I took for you that morning we went shopping. It wasn't a rug cleaner. It was a kennel. They wanted to tell you they could take Gruffy, after all, in case you hadn't found another place to board him. Which you had, of course. What were you going to do? Pretend later you'd found another dog who looked just like Gruffy?"

Joanna hastily drained her glass as Jane went on: "I wonder it didn't occur to you that it was Larry who took your father's pills."

"What are you saying?"

"Neither of us had altogether believed you were seriously intending to kill yourself, and after I found out about Gruffy we were certain. But it was too good a chance to pass up. Larry was going to dissolve those pills in your coffee the very night you killed him."

"You're lying!"

"Am I?" Jane stood up, still holding her untouched glass. "There won't be any question, you know. You've made sure of that yourself. I'll say I left you in a very depressed state of mind."

Joanna's lips struggled to form a smile. "You're insane. You're trying to frighten me. I've no intention of killing myself now. Why should I? I'll never lose Larry to you or any other woman."

"How true, Joanna. You and Larry will always be together. I was keeping those tablets for Larry just to make sure you didn't find them. Ah, you've finished your drink already. Good girl. Beginning to feel a bit drowsy, are you?"

Carrying her glass, she moved to the railing and dumped its contents to the ground far below the terrace. Joanna sank into a chair, too weak to make it inside to the telephone. Jane sat on another chair and appraised her.

"Joanna, darling, you'll look divine in that midnight-blue."

Barbara Owens

The Line Between

They pronounced me fit for departure in the spring. I was surprised to find a little sadness mixed with my relief. A metamorphosis was beginning at the Birches—grounds ripening to lush greens, birds and flowers returning to take up summer residence. My six months there hadn't been so bad. Expensive, yes—a sanctuary for the well-to-do to work out their privileged nuttiness. Well, I had worked mine out, it seemed—time to go. I didn't mention my small regret to Joe Ryan during our last conversation in his office.

"You'll be fine, Shirley. Check in with Paul Baker next week and keep seeing him until you both decide it isn't necessary any more. Now, an important piece of advice: take it slow. Don't go back to work for at least six weeks, okay?"

I liked Dr. Joe. A sincere young man, kind, totally committed to his work. I identified with that completely.

"I promise. Believe me, I'm aware of what happened. And how. I hate to keep reminding you that I checked myself in here."

He smiled. He had warm eyes. "And I hate to keep reminding you that one of your last acts outside was sitting in a restaurant screaming at a character from one of your books."

Warm eyes, but all the delicate subtlety of a tank. He'd often assured me it was because he cared.

"Yes, well—I got too close. That's the only way I can write—my people have to be real to me. This time—"

"This time you crossed the line, Shirley, between reality and illusion. I must be convinced you recognize that before I'll let you go."

"That expression's trite, you know—the line between et cetera." It was a feeble counter.

"And classic in cases like yours."

Reluctantly, I relented. "You're right—I crossed it. But only momentarily. I'd been working too hard. Honestly, I think I needed rest more than anything. It won't happen again."

He hugged me at the door. "Remember the percentage if you use any of my ideas. If not, I'll sue."

It felt good to laugh. "Joe, if you only knew. Scratch any dentist, cab driver, bag boy at the market. Underneath is a writer with no end of burning ideas."

"You're a good one, Shirley. Just stay back of the line, okay?"

It was done. I was going back into the real world again. Kate, my favorite attendant, stopped by my room as I was leaving.

"Shirley, I've been working up nerve to do this since you came. Will you please autograph this for me?"

The book was like a living thing in my hands—*Before We Die*, by Lora Chasen—my latest, still selling well after a year.

"It was terrific. I believed in those people. I wouldn't mind meeting Tim Brannigan, that's for sure."

Such a pretty girl. I smiled and handed it back signed. "I've met him. Believe me, it'd be worth it, Kate."

Quick color rose in her cheeks. "I'm sorry, I didn't mean—oh, you're pulling my leg. You take care now. I'll be watching for your next one."

During the cab ride back to New York, I thought about my next one. It had been nagging me for weeks, demanding to be born. Everything was coming together, ready to get put down on paper. No—I'd promised Joe Ryan. It would have to wait. Those people weren't going anywhere until I set them free.

Finally I was opening my apartment door. Home. My refuge. Paige had cared for it while I was away. My plants had grown, my refrigerator was stocked. A note stuck in my beloved Selectric said Paige would be up for dinner at seven, bearing food. It felt great to be there. Things were back to the way they should be.

I had mail and messages on my answering machine, but they could wait. A shower and nap—for the first time in months my life was my own. The bad times were over, left in the capable, caring hands of Dr. Joe. There was no need to dig them up again—ever.

I should have known better.

She arrived, red hair flying, crackling with inner fire. Paige Stark had been blessed at birth with an electric current that never dimmed. We had scarcely spread the Chinese delicacies she had brought in front of us at the kitchen table before she started in.

"It's absolutely terrific having you back. Are you really, really fine?"

"I really, really am, Paige. Believe me, they wouldn't have released me any other way."

"Was it awful? You can tell me."

Sweet-and-sour sauce stalled in my throat. "Let's put it this way— I've been known to have more fun. You should know—you were there through most of it. Your coming meant a lot, Paige. You were the only one who did, you know."

Her eyes widened, sending off heat. "Well, because you made me promise not to tell anyone where you were! Lots of people asked about you. All the time. Constantly."

Carefully, I sipped tea. "I don't remember telling you that."

"Well, you did. The night I drove you up there." She shifted gears quickly. For a fashion designer, Paige was unusually perceptive of the people inside the clothing. "Oh, it doesn't matter. You're back and I'm glad. When can you get back to work?"

"I'm not supposed to rush things, but I feel ready tonight. The next one's writing itself inside my head."

She was silent for several minutes, surely a record for Paige.

"Shirley, I've done a lot of thinking about you—and things—while you were away. Have you ever thought—maybe it would be good— look, damn it, you're forty years old. You have no husband, no lover, nothing but your work. Maybe you need someone—to settle down a bit —a lifestyle change."

My expression made her laugh. "I know what you're thinking. You've always said I was loose. But at least I've had someone or something in my life besides my work. It helps keep me—" she broke off.

"Sane," I finished for her. "Okay, we'll talk about this once and not again. I honestly never believed it was as serious as everyone else did, including you. I was simply working too hard. My brain went into overload, I guess. I'll be more careful in the future. You see, the way I write—"

"I think that's it, the way you write. You're too intense about it, Shirley. Sometimes it's creepy."

She'd never said that to me before. Because she was my old and special friend, I forgave her. "You're right, it is intense. So much so that my work is my husband, is my lover. There isn't room for anything else. I didn't plan it—that's just the way it is."

She eyed me hopefully. "You could change."

"No. I can't. But I can start recognizing it if I come too close. Joe Ryan helped me with that. You want to hear something funny? Sometimes in the past my people became so real to me that I'd feel guilty about sending them out into the unsuspecting world when I finished with them. I remember feeling especially awful after *Dead Is Forever*. Jonas Reed was the most despicable villain I ever dreamed up."

Paige sighed. Bless her, close as we were, she'd never understand. That, too, unfortunately, is the way it is.

"Well," she said in her bright little voice, "if that's your problem, can't you write romances instead of mysteries? Then your only worry would be overpopulation."

After we laughed, back on good ground, she launched into an animated condensation of her life since I'd been gone. Listening to her, I felt privileged. Everyone needs an old and cherished friend like Paige.

In the days following, I moved back into circulation and saw Dr. Baker as Joe Ryan had ordered. There wasn't the same bond there. Baker was older and spouted theories—I felt extremely conscious of being a case, not a person, but I was feeling so good it didn't matter.

Finally, I could no longer delay getting started on the new book. We were both ready. Stacking up on food and drink, I went underground to create.

It wrote quickly. Within a couple of days the familiar cocoon closed around me. I knew there was a world outside, was aware of my phone ringing and of Paige's maternal visits, but the important world was in the typewriter and I went there to stay. Day became night became day, and it didn't matter so long as the pages piled up and my people did as they were told.

"Are you sure it's not too soon? Have you been seeing that doctor like you're supposed to?" Paige asked late one muggy evening. We sat, sated, over the remains of pizza with double everything.

"I went a couple of times. Don't yell at me, Paige. The book's going beautifully. I feel wonderful."

And I did. A key chapter finished itself during a night so late that even the streetlights looked tired, but I felt elated, immortal. Lora Chasen was going to do it again. How is that possible, one success after another, isn't it incredible, folks? It was. Lora Chasen deserved a stiff one to celebrate.

My eyes burned from strain—the kitchen was too bright. Turning out all but the small light over the sink, I sat at the kitchen table toasting myself, and was only a little surprised when I lowered the glass and saw Lenny Dupo standing by the pantry door.

I'd almost forgotten Lenny's terrible complexion. Even in the dim light every pock and pustule showed. His eyes gleamed like those of a rat cornered in a sudden beam of light.

My glass clinked to the tabletop. Lenny didn't move. It was I who finally launched the conversation. "I should have given you a mole or a scar instead, I think. You're remarkably repulsive to look upon, you know that?"

He hunched his shoulders, a movement I remembered well.

"You got to do something," he said. His voice was high, squeezed, not uncommon in so large a man. I'd worried over that voice for days before I gave it to him. "I won't let up on you till you do."

Refilling carefully, I drained half the glass before I answered him. "The last conversation we had resulted in an unexpected aftermath. You know where I ended up after that pleasant chat?"

"The nut farm," he said, and giggled—a sound that would chill the average person to the core. "I know where you been."

"Then why didn't you come to see me, Lenny? I missed you and all your charm."

His face darkened. "This ain't a social visit. You got to fix what you did to me."

I reached for my glass again, thinking briefly of Joe Ryan and his warm, compassionate eyes. "Yes, I believe you mentioned something like that the night in the restaurant."

"So? What're you going to do? I told you before—I didn't do it!"

"Do what?"

"Kill all those girls in *Before We Die*. It wasn't me."

"Of course it was! I wrote the damned thing! Nothing personal—someone had to do and it was you."

"No, it wasn't! But I know who it was!"

He hadn't moved from the pantry door, but I couldn't see anything except his awful cracked and reddened face. This had to stop. I pushed away from the table, rising on shaky legs. I locked onto Joe Ryan's steady presence and looked Lenny Dupo square in his glittering eyes.

"You are not real. You're fiction—I made you up. This conversation isn't happening because it's impossible to have a dialogue with someone who isn't real."

A sneer spread slowly across his face. "I'm as real as you are, lady."

"What does that mean?"

"You. Your name's not Lora Chasen, it's Shirley Gruber. You ain't real, either."

"That's different! A pen name isn't—" Suddenly I was cold, inside and out. "What did—how do you know my real name?"

His sneer widened. "You'd be surprised. Maybe you made me too real."

I shook my foggy head. "Now, wait—"

"I ain't waiting any more. I'm through taking the rap for something I didn't do. *You* screwed up, lady. Now fix it for me or you're gonna be real sorry."

"But—"

"Look at me!" he burst out. "Ain't I a little obvious? Anyone who looks like me is just naturally the bad guy, right? Wrong! It's always the one nobody suspects. Where you been? I'm telling you, you got took. He got away with it, but you got to straighten things out, you hear?"

I'd definitely had too much to drink. "He?" I managed, sounding idiotic. "I don't know what you're—he who?"

Air shifted inside the kitchen. Lenny's eyes flickered. Someone else was with us. As my head started to turn, a familiar voice sounded from a dim corner—warm, resonant, a hint of Ireland crooning underneath.

"Me, Lora. In his stupid way, he's trying to tell you that you fingered the wrong guy."

Tall, rusty-haired, handsome. I'd liked clothing him in browns because of his coloring and soft dark eyes. Deeply involved in the investigation, he'd been one of those instrumental in solving the case. I could understand young Kate's wistful lust for Detective Tim Brannigan—I'd had exactly that reaction in mind when I wrote *Before We Die*.

He stepped into the light, smiling. "And you know—he's right. I did do it. You losing your touch, old girl?"

My mouth finally worked. "What? Is this some kind of joke? *I* know who did it—*I* made it *up*! You think I'm an incompetent? You helped solve the case!"

"Sure. With a little altering of the facts here and there. Not hard to do when you're on the inside."

Lenny made a sound and Tim grinned at him, that endearing Irish grin. "Sorry, Dupo. You came in handy, that's all."

Something was happening that I couldn't handle. I was afraid I was going to be sick. "That's not possible."

Tim's smile turned on me. "Remember how tired you were? You lost control, Lora. I just stepped in and took over. It was easy."

He looked different. There was a new light in his eye, a manic glint I'd certainly never put there. I took firm hold on myself and stared back at him. "That's ridiculous. Your story won't hold together. I know the plot." But a terrible gnawing began somewhere in the dark of my brain.

"Check it out," he said gently, a parent to a backward child. "It's all there. Opportunities, alibis, even a hint of mystery about my past. You wrote it, darlin'. Any time Lenny could have been there, so could I."

"Now you gonna do something!" Lenny squealed. "Thanks to you, I ain't much, but I'd never do the kinds of things he done. Now you know it—fix it!"

Poor Lenny. Brannigan and I ignored him. Tim's voice lowered confidentially. His eyes never wavered from mine. "Not only that, there was more. Remember the girl we tried to get to testify at the trial? She'd gotten away from the guy, remember? She'd known who he was. Or wasn't. Well, she disappeared."

"A plot trick." He had me mesmerized. Tim Brannigan had appealed to me throughout the writing of the book and, God help me, he was appealing even now. "To heighten suspense, make the case tougher. I implied she ran away."

"Did she now," he breathed. "Do you know for sure? Is it down on paper?"

I stood very still and let the awful import of what he was saying bury itself in my bones.

He was enjoying himself. "But here's the best part. Listen carefully now. I'm going to keep on doing it. And you can't stop me. What do you think of that?"

My mind was switching off—I couldn't think any more. "You can't. The book's finished."

"Oh, but I'm not. And it's your fault, Lora. You created me." His face was inches from mine, smile tender.

Suddenly I couldn't bear to look at him, have him so close. I closed my eyes, and when I opened them I was alone. The apartment was empty. For a long time I stood there, numbed, but the gnawing grew in my brain. Before the night was over I'd reread Before We Die, poring over every word.

Morning found me at the window, staring into the street. He was right. Discounting the noble character I'd given him, every vicious killing in the book could have been Brannigan's work as well as Lenny's. And the shadows over his past were ominous—how could I possibly have ignored them? I'd camouflaged him with respectability and he'd used it gleefully. It was hideous. The worst of my fantasies had come home—I'd loosed a maniac into the streets.

I needed to talk to someone. Paige was gone, away with her latest for a weekend in the mountains. Pompous ass Dr. Baker was out of the question, Joe—no, not Joe Ryan. Anyone but Joe Ryan. I knew what he would do.

At last I fell asleep, exhausted, in the chair.

I woke in the dark. Someone was saying my name. It was deep night and Tim Brannigan leaned over me, smiling.

"You believe me now?" he whispered.

I cringed away from him.

"Read the papers tomorrow, darlin'," he said gently.

When I turned the light on, he was gone. I didn't go back to sleep.

In the morning, it was there. The newspaper shook in my hands. A young girl returning home from night class. Details were veiled, but I knew his work. Brannigan had killed a living thing.

I simply couldn't accept it. But I had to. And I had to do something—I was responsible. I had to destroy him, erase him from the page. Finally it occurred to me what had to be done. I reached for the phonebook.

I started with New York. I refused to think about the rest of the country, the world. One thing at a time. There are a great many bookstores in New York. Most people hung up on me. I couldn't blame them—I heard myself shouting the bizarre request into the phone. At last, desperate, I called my publisher. He sounded stunned. Then he tried reasoning with me.

"All!" I insisted, trying to keep my voice down, to sound rational. "Every copy of that book must be located and destroyed! I can't explain, there isn't time, but it must be done immediately!"

Murmuring something ambiguous, he hung up. Within minutes, my agent called. "Shirley, what the hell are you doing? Are you all right?"

"Believe me, this has to be done. Will you help?"

"Be reasonable. It's impossible." There was a short, thinking pause. "Why don't you come in and we'll talk about it?"

I hung up. With no one to help me, how was I going to do it? For the remainder of the day, I stayed on the phone. I begged, ordered, threatened. Every bookseller hung up. I was exhausted, beaten. Brannigan was out there and I was to blame . . .

Late in the evening, Paige called. "Hi, I'm back. Can I come over?"

"No. I'm not seeing anyone today." My voice was almost gone. I must have sounded drugged. Or worse.

There was a moment's silence. "Shirley, what's wrong? What happened?"

"I can't tell you. Nothing. Nothing's happened."

"I'm coming over."

"No. I won't be here. I'm going out." If I tried to tell her, she'd be on the phone immediately to Joe Ryan. She was my friend, but she didn't understand.

It wasn't easy to sit silently in my dark apartment and hear her call me through the door.

"I *know* you're in there, Shirley. *Please* let me in. Tell me what's wrong and I'll help you."

She could help by leaving me alone. I had to think, decide what I must do.

"Have you eaten? Let me get something for both of us, okay? Shirley?"

It went on for long terrible moments, but eventually I heard her leave.

He was standing by my desk when I turned the lights on. Such an attractive man. And that attraction had blinded me, I knew it now. He wore a self-satisfied smile.

My stomach knotted.

"How long have you been here?"

"I come and go," he said easily.

"Brannigan, that girl in the paper. Did you—? You couldn't—"

"Still not quite sure?" His smile was teasing. Then his eyes slid to the door. "What about her? What if she calls your doctor friend?"

"Paige? She won't. I know her. She'll think about it for a while, then she'll be back." I drew a deep breath. "I'm going to stop you, Brannigan. I'll see that every copy of *Before We Die* is destroyed. I'm going to eliminate you. You won't exist."

His eyes narrowed, cooled. "That's impossible. You can't do it."

"I'll do it."

For a moment his confidence seemed to slip. He looked almost as though he believed me. "I'd think it over, Lora," he said slowly.

"I have thought it over." He terrified me, but at the moment my anger was stronger. "Before long there won't be a trace of Tim Brannigan anywhere."

The chill moved back into his eyes, his look calculating. He left without a word, but I'd reached him, regained some control. Exhausted, I fell into bed ...

The phone woke me. The room was grey with early light—it was almost dawn. I didn't recognize the voice at first—it was hollow, drained, mumbling terrible things into my ear. When I finally realized it was Brian, Paige's latest, everything just slipped away.

"The police just left," he went on. "It was—" his voice stumbled "—awful, Shirley. They don't know how he got in ..."

I hung up the phone. When I raised my eyes he was there, standing at the foot of my bed. For once he wasn't smiling—his eyes were hooded, guarded. I heard a sound like an animal whimpering—and realized it came from me.

Brannigan leaned toward me. I couldn't move. "Let this be a lesson, Lora," he said gently. "Don't ever threaten me again." He was so close I could see the wildness careening through his eyes. At last he smiled, that sweet Irish grin. "Next time it could be you."

"You—you're a monster." My voice sounded broken. I hurt too much to scream or cry. "You—my God, what have you—"

"Goodnight, darlin'." He was gone. He had killed my oldest and dearest friend. To warn me. I hugged myself and rocked to stop the pain, and in that instant the solution came.

Since that night I haven't closed my eyes. I'm afraid to sleep. I never know when I'll wake and he'll be leaning over me in the dark. Besides, I can't sleep—I have work to do. Somehow I'll stay awake till it's done. I'm writing a book—a sequel to *Before We Die*. In this book I'm going to kill Tim Brannigan, and it will be as slow and horrible a death as I can devise.

An ironic thing happened yesterday. Brian left a message on my machine that Paige's killer has been caught. I don't believe it for an instant. I know who killed Paige, and I'm the only one who can bring him to justice. Each word I write brings it closer. I've never enjoyed anything more.

Of course I'm afraid. He mustn't find out. I'm sure he doesn't suspect what I'm doing, murdering him by the page. If he did, I honestly think I'd be dead by now. I have to outsmart him. The finished chapters are hidden in the lining of my winter coat—I happen to know he's allergic to wool.

So I write. And watch for Brannigan. Watch for Brannigan watching me.

William Bankier
Each Man Kills

Bernard Kingsley, the crimson lining of his dinner jacket attracting the eye, led his guests into Evan Lake's screening room. It was almost midnight. Most of them had been drinking alcohol since seven o'clock. Some were high on cocaine. The girl on Kingsley's arm showed her teeth and tongue, hissing with fake delight, pretending she thought the old man liked her.

"What have you prepared for us this time?" Kingsley asked Lake. "We don't want any of your soft-core simulation."

The filmmaker was a short, wedge-shaped man with sandy hair and milky eyes. He craned his neck to stare up at the giant land developer, whose grey head was balanced on his collar like a mossy rock. "Nothing but the best for the King," Lake said sharply. "The real thing. You won't mistake it." He left the screening room and went back where young Carlo had the film racked up on the projector. "Give them a couple of minutes to settle down," he said, "then roll it."

He glanced through an aperture. Somebody was at the liquor cabinet pouring drinks. A couple had seated themselves in the front row and were kissing, the girl's gown off her shoulder.

Lake turned away. Why did he attend these screenings? Carlo could run the film and Lake could retreat to his office and pretend to work, letting Kingsley come to him with the money when they were finished. But he knew he would stay and watch. He always stayed and watched.

He turned a rheostat, dimming the lights in the small theater next door, and gave Carlo the nod. The boy switched on the projector, peering through another aperture to check focus and making minor adjustments to the sound.

Oh, yes—sound. Sound on film. King insisted on—and was paying for—the best. The only difference between this and any other short film produced at Lake Visuals was subject matter. Evan Lake knew what sort of music the old man liked, so he lifted it from the record library and dubbed it onto the film at rough-cut stage. No royalty was ever paid to artists or composers—but that was the least of the crimes being committed.

In the theater, the music of a Chopin polonaise poured from concealed speakers. The audience saw first a silver tray, a crystal goblet and a tall carafe. A masculine hand lifted the stopper and poured red wine. The camera pulled back to reveal a tall, rugged man in evening dress, past middle age but heavy and virile.

Sipping his wine, the actor moved toward the sound of the music, which increased in volume. The performance seemed flawless, but his was the face of a stern perfectionist. The curved end of a concert grand

131

piano came into view, the lid raised. Now the camera panned down, moved across strings and hammers to encounter for the first time the woman at the keyboard.

She had been pretty years ago. Now, surprising and pathetic in this elegant setting, she appeared an ordinary housewife dressed in an off-the-shoulder gown with a diamond pendant about her neck. Her skin was mottled and lined from lack of care, her hair was not a smart length, her collarbone showed like a crossbar. Though her hands never appeared on camera (they couldn't—she wasn't really playing the piano), it was a certainty that they were red and swollen from years of rough work around the house.

Evan Lake had seen her raw-boned hands—he had been the cameraman on the set—and now he closed his eyes and rested his forehead against the cold plaster wall. But he couldn't keep himself from moving back to peer through the window, a boy outside in the cold—lonely, hungry. A hundred thousand dollars, tax-free, for one day's work. That should buy some freedom, shouldn't it? But where could he go after this?

The polonaise ended in a series of reverberating chords. Then the woman, this drab housewife, sat back with her hands in her lap. She didn't look at the man beside the piano. The expression on her face was a look of such distress, she could have been (she was) a little drunk. But there was more to it than that.

The man spoke. "Terrible. No good." He was not an actor, after all. The voice was rough, the delivery mechanical. "You got to do it again."

"It's the best I can do."

"You gotta practice. I will make you the best in the world, or—"

The scene seemed familiar. It was, in fact, based on a situation in a famous British film where the patron brings his cane down across the hands of his beautiful protégée sitting frozen at the keyboard. Lake had taken this as a starting point.

"I can't do any more." The woman began to cry and the tears were genuine. Her despondency was out of proportion to any supposed inadequacy as a musician.

The man set down his glass and came round the end of the piano. "You bitch—" He seized the pendant and snapped the chain, exposing the scrawny neck. This he grasped in one huge hand, squeezing and shaking gently. A pin fell from her hair onto the keyboard. she closed her eyes—squeezed them shut like a child trying to force herself to go to sleep.

Lake's camera came in for a head-and-shoulders shot as the masculine hands took a better purchase on her throat, one above the other. As they increased pressure, her face darkened and now her eyes popped open, her mouth stretched, her tongue came thrusting out.

But she made no noise. The only sounds now were the creaking of the piano bench, the man's grunting breath, the rustle of the fabric of his jacket.

More pressure. Still the gentle shaking back and forth. At the end, he took one hand away and grasped her hair. Then he let go of her throat and stood to one side, holding the murdered woman's head in frame for the final close-up.

The screen went dark. Carlo turned off the machine. In the silent projection room, Lake could faintly hear the reactions from the theater.

"Chrrrrist!"

"*Mmmmmm*—keep doing it—"

And Kingsley saying, "My man earned his money with this one."

The receptionist hesitated. There was something about the tall, slender young man facing her across the glass desk. His corduroy jacket was expensively tailored and the velvet shirt cost a lot, too, but it was the high cheekbones and the contrast between the deepset dark-brown eyes and the hair so pale it was almost silver. When he spoke, she detected signs of training in the well modulated baritone voice.

"I'd like to see Mr. Kingsley, please. I'm Julian Holderman."

"Is Mr. Kingsley expecting you?" She crossed her legs beneath the transparent surface and was satisfied when his eyes glanced down.

"No, but he'll see me. Just tell him Julian Holderman."

A minute later, walking into his father's office, Julian felt like a child in church. No, the sensation had heavier overtones—he was in a bank where his account was overdrawn, he was in a hospital where people were dying of incurable diseases. There was nothing good about this place or his reason for being here.

"Julian!" Bernard Kingsley approached from a blinding backdrop of sun-dazzled glass. "What brings you here?"

"Mother died last month. I wrote you as soon as it happened."

"I still have the letter. I know how you must be feeling."

"And you sent me money. That was your response, Father—a check for a thousand dollars."

"If you need more—" Kingsley gestured toward his desk like a magician about to perform his best trick.

"I wanted you to come to the funeral, or at least call me on the telephone and say something about her."

"It happened at such a busy time. Avalon Center was opening and I was completing a deal for two thousand acres on the back river."

"What about the last fifteen years? That's right, look surprised. I was eight the last time we were together. Can you remember that?"

"Fifteen years is a long time."

"You came to Toronto and visited Mother and me. I don't know how she managed to get you to come. Anyway, you did and you ended up bringing me back to Montreal for the weekend." Julian turned from the window and faced his father. "Remember the baseball game at Jarry Park?"

Blood rose in Kingsley's cheeks. He went to a sideboard and came back with something in either hand. "My ceremonial baseball," he said, showing the one covered with signatures. "And my functional baseball."

Julian took the second ball and turned it in his hands, examining the faded cover until he found the scuff-mark where it had been struck a glancing blow by a bat wielded by one of the New York Mets. "I thought you were some kind of god that day," he said quietly. "I've never forgotten it. I can still see it happening. It wasn't one of those fly balls that drop into the stands with ten people reaching up and the ball bouncing away from them. This was a line-drive foul, a frozen rope. It came at us like a shot from a cannon."

"I couldn't get out of the way."

"Everybody else did. All the heads went down in the rows in front of us. I could see the ball coming, getting bigger, and I could hear it. It was sizzling, vibrating like a comet. You half rose out of your seat, put your hand up, and—bang! You caught it and everybody stood up and applauded. My father."

Kingsley's eyes were moist. "That was one of the greatest moments of my life."

Julian began to pace the wide area of broadloom between desk and office door, tossing the ball in the air and catching it one-handed. "I thought that was the beginning of the good times. I expected a lot—ball games, hockey games, you and me and Mum around the table at home. But nothing happened."

"I've always been dedicted to my work. I put in sixteen hours most days. That's how I got here."

"You don't have to explain—I understand everything. I figured it out when you didn't get in touch with me again. First it sank in why my name is Holderman and yours is Kingsley. You never married my mother. Yes, you sent lots of money, we lacked for nothing, but she was an embarrassment to you—and so was I."

"Julian, you must sense how I feel about you."

"Shut up, Father. You didn't want your business and society friends to know about the secretary you got pregnant while you were still an agent on the way up. Fair enough. You did it your way and if it's all right for Frank Sinatra, then why not for you? See, I'm not mad. I'm just here to bring you the word."

"You *sound* mad, son." Kingsley was sitting on the edge of the desk, compelled to watch this handsome wraith pacing the carpet, tossing up the baseball—toss, catch, toss, catch. "What word did you bring me?"

"About how she died. Just so I'm not the only one who knows."

"I know she took her own life."

"That's only a phrase. It's too easy. No, you have to picture me coming home and finding her progressively more depressed. She was getting therapy but it wasn't helping. The capsules toned her down a bit, but they were no cure. A week before she did it, I heard her crying in the night. I went into her room and found her sitting on the edge of the bed, still with her dress on, and it was soaking wet down the front. From her tears. I never knew so much water could come out of a face. I sat beside her and put my arm around her—it was all I could do. 'It'll be all right,' I said. I patted her shoulder. What a useless thing to do."

"She was lucky to have you."

Julian paused in his tossing and catching. The look he gave his father was half bitterness, half curiosity. Then he continued. "We hardly ever touched each other—we weren't demonstrative. I was surprised at the feel of this fat stranger, this back like a barrel. I can't say I liked it, but at least I learned what my mother felt like. Five days later I came back and found her—"

"Julian, don't tell me any more."

"She was on the bed, on her back. Her mouth was open and her eyes were closed. The pill bottles, two of them, were empty on the bedside table. I thought of trying the kiss of life but I couldn't put my mouth against hers. Anyway, I could imagine the hell on earth she had been experiencing and now that she'd got herself out of it, how cruel it would be to drag her back and make her start feeling things again."

Kingsley cleared his throat. "You did the right thing."

"Coming here and telling you was the right thing." Julian went to the door, turned suddenly, and tossed the baseball across the room. "Think fast, Father."

The ball struck Kingsley on the chest and rolled across the carpet. He was on his knees crawling after it when the door closed.

Evan Lake used to enjoy driving through the streets of Upper Westmount because he had believed that one lucky break in the film business would see him owning one of these magnificent homes. But Bernard Kingsley had kicked that dream to pieces, left it a heap of painted canvas flats and rented props. Tonight, rolling along the wet streets to the King's house, Lake felt like a prisoner in one of those Stalag movies, summoned to have a Christmas meal with the camp commandant. He had money in the bank now, but he couldn't use it for any of the things he used to think he wanted.

Kingsley had proved that he could keep Lake in Montreal—certainly he had scuppered the filmmaker's Toronto deal. It had been easy for a man with the property developer's unlimited resources. One day everything was set for Lake to sell out his Montreal firm, move to Toronto, and buy a half share in Abco Productions. Next day he was told the deal was off—Abco was under new ownership and was no longer interested in acquiring another partner. By the end of the week, Lake had learned the new money behind Abco came from the Kingsley organization.

Lake got out of his car and slammed the door. As he walked across the paved forecourt, he looked up at lighted windows behind which elegant women moved, holding glasses of champagne. How many scenes like this had he directed for up-market television commercials? It was fashionable to pretend that this world existed only on film. Lake knew better—the glossiest productions were a pale imitation of Bernard Kingsley's lifestyle.

Lake's heel skidded on a wet leaf and he felt a sharp pain in his groin. It was confirmation of his inability to function as a man. It was also a superfluous handicap. His depression these days was enough to blot out all interest in sex—a hernia was not required. Dozens of beautiful, willing women would cross his path tonight, but Lake would do nothing but drink.

"This young man who calls himself Holderman," Kingsley was proclaiming from a dais where a dance band had recently stopped playing, "is my son, Julian. He adopted a professional name to go with his career in radio, not wanting to trade on my reputation. Or maybe he thought the Kingsley tag would be hard to live down."

Laughter, and cries of "No! Never!"

"Look at him—isn't that a face to make a father proud? And I don't mind boasting he's inherited the old man's drive. He went to Baytown and landed himself a job at CBAY as an announcer. Then after two years he moved back to Toronto where he is now late-night DJ on the top-rated station."

Through the applause, Julian looked into his drink. The revelers nearest him put hands on him and whispered their congratulations. He had to respond, but there was a look of disappointment on his face. Lake noticed it and wondered what was going on.

Later, having topped himself up at one of the bars, he encountered the young man breaking away from a couple of laughing women. "You don't like this one little bit," Lake said.

"It wasn't my idea. Who are you?"

"The King's filmmaker. Evan Lake."

"I didn't know my father was into films."

"Live and learn. I could instruct you in that particular area." Lake allowed himself a moment to think about the dangerous hint he had just uttered. Then he said, "I didn't know Kingsley had a son."

"He never advertised it. Now that my mother is dead and can't embarrass him, and now that I've gone ahead in a business with glamor attached to it, he's decided it's fun to show me off."

"I've never seen him the way he is tonight. Standing with his arm around you up there, he looked like he could eat you for breakfast."

"Did he now?" Kingsley's laugh thundered from another room and Julian's head turned like a radar antenna. "Perhaps I can make use of that."

"I get the feeling you don't like your father."

"I haven't suddenly acquired a father just because it suits him at last to acknowledge his son."

"You think Bernard Kingsley is not a very loveable man." Lake emptied his glass. "But you don't know the half of it."

"What are you talking about?"

"Let me have another double. I may become drunk enough to show you."

Julian drove Lake's car as the film producer gave him slurred directions. At the converted warehouse in Old Montreal, he had to help him out of the car and up the steps to the steel door. Together, they manipulated the key and let themselves in.

By the time they reached the screening room, Lake was getting it together again. "Drinks under there," he said, pointing to a mahogany cupboard. He opened the door to the projection room. "I'll rack up the film and be right back."

Julian poured himself a beer. Lake returned with a can of film under his arm. "Supposed to burn this soon's it's shown. Show it once, then up in smoke. Negative the same thing. Can't take any chances."

"And you say this is a film you made for my father. With his money?"

"'Sright. Lots of money. For the star, ha ha. For me. Tons of money to make me happy and keep me quiet. 'Swhy I'm the joyful fellow you see before you."

"And you have to burn the film? It must be hot stuff. What is it, a skin-flick?"

Lake frowned. He held the can of film with both arms pressed against his chest. "Snuff," he said.

Julian looked puzzled. "It's enough?"

"No, no." Impatiently, Lake shook his head, trying to make his meaning clear. He put thumb and forefinger to his lips, wetting them with his tongue. He pressed them together like a man pinching a candle flame and imitated the sound of the extinguished flame. "Snuff," he said. Suddenly his eyes filled up and tears poured down his cheeks. He turned and hurried away with the film into the projection room.

Julian sipped his beer, thinking he had just seen something like the old silent version of *Phantom of the Opera*.

When the film began, Julian watched the girl pretending to play the piano and wondered at the terrible casting. She was no actress, she was somebody's mother. The Chopin rendition was superb—he thought he recognized Brailowsky.

The appearance of the dangerous-looking man with his goblet of wine at first seemed ludicrous. He reminded Julian of somebody—there was a vague resemblance in build to his father. What happened next was so shocking, so revolting, he could hardly believe it.

"He's killing her!" He was surprised to hear his own voice in the darkened room.

Lake had crept in from the projection room. "Kingsley gave her twenty thousand dollars. In advance."

The last frames of the film clattered through the unattended machine. The screen went white but the two men remained in their seats staring straight ahead.

"I never knew there was such a thing." Julian sounded drained. "But of course. If they can think of it, they'll do it."

"Snuff films. There aren't many. If he were alive today, the Marquis de Sade would be into this." The alcohol was wearing off, Lake was becoming articulate. "I read about de Sade. He had a machine like a carousel that went around and up and down with people fastened on it. Their heads were cut off one at a time."

"Oh, shut up! Christ!"

"It's imagination. As you say, if they can imagine it, they'll do it. All it takes is money. And your father has plenty of money."

"But the woman—why did she agree to it? Was she drugged?"

"Not that I saw. She had a couple of drinks," Lake remembered. "Kingsley let her name her price and that's what she asked. She sent it to her daughter and grandchild in Vancouver. The girl went out there pregnant with some musician and he abandoned her when the baby came."

"Tell me the old, old story," Julian said.

"It must be horrible to go that way, but no worse than dying of cancer." Lake was now the philosophical drunk. "In a way it makes sense."

"What makes sense?"

"It's like a woman who's never had any insurance being able to acquire a policy on her deathbed. You try to get that from Mutual Life and see what they say. But Kingsley says okay. He pays in advance, too. As long as you let him organize the death and take pictures of it."

"You aren't telling me you approve of this." Julian was disgusted. "Yes, you are, I can tell. You're his accessory."

"No, I'm his slave. And I *don't* approve. I believe I'm doing the Devil's work."

Julian Holderman went exploring the dark streets of Old Montreal. He found a tavern with sawdust on the floor, an old man in an overcoat on this warm summer night, a soundless television screen flashing high up under the ceiling. He sat at a table near the open door and drank two quarts of beer. Outside, car tires sizzled on glistening pavement.

He left the tavern and walked on, his shoes skidding over wet cobblestones. He thought about who he was but had trouble getting a fix on his identity. The listeners to his radio show seemed to know; they wrote him letters or telephoned in and chatted with him on the air. Every one of them probably had a clear mental image of Julian Holderman, but Holderman himself felt insubstantial if not invisible. As he walked, he felt a lightness of body, almost as if some force was trying to draw him up into the sky. Was he going to do a Judge Crater and disappear from the face of the earth?

He came to a nightclub entrance, an open doorway revealing a staircase bathed in rose-colored light. He could hear a tenor saxophone inside the club playing fast, competent variations around the tune, "Taking a Chance on Love." He went inside and climbed the stairs.

The club was almost deserted—three customers, one bartender, and four musicians on stage. Julian sat down and ordered a beer from a beefy gangster in a dress suit complete with cummerbund. When the song ended, he applauded and the musicians squinted into the darkness to locate the source of the unexpected approval.

After completing the set, the saxophone player wandered close enough to Julian's table for him to say, "Very nice, good sound."

The musician joined him and accepted a drink. He was a slight, dark-haired man in a crisp suit that looked alien to Holderman. He was from someplace in New Jersey and his name was Al Dibbs. They talked about jazz for a while and Dibbs mourned with Holderman the passing of the great tenor years. Yes, admittedly he patterned himself on Stan Getz, Zoot Sims, all the disciples of Lester Young, and yes, he was out of style, standing up there blowing chorus after chorus of the standards—but the alternative was to join some rock group where everything was amplified and out of tune and it didn't matter because the kids kept yelling all the time you were playing.

"At least you're being true to yourself." Julian felt very drunk as he told the musician about his DJ show and his wealthy father and tried to describe his feeling of not being anybody at all. He ended up saying, "I'm not stupid, I know what it is. All my life my father ignored me. Now all of a sudden he's paying attention. But it's too late. It's as if I never existed."

"If you've got money behind you, don't knock it." Dibbs was rolling a thin, brown cigarette. "My old man comes to see me every day when I play anyplace near Paramus. I keep giving him money to get a shave but he spends it on booze."

Julian left the club and tried to find his way back to the main streets. Feeling sick, he lurched down a lane and threw up into an empty garbage can. He wandered on and emerged from a maze of alleyways onto a street of brightly lit restaurants and theaters.

He drifted through a fragrant doorway and had coffee at a window booth. At the cash register, looking for his money, he said something to the middle-aged blonde behind the counter and smiled. Suddenly, like a watchdog off its chain, a barrel-shaped man with glazed eyes came at Julian from where he had been standing beside the counter. He made no attempt to throw a punch but he chested Julian back, treading on the toes of his shoes.

A sharp call from the cashier brought the man to heel. "Emil!" Julian paid and went away, swallowing his impotent anger, unable to forget the look in the eyes of the cashier, who must have wondered why a healthy young man did not even complain when he was walked upon.

Back in Westmount, the party crowd had dispersed and most of the house lights were out. Julian paid the taxi and went inside. His father met him at the top of the stairs. "Tied one on, did you? Well why not? You should have heard what everybody was saying about you. They didn't know I have such a good-looking son."

"I'm going to bed, Father. I don't feel well."

"We'll talk in the morning." The old man followed the boy to his bedroom door. "I've got a good idea. The number-one station here needs a chief announcer. I was asking some questions. The job is yours."

"I don't think I want that."

"Consider it. Take your time."

Julian closed the door behind him and as he crossed the room, he extended his arm and knocked a carriage clock, a china bowl, and a crystal vase off the top of the dresser onto the floor, where the bowl and vase smashed and the clock made a grinding noise.

"Are you all right?" Kingsley's voice sounded worried outside the door.

"Don't come in!" Julian stood in the dark, trembling, taking deep breaths, resisting an urge to push some heavy piece of furniture through the floor-length windows at the end of the room.

In the morning, Julian left the house without speaking to his father. He walked down the hill and made his way to a restaurant, where he had toast and coffee and tried to read a newspaper. Then he went to a pay phone and rang Evan Lake.

"It's me."

"I thought I'd be hearing from you. What did you get up to after you left here?"

"Drinking and thinking. And being sick."

"Never think."

"I've decided what I'm going to do."

There was silence on the line. Then Lake said, "The moving finger writes ..."

"You're a poetic bastard. Good. Maybe you're in favor of justice. I want you to do one of those films. Using me."

There was silence on the line, then: "It's as if I knew you were going to say that."

"I've said it."

"I've always thought Kingsley is crazy. He's passed it on to you."

"Will you do it? You don't like him any more than I do. He's made you a slave, you said so yourself."

"I never said I was Spartacus." Lake pondered. "If he found out I used his son in a snuff film, I wouldn't last a day."

"You don't know I'm Kingsley's son. My name is Holderman. I'm a drifter who came to you for money. Did my father see you at the party last night?"

"No. I told him earlier I might not make it. I happened to drop in later. I don't think he saw me."

"Then you're clear. Will you do it?"

"Give me time to think about it."

"There is no time. It has to be done now."

"I've thought about it. Yes. God yes, I'll do it. Come to the studio tonight."

Julian packed his bag and told his father, as he waited for the taxi to arrive, that he was going back to Toronto.

"When will I see you?" Kingsley was watery-eyed with disappointment.

"You'll see me when you see me."

Julian directed the cab to Central Station, where he stowed his bag in a locker. Then he walked down the hill into the old town. He found his way to the warehouse studio and rang the bell beside the steel door. A buzzer released the lock and he went inside.

He discovered Lake setting up a camera in the studio. The set had been prepared and the lights were slung, but the crew had gone away except for a dark lad sitting at a tape recorder with a directional microphone at his side.

"This is Carlo," Lake said. "We're waiting for the talent. You've got time for a drink before you get into your costume."

"Father musn't see it's me at the start of the film. If he does, he'll stop watching."

"I thought of that," Lake said. "Leave it to the old master." He turned to his sound man. "Have you got the other tape, Carlo—the one I had recorded this afternoon?" As Carlo placed the reel on the machine, Lake explained, "I wanted a touch of class, like the Chopin in the film you saw. So I gave it some thought. I had an actor in here today on another job and I asked him to record this. When I dub the sound track onto your film, I'll use this as a prologue before the action starts. When you're ready, Carlo."

The boy pressed a key and a cultivated voice issued from the speaker:

"Yet each man kills the thing he loves,
By each let this be heard,
Some do it with a bitter look,
Some with a flattering word,
The coward does it with a kiss,
The brave man with a sword!"

As the voice stopped speaking and Carlo switched off the machine, they heard heavy footsteps on the stairs. "Drink up, Julian," Lake said. "Here comes the talent."

Evan Lake, for one of the exceptional times in his life, became aggressive on the telephone. "I don't care how busy he is, we're all busy. This won't wait. Put me through to Kingsley."

As he came on the line, Bernard Kingsley sounded weary. "Whatever it is, Evan, not now."

"You've become impossible, King. I've been trying to get through to you for over a week."

"I'm working hard these days. Therapy. My boy went away and I don't know where he is. He hasn't reported back to his job in Toronto."

"I'm sorry."

"Did you meet him? Everybody in town was at the party up at the house."

"I couldn't get there. Listen, King, I've made a film that tops everything I've done for you till now."

After a pause, Kingsley spoke with a little more life. "You were just paid for the other one."

"I know. But somebody came along who was perfect. I couldn't take a chance on losing him—these drifters change their minds and disappear."

"It takes a while to get a group together."

"Why a group? Why not a command performance?" Lake waited, heard no objection. "Indulge yourself for a change. Come over tonight. Come now—there's nobody here."

"I could use a pick-me-up."

Kingsley arrived at the studio on foot, a taxi having dropped him at the end of Jacques Cartier Square. Lake answered the bell, their eyes met, nothing was said. The producer led the way through the catacombs to the studio.

"There's a drink, King. Sit you down. We'll start whenever you're ready."

"Roll it."

In the projection room, Lake nodded to Carlo and took his place at the aperture. The projector began to whirr and the screen went bright, then dim as the opening scene came up—a stairway between stone walls, a construction of skillfully painted flats. A man in the costume of a medieval soldier stood guard, a broad sword held casually in both hands across one shoulder. He was, in fact, the same man who had played the disciplinarian in the previous film. His resemblance to Bernard Kingsley had been increased by the application of a neat, grey moustache.

Now a younger man, tall and slim, entered at the top of the steps and began to descend. He, too, was in medieval costume but his face was concealed behind a black mask. When he reached the bottom of the steps, the guard blocked his way, sword at the ready. The young man was hot-blooded; he drew his rapier and began an unequal duel with the heavier man wielding the broad, two-handed sword in aggressive sweeps. As they fought, the sound of steel on steel faded to permit an actor to recite Oscar Wilde's words:

"Yet each man kills the thing he loves ..."

As the verse ended, the duel reached its climax. The younger man lost his footing and fell back hard across the steps. The guard lifted his sword like an executioner's axe and brought it down with all his strength.

In the silence that followed, the camera stayed with the victor's hand as he bent to the almost severed head and removed the mask. In death, the young man's features were composed, handsome, as if he had fallen asleep. There was no doubt it was Julian Holderman.

Lake left the projection room and hurried to his private office. When Kingsley came in without knocking, he was sitting at his desk with a whiskey bottle and two full glasses in front of him. The millionaire was stunned. "You madman, what have you done?"

"They get better, don't they?"

"That was my son. Didn't you know he was my son?"

"He said his name was Holderman."

"His mother's name. We were never married. You've killed my son!"

"He had me send the money to a woman in Vancouver. I thought he was another West Coast drifter."

"I don't believe you. You're lying."

"Sit down. Here, have a drink, you need it more than I do. Could you be mistaken?"

Kingsley drained half the glass. "My own son? He was at the house this week. If you'd been there you would have seen him." He thought again. "Somebody told me they spoke to you at the party. You must have known."

Lake set down his empty glass. "If you drink up," he said, "the pain won't be as great."

There was a sharp rap and the door opened. Carlo came in with two metal cans which he placed on the desk. "The film and the negative, Mr. Lake."

"Thanks, Carlo. Lock up downstairs, okay? And thanks for everything."

The boy went out and Lake followed him to the door, snapping the latch, trying the door to confirm that it was locked. He came back to his seat, staggering, opened a tin, and took out a reel of film. "To be destroyed after one viewing, right, King? Nobody must ever know how we enjoy ourselves."

"Collusion!" the old man coughed over the word. "You *knew* it was my son." He tried to stand but his legs gave way. He felt numb from the waist down. "What was in that drink?"

"Good, the drug is working. I'm feeling it but I wasn't sure about you." Lake began unrolling the film, covering his desk and the floor with a cascade of celluloid. "You'll be glad you drank it. As I said, it will reduce the pain."

Kingsley was sobbing. "I can understand *you*, Evan. You've never liked me. But why my son? Did you drug him, too? Was he insane?"

"He was a lot saner than either of us," Lake said, knowing he would have to act fast while he could still use his hands. "A highly motivated young man. He hated you, King. And this was the best way he could think of to show you."

The old man closed his eyes. He opened them again when he heard the sound of Lake's cigarette lighter. Lake was touching the flame to the unraveled film and it was catching fire, the flames spreading rapidly across the desk and onto the spillage of film on the floor. Kingsley tried to get up but it was as if he was fastened to the chair.

"The phone!" he screamed. "Call for help!"

There was a rumbling sound and the room shook as the carpet, papers, furniture, drapes all took fire.

"Too late." Lake's teeth were set, his nostrils flared, there was not much oxygen left to breathe. "Get used to the fire," he said as the inferno engulfed their chairs. "Where we're going, it never ends."

Patricia Matthews
Death at Gopher Flats

Scarecrow was washing his feet again.

Looking out of the window of my trailer, I watched his angular figure slosh up the low hill toward Gopher Hole Number One, where he had been working all week.

Scarecrow was called that because no one in the Gopher Flats Campground knew his name, and I knew he was washing his feet because he was wearing—in addition to his usual outfit of ragged jeans, filthy plaid-flannel shirt, and almost disintegrating Levi jacket—his worn, thigh-high rubber wading boots.

Scarecrow had arrived at the flats about a month after I did, and although he was an incongruous figure he was scarcely noticeable among the collection of characters that made the camp their winter home.

He arrived one day in a battered yellow Volkswagen that must have been at least twenty years old—a tall gaunt figure in worn clothing with an old wide-brimmed felt hat pulled down so low over his face that his features were barely discernible. Under the disreputable hat and the scraggly brown beard and long hair, he was like a man in disguise. It was impossible to tell his age.

He was friendly enough in his vague way, and would answer when spoken to, but he would never tell anyone his name. The kids in the camp started calling him Scarecrow and the name just sort of stuck.

But back to the foot-washing business.

I'm an early riser—most of us in the camp are, except for the snowbirds—and when I'm making my coffee in front of the kitchen sink I get a good view of the camp waking up. And one day about a week after Scarecrow arrived I saw him leave his tent with his dry rocker over his shoulder, wearing a pair of high rubber wading boots.

Now, a cop is always curious about anything unusual, it's part of the job—and although its been many years since I retired from the Los Angeles Sheriff's Department, my curiosity didn't retire with me. Coffee forgotten, I watched with some interest as Scarecrow walked over to the canal, removed the boots, filled them with water, then put them back on and headed toward the hill that led to Gopher Hole Number One.

When I got the answer to the puzzle, it turned out to be very simple and, in a rather peculiar way, logical. Scarecrow told me that by the time he walked up the hill to his diggings in the water-filled boots his feet would be clean. Of course, I never did quite figure out why he should worry about his feet when the rest of him was usually filthy, but I long ago decided that most of us seldom understand other people's priorities.

Waving to Scarecrow, I looked over to where the members of the Jenks family were descending from the back of their tiny blue van with

THE BLUE JAY painted on its side in awkward white letters. Watching the Jenks greet the morning was like watching that circus act where an impossible number of clowns continuously came out of a tiny car: first Jake, tall, and fat somehow, despite the fact that there was never quite enough food for the family; then Jolene, his wife, as small and desert-dried as a mesquite, and just as tough; and then the kids, all four of them, ranging in size and age from Jimmy, who was eighteen, down to little Johnny, who was eight. In between were the two girls, Janine and Janice, aged fourteen and twelve.

Like a number of the campers at Gopher Flats, including Scarecrow and old Scotty, they were professionals—meaning that they made their living, such as it was, strictly from the gold they mined. Or I should say, Jolene and the kids made their living, while Jake, who pleaded a bad back, sat by and supervised.

It was surely something to see that tiny woman and those kids digging out heavy boulders, working the dry rocker, and hauling the black sand back to camp for panning. They were like ants, industrious and seemingly indefatigable. I didn't care much for Jake, but I truly admired Jolene and the kids. They were real survivors, and managed to keep starvation at bay by selling their gold to the snowbirds who came to Gopher Flats in their fancy campers and trailers to avoid the winter weather at their permanent homes.

Most of the rest of us were recreational miners—retired folks and couples and families who loved the outdoors and made a hobby of panning or mining for gold on weekends and vacations. As for myself, during the thirty years I spent in the Sheriff's Office, my mining and hunting trips were what helped me keep sane. The open sky, the mountains, and deserts helped me remember that there was more to the world than mean city streets, dope addicts, murderers, and rapists.

After my wife died and retirement time came around, it seemed the natural thing to me to sell our house, buy a nice comfortable little travel trailer, attach it to my Scout, and head for the hills and deserts. I've never regretted it. I spend my time where and how I want to—hunting in Wyoming, fishing in Oregon or Washington, mining at the camps set up for recreational mining by the Bureau of Land Management or at one of my own claims up on the Piru Creek. It's a good life. And I meet a lot of nice people and fascinating characters, like Scarecrow and old Scotty.

To speak of the Devil, at that moment I saw Scotty pass by my window carrying two gallon jugs, obviously on his way to the water hole from which we all haul our own water.

My trailer window was open to the fresh desert air and I stuck my head out and asked if he wanted to stop on the way back for a cup of coffee. He grinned. "Shore would. Beats drinkin' my own. Never did learn to make a decent cup of coffee."

By the time he returned, carrying his two full jugs, the coffee was brewed and I had browned a pan of the packaged biscuits I'm partial to and scrambled a half dozen eggs. It didn't take much persuasion to get Scotty to share the meal as well as the coffee, and he tucked in with a hearty appetite, smacking his near-toothless gums and washing the food down with huge swigs of coffee. Whenever I could, I asked Scotty, Scarecrow, or one of the other professionals to share my simple meals. Most of them existed on the edge of real hunger, and those of us who could usually tried to help them out.

I suppose I worried about Scotty more than the others because of his age. I'm no spring chicken myself, but Scotty looked to be at least twenty years older than me, and it seemed to me that he grew more bent and moved more slowly day by day. He seemed to be as ornery and chipper as ever mentally, but still I worried about him.

Looking at him now, wearing the same dark suit-pants and jacket he'd been wearing ever since I knew him, I leaned over to pour him more coffee, thinking of the stories that were going around the camp. If the stories were true, then Scotty didn't really need my meals, or my pity, but I'd certainly seen no sign that they were. His small trailer was old and ratty-looking and his pickup truck looked as if it was on the edge of collapse. Surely, if he had all the dust and nuggets hidden away that they said he did, he'd live better. I made a decision.

"Scotty, that old suit of yours looks as if it's seen better days. Look, I have some jeans and a couple of good flannel shirts that I've—outgrown, you might say. They're just taking up closet space. Why don't you take them and use them? You'd be doing me a favor."

Scotty grinned at me, exposing one of his remaining teeth. "Thanks kindly, Roy, but I'm sort of attached to this here old suit. It's my lucky suit, you might say. Wouldn't feel comfortable in anything else, and that's a fact."

I grunted. "Well, you'd *look* a damn sight better in something else. That suit's going to fall right off you one of these days and then where will you be?"

Scotty leaned back in his chair, pulled out the red suspenders that held up his baggy pants, and let them snap against the top of the old-fashioned long johns he wore both as shirt and underclothing. "Why, Roy," he said with a cackle, "this suit will last as long as I will, and that's a fact."

I sighed and gave up. As frail as the old man was getting, it was probably true.

Scotty sat down his now empty cup and wiped his lips on the paper napkin beside his plate. "Want to come work by me today? I'm working down in the old river bed. Found me some good color yesterday."

I knew that this was Scotty's way of trying to thank me for the meal and my good intentions, and since I was pretty discouraged with the site I'd been working I agreed. In the B.L.M. camps there were no staked claims. Anyone could work wherever their fancy drew them, and if you found anything hot it was well to keep it to yourself, because if you didn't there would be twenty people working in the same spot the next day.

Still, sometimes someone would share a hot spot with a good friend, or to return a favor, and often people worked together simply for the company.

"I've got to clean up here, but I'll meet you soon as I'm done. What part of the bed are you working?" I asked.

"Where it just begins to narrow. Right by that big rock. You know the one that I mean?"

I nodded. "See you there in about half an hour."

By the time I got to the river bed, Scotty was there before me, bent over, digging near the big rock he had mentioned.

Not far away I saw a tall thin figure that made my heart sink. Mary Fairchild. She was talking to another figure I recognized, Tom Harris, the gold buyer. Near them stood Mary's teenaged son, Bubba.

I pulled my hat down and tried to pretend I hadn't seen them, but Mary sighted me and waved gaily, giving me a big grin that I couldn't help but see, far away as I was. There wasn't a thing I could do but wave back, which I did as casually as possible.

Mary's a widow, and she's had her eye on me since I came into the camp. Without undue modesty, I'll have to admit that despite the fact that I've accumulated a few years the ladies still seem to consider me a good-looking fellow.

I'm not tall, but I've still got the shoulders and chest I developed in my boxing days, and my hair, while partly grey, is thick, curly, and all my own. And I'll also have to admit that the sap is still running, and that as much as the next man I appreciate an attractive woman. Unfortunately, the widow Fairchild did not fit the bill. She was probably younger than I was, but looked older. Thin as a rail, with leathery skin and what seemed to be an unusual number of teeth, she was nothing to stir a man's blood. Of course, looks aren't everything, but her personality was no better than her looks, and so I tried to avoid her when I could.

I walked over to Scotty. "Finding anything?" I asked.

He stood up and leaned on his shovel. "I panned out a little color last night from yesterday's batch." He grinned. "I see yo'r lady friend's noticed you."

I shook my head. "It's the curse of my good looks," I told him, smiling.

At that moment I saw Bubba heading toward us. Bubba was a nice kid as teenagers go, but he was a little slow. Sort of an innocent, if you know what I mean. "Howdy, Mr. Scotty. Howdy, Mr. Wylie," he said in his odd, squeaky voice. "You findin' anything?"

Scotty gave him a grin. "Not much, son. Not much."

Bubba squatted awkwardly and picked up some river-bed gravel, letting it run through his fingers. "Mr. Scotty, is it true what they say in camp? About you, I mean?"

Scotty pulled a filthy red bandanna from his pocket and wiped his face. It was only nine o'clock, but the air was already getting hot. "What is it they say, son?"

Bubba didn't have the sophistication to be embarrassed by his own question."They say you have a lot of gold you've found hidden someplace—maybe someplace here in camp." His rather beady eyes looked at Scotty questioningly, and Scotty shook his head.

"You can't believe everything you hear, son. Now, do I look like a man who has a lot of gold? Roy here was just telling me this morning that I look like an old tramp."

Bubba looked disppointed. "But they say you do have," he insisted. "They say you could be rich if you wanted to."

Scotty was saved further demurrals by the arrival of Tom Harris. Dressed like a snowbird in plaid slacks, an Izod shirt, and running shoes, Harris beamed at us. "Hi, Scotty. Roy. Anything for me today? The price is up, you know."

I shook my head. I'd been keeping the small amounts I'd garnered. I didn't need the money right now, and I liked to look at it.

Scotty shook his head, too. "Haven't been doin' so good," he said with an expression of sadness I knew wasn't real. "Had a real bad week."

Harris eyed him sardonically. "That's not what I hear. I hear you've been doing very well—that you *always* do very well. Are you sure you don't have any dust or nuggets to sell? Remember, it's like they say—you can't take it with you."

Scotty let out a bray of laughter, his eyes now full of mischief. "Who says I can't? Maybe I'll just fool them, who knows?"

Harris shrugged. "Well, if you change your mind, let me know. You can always reach me in town."

As he walked away, I turned to Scotty. "Listen, old friend," I said, "I wish you wouldn't encourage those stories about a gold cache. It could get you into trouble."

Scotty waved my words away with a hand marked by years of digging. "That's the cop in you, Roy. Always worryin'."

I gave an exasperated sigh. "Scotty, I'm serious. Some of the people in camp believe those stories—and although most of them are honest enough, there are always a few bad eggs in the bunch. You don't want to find yourself murdered for a batch of nonexistent gold, do you?"

His old eyes softened and he patted my shoulder. "It's all right, Roy. I can take care of myself. Been doin' it for over sixty-five years, ever since I left home. Now you get to diggin'. The sun's gettin' high."

I worked until about one o'clock, when the heat grew uncomfortable, then I figured I had enough sand to keep me busy panning the rest of the afternoon. Scotty, too, was ready to pack it in and we walked back to the camp together, where we parted, each going to our own trailer.

I had me a good wash, a cold glass of apple cider, and a thick ham sandwich, after which I took a good nap.

When I awoke it was about three. A bit of the heat had left the air, so I got my water jug, my gold pan, and my day's collection of sand and sat under my awning in the shade.

Panning is a careful business, but it's also relaxing, and once in a while I would look up from the pan to see what was going on in camp.

I saw the Jenks coming back from their dig, Jolene and the kids carrying the bags of sand and the dry washer, with Jake strolling along behind them holding his back.

I saw Bubba Fairchild with a group of other kids, gathered in a huddle as if they were deep in conversation.

And later, when it was almost dark, I saw Scarecrow, his angular figure outlined against the darkening sky, passing by my trailer in the opposite direction from his own camp.

Curious as always, I called out to him. "Scarecrow—where are you off to?"

He stopped in front of me, lowering his head as he always did when he talked. "Going to see Scotty. I found something today I want to ask him about."

"Well, he's the one to see," I answered. "He's the most experienced miner around here." Scarecrow only nodded at this, and then, with an ungainly jerk, started moving again. I watched him disappear into Scotty's trailer and then went back to my panning so I could finish before dark.

There was quite a bit of color in the sand I had dug that afternoon, and when I was finished I had perhaps a quarter pennyweight in fines in my little bottle. Not a bad day's work.

That night there was going to be a pick-and-sing, so as soon as it got too dark to work I fixed myself a quick supper and put on a clean shirt. The pick-and-sings were an informal sort of get-together that we had every few weeks or so. Several of the people in the camp could play musical instruments, and we'd build a big bonfire and sit around it and sing, and maybe dance a little. There were marshmallows for the kids, and anybody that wanted anything to drink brought their own. Since there wasn't a lot to do around the camp at night, these parties were pretty popular.

By the time I got there, the music had already started. Jolene Jenks was there with her fiddle—she was a talented country fiddler—and young Ed Johnson was there with his guitar. A nice, pretty lady named Nancy Flanders was playing the autoharp and a man I didn't know was thumping one of those basses you make out of a washtub.

They were sounding pretty good, and I was pleased that they were playing one of my favorites, "Wildwood Flower," but one of the regulars was missing—Jake Jenks, who played the mandolin. When the number was over, I walked up to Jolene. "Where's Jake tonight?"

She shrugged. "He says his back's hurting him. He's resting in the camper." I shrugged back and gave her a smile. Usually Jake's back only kept him from things that might involve work. When it was party time, he was usually the first one there.

I also noticed that Scotty wasn't in the crowd around the fire, and that was unusual, too—there was nothing Scotty liked better than a good songfest. He knew all the old songs and he played a mean harmonica, too. Well, perhaps he had something else to do.

The pick-and-sing went on until about eleven when we broke up and went to bed. It had been a nice get-together and I went to sleep in a pleasant mood.

It wasn't until late the next day that I realized Scotty was missing from more than the pick-and-sing.

I didn't see him go by in the morning, but I'm only at the window when I'm fixing my coffee and cleaning up, so I don't see everything. I thought sure he'd be digging at the same place, but when I arrived at the old river bed he wasn't there. Instead, Bubba and Mrs. Fairchild were working his hole, at which I took offense. As I said before, you can't stake any claims on Bureau of Land Management land, but there is sort of an unwritten law that you don't barge in on a digging while someone else is working it. Just because Scotty was late in getting to his dig didn't give them the right to take it over. Still, it wasn't my business. Scotty could take care of the matter himself when he got there.

The thing was, he never did. I stayed until about one-thirty, working and trying to avoid the occasional glances of Mrs. Fairchild, but there was no sign of Scotty.

Walking back to camp, I tried to tell myself that the old man had probably decided to work somewhere else, but somehow I didn't believe it. That old sixth sense that served me so well as a cop was working overtime. I had a feeling that something bad had happened.

When I got to camp, I didn't stop to wash up but went over to Scotty's trailer. The truck was there, but when I knocked on the door I got no answer. However, the door was open and I went in, wrinkling my nose at the miasma of odors that met me. Scotty was not a neat housekeeper.

I pulled up the blinds, letting in the light, and saw, with a sense of shock, the wild disorder. Scotty wasn't a neat housekeeper, but this wasn't his usual clutter. Someone had obviously searched the place. There was an empty whiskey bottle on the table. I picked it up and smelled it. The odor of liquor was strong. Scotty wasn't a heavy drinker, but once in a while he'd buy a bottle od cheap whiskey and tank up. If he had done that this time, he should be here in the trailer, sleeping it off—but he wasn't.

Really beginning to worry now, I left the trailer and checked with the otherr campers, most of whom came back to camp during the heat of the day. Nobody had seen him.

Last of all, I talked to Scarecrow, who I'd seen go into Scotty's trailer last night. Trying not to sound like a cop, I asked him how Scotty had seemed last night.

"Like usual," Scarecrow said.

"He didn't seem sick or anything?" I asked.

Scarecrow shook his head. "No. Seemed fine. Just like always."

I pushed on. "Was he able to give you the information you needed?"

Scarecrow nodded again. "Yes."

And that was all I got out of him.

By the evening, Scotty still hadn't showed up, and by now everyone in the camp was worried. Scotty was a real favorite among the campers. He had done more than one of them a kindness, and he was always ready to share his knowledge and experience with beginners.

In the morning, he was still missing, and so we got together and spread out to search the area. If Scotty *had* been drinking the night before, it was possible he had wandered off. He often liked to walk the desert at night, like an old coyote. 'Specially if there was a good moon. Feeble as he was getting, if he was really sloshed he could have fallen and hurt himself.

But we found no sign of him. It seemed that it was time to report his disappearance to the authorities.

The next two days were not pleasant. The local police were efficient and polite, but there is no way to make questioning enjoyable.

I talked to them, told them who I was and that I would be glad to lend a hand, but I could tell it didn't impress them much. They did, however, tell me more than they would have told a civilian, and I learned that they considered Scarecrow their prime suspect. "Suspect of what?" I asked them, and they told me they were pretty certain old Scotty was dead. In talking to the campers, they had been told the stories of Scotty's supposed gold cache, and as far as they were concerned that was motive.

The fact that Scarecrow had been to see Scotty and was apparently the last to see the old man was the opportunity. They said that they figured Scarecrow killed the old man for his gold, which he had found after searching Scotty's trailer, and had buried the body somewhere near the camp. They began the painstaking searching and digging they hoped would turn up his body—no easy task in a place like Gopher Flats, where the ground was riddled with holes and diggings.

As for myself, I felt they were wrong. I couldn't see Scarecrow as a murderer. He was too retiring, and too timid. It didn't feel right.

For a while I wondered about Bubba and his gang of teenaged friends, or even Bubba and has mama, but finally dismissed them, too. I wouldn't put anything past the widow Fairchild, but even though Bubba wasn't awfully bright he was a good kid. And he liked Scotty.

And then the police found the nugget buried under Scarecrow's dilapidated tent. It was only the one nugget, but it was pretty large and it convinced them that Scarecrow had found Scotty's cache.

Scarecrow kept insisting that he'd found the nugget himself, that in fact it was the reason he went to Scotty's trailer that evening, to show it to Scotty and ask his advice about the site where he was digging. but they didn't believe him—they arrested him on suspicion of murder and hauled him off to the nearest jail while they continued the search for Scotty's body.

I felt real bad about Scarecrow. He had looked scared as hell as they hauled him away. I knew in my gut that he hadn't killed Scotty, but that was a lot different than proving it.

I didn't go out to dig that day, but sat in the shade of my awning, thinking. It was obvious that *someone* had searched Scotty's trailer, and I was pretty certain it wasn't Scarecrow, so who had it been?

I thought back to the night before, trying to remember every detail. Item one: if Scarecrow was telling the truth, Scotty was alive and in his trailer early in the evening. Item two: Scotty hadn't shown up at the pick-and-sing, which had started about eight o'clock. Item three: others not at the pick-and-sing were Scarecrow and Jake Jenks. Item four: it wasn't unusual for Scarecrow to be absent, but it was unusual for Jenks and Scotty not to be present.

I spent most of the day mulling over the case and by dark I had an idea that might lead me nowhere, but one I felt impelled to try.

The first thing I did was to go to Mort Simmons' camper. I knew Mort pretty well. He was about the right size and he was the kind of man who would help me without making too big a thing of it. I talked to him and his wife Suzie and, with Suzie's blessing, he agreed to help me.

A few minutes later, Mort and I were at Scotty's trailer and I was searching through Scotty's closet for clothing that might approximate the old suit he usually wore. We found only an old jacket and mismatched pants, but in the semi-dark I figured they would do.

It took about an hour to get my little scene set up, and then I took myself over to the Jenks van. It was dark and the family was obviously already in bed, but so much the better.

I pounded on the side of the camper, hoping I was waking Jenks out of a sound sleep, but it was Jolene who stuck her head out the door. She blinked at me in the light from the full moon. "What on earth? Oh, it's you, Roy. What do you want?"

I made my voice sound worried. "I've got to talk to Jake, Jolene. It's important. Would you get him out here?"

She grunted and disappeared back into the van. I heard the rasp of Jake's voice and then he appeared, rubbing sleep from his eyes. "What the hell's this about, Roy?" he said in his whiney way. "You oughtn't rouse a man from a good sleep."

I took his arm, and pulled with some urgency. "I need your help, Jake. Something's going on and I can't handle it alone."

With most men, this would have appealed to their masculine vanity, but with Jake, it only made him whine the more. "Why me, Roy? I need my sleep. My back's been killin' me."

"You're the closest one, Jake."

I was pulling him along now, and he was following unwillingly. When he began to see where I was leading him, he held back still more. "You're headin' for Scotty's trailer, Roy. Why you takin' me there?"

I continued to pull him along. "Because I saw a light. You see it?"

There was a faint glow coming from the window of Scotty's trailer. Jake was looking at it with terror. "I see it. Shore, I see it. Let go my arm, Roy. I'm tellin' you I don't want to have nothin' to do with it. You get someone else."

"Don't tell me you're afraid," I said, making my voice scornful. "We're here now and we've got to see what's going on."

We were at the trailer and I opened the door with one hand, keeping my hold on Jake with the other, but I couldn't get him to enter the trailer.

"Jake," I said softly, "if you don't go into the trailer, I'm apt to think you have some special reason not to. And if I thought that, I'd probably have to talk to your wife, and maybe the police. Come on—what's there to be afraid of?"

"Nothin'! Nothin' at all!" he said, but his voice belied his words.

"I'll go first," I said, still pulling on his arm, and slowly, gingerly, he followed after me into the dimly lit trailer.

Now we were both inside and I said cheerfully, "Well, I guess it was nothing, after all. There's no one here."

I could hear Jake give a sigh of relief, and then I felt him stiffen and make a low noise deep in his throat. In a dark corner, something was stirring.

I'll have to admit that I felt a chill up my own spine as a bent figure moved into the half light and a raspy voice breathed Jenks' name. I looked up at Jenks, who was white as a sheet.

"Jake," the figure whispered, "Jake, why'd you do it? Why?"

Jenks gave a womanish screech and sagged back against the door, which I had latched behind us.

"I didn't mean to!" he cried. "It was an accident! Don't touch me! Don't touch me!"

Mort, who did look a lot like Scotty in the old clothes and the dim light, stretched out a clawlike hand.

Jenks sagged to a sprawl on the floor, his hands over his face. "I didn't mean to! I didn't! I only wanted the gold! You wasn't usin' it, and me and my family are poor as dirt. I only wanted the gold!"

"Tell me what happened and I'll make him go away," I said, motioning Mort back into the shadows.

The story came tumbling out. "I—I bought a bottle of whiskey. I know he liked a drink now and then. I thought that if I got him drunk he might let something slip about where he'd cached the gold. But he wouldn't talk, least not about that.

"Pretty soon we was both drunk, and I started to get mad. The old bastard, sittin' on all that gold and us with nothin'. I wanted to hit him, to beat it out of him, but I was afraid someone would hear me, so I took him away from the trailer, down by the catch-water pond, and I began to hit him—"

I felt sick in the pit of my stomach, thinking of this pile of dirt beating that helpless old man, but I made my voice calm. "And then what?"

Jake's voice was blurry. "I only hit him a couple of times. The last time, he fell backward into the pond, and he disappeared."

I tried to contain my anger, but my voice was growing louder. "What do you mean, he disappeard?"

"He disappeared. He went under the water." He didn't look at me. "He never came up."

"Didn't you try to pull him out?"

Jake was blubbering now. "I tried, but I couldn't reach him. He was deep under the water and I don't know how to swim! Wasn't nothin' I could do but go home!"

I sat silent for a moment, thinking over what he'd said. I didn't know whether or not Scotty could swim, but normally a man doesn't go into the water and just disappear beneath the surface.

And then the answer came to me. All the little bits and pieces that hand't made sense came together in a clear picture.

Motioning for Mort to come out of his corner, I thanked him for an acting job well done and together we tied Jake up and locked him in the trailer until I could turn him over to the police in the morning.

It only took about a half hour of dragging to snag Scotty's body. There were eight of us around that pond when they grappled him up, including a handcuffed Jenks, and none of us were looking too good. I've seen a lot of bodies pulled out of a lot of water, but I never felt worse over any of them.

When they stretched him out and turned him over, Jenks began to blubber, but I paid him no attention, just walked up to the officer in charge, who turned and looked at me.

"Well, you were right about this much," he said quietly. "Let's see if you were right about the rest. You do the honors."

Kneeling by my old friend, I took out my pocket knife and, with some effort, lifted the front panel of his coat. Using the knife, I slit open the seam, and the sun glinted on the small nuggets that spilled into my hand.

I had guessed right. Scotty had indeed had a cache of gold collected over many years, but it wasn't buried under his trailer or in some secret spot. The old cuss had sewn it into small pouches, which he had then sewn into the lining of his old suit. No wonder he had grown more bent and had walked with more difficulty every day. He was probably carrying sixty pounds of fines and nuggets in his clothes.

The lieutenant, standing behind me, let out a soft whistle. "So that's why he didn't come up. He was intoxicated, he'd just been struck, and the weight of the gold was enough to keep him under long enough to drown."

I noded, wondering what Harris, the gold buyer, would say when I told him that Scotty *had* taken it with him, after all.

Warren B. Murphy
A Public Duty

The brass-trimmed dark-oak carriage stopped in front of the open door of my small clinic and was surrounded so quickly by a cluster of children that it seemed they had been lying in wait for it to arrive.

Sir Charles stepped from the carriage and, as he always did when visiting me, looked around with an expression that could only be characterized as disgust.

It is not a pretty place where I am. In fact, to call my neighborhood "dilapidated" would be to accord it an honor it does not deserve, since "dilapidated" implies that the area was at one time better than it is now. The truth is that this area of London where I now work has never been better. It was a slum in the Dark Ages and a slum it remains. It is an area of transients, people who come and people who go. Those who stay do so only to die. My only long-lived, abiding neighbors are poverty and ignorance and evil.

Still, I practice my profession here because I think it is incumbent upon one to do what he can to improve the quality of life of those less fortunate. Also, I would be less than honest if I did not confess that I somewhat like the admiration I receive from those who are forced to live in this area. Most of them think I am a fool, but even those believe me a well intentioned fool and that is enough for me. Man does not live by bread alone, as the Good Book tells us.

Sir Charles was shaking his head, more in sadness than anything else, and the clump of children around him were shouting. "Ha-'penny—ha'penny for bread, kind sir!" Then the uniformed driver of the carriage shooed them away lest a bold one manage to steal from Sir Charles' person something of more value than a halfpenny.

Yes, these children are thieves. But do not censure them, good people. They are the outcasts of society—coatless, shoeless, most of them the children of the prostitutes who prowl these streets—and they are no better or no worse than we would be would the Great God demand we change places with them.

The children hooted as Sir Charles walked briskly toward my open door. In his hand he carried a small canvas package. As I stepped forward to greet him, I wondered how many of the pitiful urchins on the street knew that the man they were harassing was Sir Charles Warren, superintendent of the Metropolitan Police and the highest-ranking law-enforcement officer in all of London.

"Good morning, General," I said. "It's a pleasure to see you again." Even as I spoke, I closed and locked the door behind him. His business with me is usually confidential and a locked door would spare us from being disturbed.

"And you, Doctor," he said. "How unfortunate that the only time we meet is when I have a favor to ask of you."

"It is I who am favored by sometimes being able to help," I said politely. "Supporting those in authority is one of the prices we pay for civilization, however imperfect it may be."

As befits his military background, Sir Charles is a brusque man and he seems uneasy when confronted with simple polite conversation.

"Yes, yes," he harrumphed. "Yes, yes, indeed."

Let me digress to say why Sir Charles had come to see me.

The state of forensic medicine in England is quite pitiful and it is only in the last few years that the police, under the guidance of such excellent men as Dr. George Bagster Phillips, have begun to make any strides in this area at all.

Sir Charles, under whom I served in the Army, knows that because of the neighborhood in which I work I am more familiar with knife wounds and gunshots and violent death than anyone under his direct command. These things, unfortunately, are the raw material of my practice: criminals so vicious they would steal the coins from a dead man's eyes, prostitutes so vile they reek with the unholy stench of their corrupt trade—these are my patients. Yes, I would vastly prefer to be treating the ague but I fear that such will not be the case so long as my clinic is located where it is.

At any rate, I have assisted General Warren on a number of occasions when his official resources have failed him.

Without waiting for an invitatioin, Sir charles walked to the cubicle in the rear of the single large room that was the clinic. There I maintained my small laboratory and office.

Once inside, he opened the canvas package he was carrying and removed from same a bloody strip of bandage, a blood-stained scrap of flowered material, and a man's necktie, spotted with blood. He placed them neatly on my desk and I glanced at this odd baggage, then at Sir Charles questioningly.

"Do you remember the Strewe case?" he asked in the blunt fashion which could be both personally and professionally offensive. However, I took no umbrage since I know the man well.

"I am afraid not, Sir Charles."

"It was four months ago, at the end of April. Mrs. Amanda Strewe was bludgeoned to her death in her home in West End. The instrument of death was not found. The body was discovered in the front parlor by the maid, who was returning to duty after being absent the morning to attend the funeral of a relative. The maid said that when she was unlocking the front door she thought she heard a groan, so we believe that if she had arrived only moments earlier she might actually have seen the murderer."

I nodded and Sir Charles continued:

"My men were on the scene in a very few moments after crime was committed. An inspector was immediately dispatched to inform Mr. Arthur Strewe of his wife's demise.

"Mrs. Strewe was independently wealthy but her husband operated a small construction company. When our inspector arrived there, he found that Mr. Strewe apparently had just suffered an accident. There was blood on his clothing and a large cut on his right hand. He said he received the injury while repairing one of his lathing machines.

"The inspecctor helped bandage Mr. Strewe's hand and brought him to headquarters, where his statement was taken. He seemed very distraught and the officers in charge of the investigation were inclined to leave it at that."

"But something intervened?" I interjected. Sir Charles nodded and slowly lit a cigar and exhaled a long plume of smoke. He had forgotten that I detest the smell of tobacco, but I felt that saying so might inhibit him and so I suffered in silence.

"During the regular course of the investigation," he continued, "officers talked to neighbors and found that Mr. And Mrs. Strewe had often engaged in loud arguments in the several months prior to the killing. And the maid told our inspectors that it was Mr. Strewe himself who told her that she should take the entire day off to attend to her family funeral. She said it was just the fear of losing her position that caused her to return early, directly after the funeral."

"What of the blood on Mr. Strewe?" I asked. Sir Charles blew another noxious plume of smoke and said:

"Strewe said that he was working the entire morning in the back of his shop, attempting to repair a machine that had been troublesome for some time. There *were* traces of blood on the machine. Mr. Strewe's secretary, whose office is elevated and looks over the entire floor of the factory, stated that she could see Mr. Strewe the entire morning and that he never left the repair room. And that is where the matter stands."

"And you are not comfortable with it," I offered.

"Exactly."

"You think that Mr. Strewe went to work that day, then slipped home to murder his wife. He fled quickly as the maid returned, repaired to his factory, and cut himself to explain the blood on his clothing."

"I do," Sir Charles said.

"Why?" I asked boldly.

Sir Charles hesitated briefly and worried the end of his cigar. "There is no reason precisely," he said. "But I have spoken to Mr. Strewe myself. His eyes are shifty, Doctor. I do not trust the man."

"But you have no real evidence on which to base a charge?"

He nodded.

"What has made it so imperative that you come now to speak with me of a crime four months old?" I asked.

"Because Mr. Strewe is leaving tomorrow for a tour of Europe. He has liquidated many of his wife's assets and I honestly suspect he may never return. If other evidence does come to light, we will not have him within our jurisdiction. I am not pleased at that prospect."

"Nor am I," I said fervently. "If he has murdered an innocent woman, he should not escape punishment. It mocks all that we believe in. So these items, then, are from the Strewe case?"

"Yes," Sir Charles said. "The flowered fabric is from the dress the poor woman was wearing when she met her death. The bandage is that from the right hand of Mr. Strewe, and the necktie is the one he was wearing when interviewed at the factory by our inspector. I thought . . . well, rather, I hoped, Doctor, that you might find something in these items that we have overlooked."

"I see you have not forgotten that I have been doing some research with blood," I said.

"No. That memory is what impelled me to come here," he said. "Do you think you might be of some assistance?"

"I will try. It is my public duty," I said.

"Would that all citizens thought as you, Doctor," he said, clapping me on the shoulder.

"Many do," I demurred.

"But few are willing to give more than words. You give all," he said.

After he left, I relocked the clinic door and went to the meager equipment in the rear laboratory. I was pleased that Sir Charles had remembered my mentioning almost a year before that I had been experimenting with blood. In truth, one can hardly be less than an expert on blood when confronted with the kind of medical practice which is mine.

Put simply, I believe that there are various recognizable forms of blood, each of which is distinguishable from another. I call these forms "fashions," although I do not yet know how to classify them or what purpose they serve. Someday, if my other duties permit, I may write a monograph on this subject for the *Lancet* in order to stimulate others to research.

These fashions of blood are not visibly different to the eye, not even under a microscope. What is visible, however, is that two differing fashions seem to clash when the cells of one are mixed with the serum of another.

I have developed a simple but effective process for reliquifying dried blood which I now use to prepare samples for analysis.

The work is slow and tedious. Charity clinics are not in the forefront in the purchase of new scientific equipment.

I was able to determine that the blood on the bandages taken from Strewe's hand was quite clearly of one fashion and the blood on the scrap of dress fabric was another. But the blood on the necktie was somehow quite different and it defied my attempts to analyze it and fit it into one of the other two fashions. The cells from it seemed to cluster when mixed with the serum from either Strewe's or his wife's blood fashion, and this should not have been the case.

Could it be the blood of yet a third party? And could it be that the blood on the necktie was a totally different fashion from any I had encountered before? The latter prospect filled me with something akin to fright, for it has been the cornerstone of my modest theory, confirmed many times by my direct research, that there are basically four blood fashions. If I were now to find a fifth, what would prevent there being a sixth and a seventh? Perhaps there might be almost as many fashions of blood as there were people on earth.

Somehow I did not think that this could be.

I bent to my task with even greater effort, spurred on by the idea of Arthur Strewe, if he were indeed a murderer, escaping prosecution for his crime. Such a thing should not be permitted in a civilized society.

It was late at night—I did not know how late—when my patience was rewarded: I finally determined that the blood on Mr. Strewe's tie was a mixture of two fashions, that of his wife *and* his own. That explained why the cells in the sample had clustered when mixed with the serums from the other two blood samples.

In an instant it was clear to me what Strewe had done. He had killed his wife, but when the maid returned unexpectedly he had fled back to his place of business. He knew the police would soon be there. When he saw the blood drops on his necktie, he arranged to cut himself on some machinery and to flick some blood from his cut hand onto the tie.

In the interests of both good science and good citizenship, because accusations of murder should not be lightly made, I performed all my tests for a second time. There could now be no doubt of the result. The blood of Mrs. Amanda Strewe was on the necktie of her husband.

I wrote a note relating my findings to Sir Charles.

"Since this technique of mine is yet experimental," I wrote, "it might be difficult to have it accepted as evidence in a court of law. However, I think it might be fruitful for your men to interrogate with great care the secretary who swore to Mr. Strewe's presence at work on the morning of the murder. If I am correct, and I believe I am, then she is lying. It might be possible that she herself was the cause of the frequent arguments between Mr. Strewe and the poor deceased."

Because I understood these things more clearly than does Sir Charles, I wrote further: "That she was the mistress of a married man clearly stamps this woman as no better than a common prostitute. As all prostitutes do, she will lie. But if your men threaten her life or her safety, she will turn on Mr. Strewe instantly and tell you the truth. It is the nature of such women to think only of themselves."

I reread the note before signing it. For a moment I was amused because my handwriting—which is barely legible at best—seemed to reflect my fatigue. It seemed hardly recognizable—rather just a sad scrawl across the page. I sealed the note in an envelope and wrapped it and the exhibits back inside the piece of canvas Sir Charles had brought to the clinic many hours before.

My body ached with weariness, but it was a pleasant fatigue, the kind that comes to one who has battled against the odds, who has done his best and has triumphed. I felt as the good St. Paul must have: "I have fought a good fight; I have finished my course; I have kept the faith."

It was a feeling I had experienced before and always cherished. It was truly the only reward of my work.

Glancing at my pocket watch, I was astonished to see that it was already after 2:00 A.M. I unlocked the front door of the clinic and stepped outside. The heat of the late August day had given way to a nighttime threat of autumn chill. The streets were silent and empty. Most of those who prowl this area after dark seeking partners in evil debauchery had apparently fulfilled their quests.

At the corner of Union Street a halfblock away, I saw the constable on duty and stepped into the center of the cobblestoned roadway and waved to him.

He recognized me because I often work late and said, "Good evening, Doctor."

"Constable Neil," I said, "I want you to bring this package to your police station. It must be delivered to Metropolitan Police Headquarters as soon as possible."

"Can't do that, Doctor. Sorry. I'm on a fixed point and not allowed to leave."

"This package is for Sir Charles Warren," I said sternly. "It contains evidence in a crime."

He looked apprehensive, then attempted a small smile. "Getting into police business now?" he said.

"General Warren has asked me to look into something for him," I responded. "I think we may have been able to catch a murderer. But time is critical."

"*You* did it?" he said.

"I assisted in my own small way."

He looked at me with awe. "A public duty," I added. "Something one must do."

"There should be more like you, sir," the constable said. He took the canvas package from me and seemed to weigh it in his hand while deciding on a course of action. Then he nodded to me.

"Well, if it's for Sir Charles himself, I don't see how I can be getting into much trouble," he said. "I'll get it to the station right now."

"Thank you, Constable Neil. I know Sir Charles will appreciate it."

"As you say. But you look like you should be getting some rest, if you don't mind my saying so, sir," Neil offered before saying good night.

As he walked swiftly away, I re-entered the clinic. My mood was now euphoric. There is no grander feeling than knowing one has done his part in making a better world by helping to remove some of the evil from his midst. I only wished that I could do more. There is so much evil here in London in the year of Our Blessed Lord one thousand eight hundred and eighty-eight—it surrounds us, engulfs us, overwhelms us.

I took my worn leather medical bag from under my desk, locked up the clinic, and went out into the street. A fog was beginning to settle over the city as I walked to the corner and turned left on Whitechapel Road.

Up ahead I heard footsteps, and through the gathering mist I saw a woman walking into Osborn Street, singing drunkenly to herself—another of the degenerates who corrupt our city. I felt a bitter taste in my mouth. Seeing her had ruined the spirit of exultation I had so recently felt.

Yet, inexplicably, I quickened my stride—and in so doing heard something come loose inside my medical bag. I opened it and found inside the autopsy knife that lamentably I must use so often in my practice.

I paused. From somewhere in the fog I could still hear the faint sounds of the woman singing, offkey and tuneless. I put the knife inside my coat pocket, closed the medical bag, and turned quickly into Osborn Street, suddenly exhilarated again.

Constable Neil had told me I should get some rest but now I neither wanted nor needed rest.

Besides, I told myself as I again saw that evil creature lurching drunkenly through the street only fifty yards before me, one can truly rest only when one's work is truly done.

And mine had just begun.

Hugh Pentecost
Jericho and the Lady Jogger

It was good to be home again. John Jericho, the giant red-bearded artist, had spent the last several months in the Middle East, watching Christians and Moslems storming at each other, slaughtering women and children and old people who had no real involvement in the conflict. Jericho's artistic career had been changed in the last few years into a crusade against the terrible violence he saw as a world sickness, flourishing everywhere. His vigorous paintings of scenes of terror, torture, and death were meant to be messages to those with a capacity to think, messages about the total annihilation they faced at the hands of war-minded men.

Home to Jericho was a studio apartment in Jefferson Mews, located in New York City's Greenwich Village. It was more like a waystation, a stop-over place between excursions to the scenes of violence around the world. The apartment consisted in part of one large studio room with a picture window looking out over the rooftops of the old-fashioned buildings and down onto the Mews itself. Coming back here was to make new contact with books he loved, paintings he cherished, mementos of past travels, and to sleep for a night or two in the king-sized bed that took up almost all the space in the small bedroom. Stopping off here was a way to refresh his energy, to blot out for a few hours the ugliness of the troubled world outside.

Jericho's long flight home from Beirut had not gotten him back to his apartment in the Mews until after midnight. There was no reason why he shouldn't have slept late in the morning, but some inner alarm clock had him up a little before seven. He started coffee in the coffee machine in his kitchenette, showered, dressed, and, with a mug of coffee in his hand, went to the window that looked down on the Mews. It was important to him to observe that things were as they always were.

Across the way old Tom Tobias had already put out his display of fresh fruit and vegetables under the awning outside his store. On summer days, the outdoor stand was always there. A few doors down the street, old Mrs. Greenbaum was sweeping the steps and the sidewalk in front of her brownstone. In a minute or two the girl jogger would emerge from the tunnel made by an overpass at the north end of the Mews, her running controlled, rhythmically a perfect model for the joggers who had become epidemic in the early hours of the morning in the city. You could tell time by that girl, Jericho told himself.

But that morning the girl didn't appear on time. Frowning, Jericho glanced at his watch. Eight minutes past seven. She was three minutes late. For some reason it distressed him to find a routine broken here in his predictable world. Maybe the girl was sick, or on vacation, or she'd moved away somewhere. But then she emerged from the tunnel—not jogging in that marvelously controlled fashion, but sprinting down the Mews as if her life depended on it. Something new? A change in her routine? There was no reason in the world why she shouldn't sprint if she wanted to, and yet Jericho had just come from a world where anyone running like that was motivated by terror.

Tom Tobias waved cheerfully as Jericho walked across the Mews to the fruit stand. "Welcome home, Mr. Jericho," he called out. "When you get back?"

"Last night, early this morning," Jericho said. "How have you been, Tom?"

"Always the same—except for my arthritis," the old man said. "Help yourself to an apple. Those Vermont Macs are the best. Go ahead—on the house."

Jericho took an apple and had a bite from it. It was delicious. "I looked out and there you were, Tom. And there was Mrs. Greenbaum. And there was the girl jogger."

"Went by like a bat out of hell this morning," Tom said.

"I noticed."

"I never see her run like that before," the old man said. "I see her every morning for the last three years, but never before like today. Late for something, I guess."

"Maybe," Jericho said. He took another bite of the apple. "You know her name?"

"Greg does." Tom turned toward the shop. "Hey, Greg!"

Greg Tobias was Tom's son, about thirty, the only family the old man had left after his wife died a few years back. He was dark, good-looking, and a little arrogant, Jericho thought, but with a bright smile.

"Hi, Mr. Jericho. Welcome home," Greg said.

"Mr. Jericho was asking about the lady jogger. You know her name."

"Miss Collins. She teaches at the high school."

"She teach you when you were there?" his father asked him.

"Come off it, Pop. She's younger than I am. She teaches phys ed—to the girl students."

"But she interests you?" Jericho asked.

Greg's smile widened. "I kind of take notice."

"You should be looking for a girl to settle down with," his father said.

Jericho tossed his apple core into a nearby trash basket and strolled on down the Mews, stopping to say good morning to Mrs. Greenbaum. The Mews was only two blocks long, entered at one end through the tunnel provided by the overpass and exiting at the other end onto a main thoroughfare. There was no vehicular traffic in the Mews except for street-cleaning equipment and garbage-collectioin trucks. You could hear the sounds of the busy city drifting through the alleyways and over the low rooftops, but the Mews itself was unhurried, a few hundred yards of peace surrounded by the big city's turmoil.

Jericho walked through the tunnel at the north end of the Mews. It was only long enough to accommodate the four-lane highway that crossed above it leading to the West Side Highway and it was dark except for the daylight at either end. He emerged directly opposite the red-brick high school. If this was Miss Collins' starting point for her morning jog and if she started at the same time each day, there would be nothing to interfere with her passing through the Mews at exactly the same time each day.

Students had already begun to collect for the first classes of the day and a girl directed him to the office where he might find Miss Collins— Room C at the rear of the main hallway on the first floor. He reached Room C and knocked on the door.

"Come in!" A clear, cool, friendly woman's voice.

She was sitting behind a desk just inside—ash-blonde, bright-blue eyes, the exquisite figure he had until now only seen in running shorts and a T-shirt concealed by an attractive dark-brown linen dress.

"Miss Collins?"

"Yes. May I help you?"

"You don't know me, Miss Collins, but my name is John Jericho and I live in Jefferson Mews."

"John Jericho, the artist?" She looked pleased. "Oh, my—I've seen your paintings in the Modern Museum, Mr. Jericho. They're beautiful— but rather frightening, you know?"

"They're meant to be," Jericho said. He hesitated. "Miss Collins, when I was a kid my father told me a story about seeing a boy running at full speed past his house. He called out to the boy: 'Where are you running to, Joey?' And the boy called back to him: 'I'm not running to, Mr. Jericho, I'm running from.' I watched you run through the Mews this morning, Miss Collins. You were running from, weren't you?"

She was quite still, almost frozen where she sat. "I don't think I understand, Mr. Jericho."

"As an artist, my subject is people," Jericho said. "I've learned to read body language. This morning you weren't running for exercise when you passed below my window. You were running from something."

She took a deep breath. "That is really quite extraordinary, Mr. Jericho."

"If I'm being a busybody I'll just take off," Jericho said. "But I saw what I saw. You were running as if someone or something had frightened you out of your wits."

"I appreciate your concern," she said. "It's rather amazing to find out that someone noticed—and cared."

"I'm right, then?"

She nodded. "I—I've been jogging this same route for the last three years."

"I know. I've seen you. This morning was different."

"I change into my jogging clothes and shoes here in the locker room every morning at seven."

"And pass by my studio at five after severn. It was nine after when you came by this morning. I can tell time by you, Miss Collins."

"It started two days ago," the young woman said. "As I entered the tunnel under the overpass, I saw someone in the shadows. I was startled. It was a man wearing a kind of comic Halloween mask— Richard Nixon with Draculalike fangs hanging over the lower lip. Some kid, I thought, playing games. He waved at me and I waved back. That was all. But yesterday, he was there again. This time he gestured for me to stop, but I didn't. I just waved at him again and went on. I saw that he was crippled as he took a step toward me—right leg stiff at the knee, almost dragging behind him as he tried to move toward me."

"You couldn't have been too frightened if you went back this morning," Jericho said.

"As I said, I thought it was some kid playing games with me. I thought if I ripped off the mask it would be someone I'd recognize and we'd both have a good laugh."

"Do you know someone with a crippled leg?"

She frowned. "No. I thought it might be part of the disguise."

"Did you report it to anyone or tell anyone about it?"

"No. But this morning was different. He had stationed himself right in the center of the tunnel, and there was no way to get past him if he wanted to stop me. So I stopped and told him I'd had enough of this. He made a kind of growling sound behind that grotesque mask and then grabbed me. This was no kid, it was a man with powerful hands. I realized I was being assaulted. Well, I'm a phys ed teacher, I know a little about karate. I gave him a sharp chop to the side of the neck, and as he staggered I ran. I was running *from* all right, Mr. Jericho."

"You've notified the police?"

"No."

"Why not?"

"I can't describe the man. All I could do would be to attract attention to myself in a way I wouldn't like. I can imagine some people saying I'd invited the attack by running around in shorts and a T-shirt. All I can do is find a new route where there's no dark tunnel."

"And leave this character to molest somebody else?"

"What should I do?"

"I *should* advise you to go to the police."

"You say you *should* advise me. Does that mean you aren't?"

Jericho nodded. "You can't describe the man because of the mask. There's the game leg, of course. I wonder if it's real, or if you're meant to describe him as lame if you were to go to the cops. That would have them looking for someone who doesn't exist."

She nodded. "I don't think I have any choice but to do my jogging somewhere else."

Jericho smiled at her. "What's your first name, Miss Collins?"

"Sue." She smiled back at him.

"There's something we could try, Sue. Tomorrow morning early, I can stash myself in the tunnel. You follow your usual routine, at the usual time. If your friend shows up, I'll be there to handle him. If I catch him in the act, we'll have more than enough for the police."

"And if he doesn't show tomorrow?"

"You say he's come three days in a row. Why not four? This time he may be prepared for your karate skills, but I'll be there. If he doesn't show tomorrow it could be because he wants to see if you've provided protection. If he sees you haven't, he'll probably try the next day. I've got two or three days in New York. I could try a second time."

Sue Collins hesitated.

"I'd like to rid my neighborhood of his creep," Jericho said. When she didn't answer, he laughed. "Are you wondering if I might be the guy, trying to make sure you're there tomorrow?"

She laughed, too. "He's about my height," she said. "The top of his head would just about come under your chin. Okay, John," she decided. "If you're willing to put in the time, I'm game."

Later Jericho would blame himself for a piece of carelessness that could have had fatal results. For months he had seen and read about the worst kind of violence—bombs in buses that killed innocent and un-involved people, a suicide driver who drove an explosives-laden truck into an enemy compound, killing himself and nearly three hundred others. You couldn't compare that kind of horror with a pervert wearing a comic mask. It was ugly but not life threatening. Seeing to it that Sue Collins be allowed to exercise without interference didn't suggest danger to Jericho. A face-to-face encounter with some kind of nut didn't create any misgivings. Perhaps it was vanity, but Jericho would have faced any one man, no matter what his size and skills, without anxiety. He had complete confidence in his ability to take care of himself. This self-confidence almost cost him more than he was prepared to pay.

When he left Sue Collins' office that morning, Jericho went back to the tunnel at the north end of the Mews. He meant, quite sensibly, to have a good look at the terrain where his encounter with Sue's attacker would probably take place the next morning. The overpass formed an arch over the Mews and the underside had been bricked in. In all the years he'd lived in the Mews, Jericho had paid little attention to what everyone called "the tunnel." His studio was located at the other end of the Mews and his normal access to and from the rest of the city was at the opposite end from the tunnel. In the daytime, the tunnel was dark except for the light that came from each end. It was brighter at night, when four bare electric-light bulbs, part of the city's street-lighting system, provided illumination.

On a bright, sunlit summer day like this one, the tunnel wasn't dark. Jericho walked in from the north end, the route Sue Collins took on her morning run. There was no place to hide except possibly behind a large wooden box with a sloping top at the south end. That box, Jericho knew, was used to store sand and salt in the winter months to keep the cobblestone walkway from being slippery. He lifted the unlocked lid of the box and saw that it was empty, normal for an August day. There was nothing else unusual except an area in the west wall, in back of the box, where there could have been a door a long time ago. It had been covered by a piece of sheet metal that had rusted and wrinkled with time. As he stood looking around, Jericho's ears were assaulted by a rumbling thunder that shook dust from the old brick walls. He glanced up, aware that some kind of heavy truck was using the overpass to get to the West Side Highway. That kind of thunderous passage must take place end-lessly, day and night.

Jericho walked out of the south end of the tunnel and along the Mews to his studio. There would be nothing to do about Sue Collins' masked molester until the next morning when he would go back into the tun-nel while it was still dark, hide behind the wooden box, and wait. Meanwhile there was a day to live. He had brought back bundles of sketches from the Middles East, some of which would be transformed into major paintings. They had to be catalogued and considered.

Shortly after supper, he phoned Sue Collins at a number she had given him.

"No change of mind?" he asked her when she answered.

"Not if you still want to try."

"I'll be going out there while it's still dark," Jericho told her. "Four or four-thirty. I don't want to waste my time out there for that long if you change your mind."

"I'll be coming through just after seven," Sue promised.

"See you then."

"I'll count on it," she said.

"If your chum doesn't show, I'll buy you a fancy breakfast," Jericho said.

"And if he does?"

"I'll still buy you a fancy breakfast—after we've turned him over to the cops and seen him booked."

Jericho had disciplined himself to be able to sleep whenever the opportunity was at hand. Shortly after nine he put away his sketches, set the alarm clock beside the bed for four in the morning, and slept.

At five minutes to four he woke without the alarm, made coffee, showered, dressed, and was ready.

At twenty-five after four, he left the apartment, walked out the south end of the Mews, and circled around to the north end and the tunnel.

The four garish light bulbs burned in the tunnel, revealing a faint film of dust drifting down in the wake of a heavy truck thundering across the overpass. Jericho walked in as far as the sand-salt box and selected a place where he could sit down behind it, out of sight.

It was after five o'clock before anyone came through the tunnel on foot. It was a young boy with a pushcart loaded with morning papers which would be stuck in mailboxes or shoved under doormats in the Mews.

As six o'clock approached, a few people with early-morning jobs came out of the Mews and through the tunnel, unaware that he was behind the wooden box, waiting and watching.

At six o'clock, the light bulbs went off. Sunlight brightened each end of the tunnel, but the inside was suddenly much darker.

A group of young men, some of whom Jericho knew, came through the tunnel from the Mews, members of a construction gang, headed for work, each wearing a hardhat decorated with the drawing of a white buffalo. In the Mews they were known as "the Buffaloes." There was a great deal of laughing and shoving and horseplay. Their catcalls echoed eerily in the tunnel.

Jericho glanced at his wristwatch. Ten minutes to seven. In about twelve minutes Sue Collins would come jogging through and the masked man would be waiting for her—or he wouldn't. Jericho changed to a crouching position from which he could move quickly. If the molester was coming, it should be any moment now. If he did come, it was Jericho's plan to wait until he tried to stop Sue Collins, then take him in the act. Trucks thundered overhead. Jericho felt the dust drifting down on his head and shoulders.

Then he was struck by a violent blow from behind, and he blacked out . . .

Jericho opened his eyes. There was a splitting pain at the back of his head and he realized he was lying somewhere in bright sunshine—outside the tunnel. He tried to focus on faces that were crowding over him. There was old Dr. Holland who lived in the Mews. Greg Tobias, Mrs. Greenbaum. And Sergeant Mulloy from the local precinct. Dr. Holland smiled at him.

"Welcome home," he said. Then, when Jericho tried to push himself up to a sitting position: "Take it easy, son."

"What the hell happened?" Jericho asked.

Greg Tobias answered him.

"I was on my way back from placing an order for my father at the wholesale fruit market," he said. "I saw you sprawled over the sandbox in the tunnel, blood on the back of your head. I dragged you out here and called the doctor."

"I've stopped the bleeding," Dr. Holland said, "but we better get you to the hospital. Somebody hit you a hell of a clout, Mr. Jericho."

Jericho looked at his watch. A quarter past seven. "The girl?" he asked. "Is she all right?"

"What girl?" Sergeant Mulloy asked.

"Sue Collins, a teacher at the high school," Jericho said. "She was due to jog through the tunnel just after seven. I was waiting there for her when the roof fell in on me."

"She didn't come through this morning," Mrs. Greenbaum said.

"She had to!" Jericho said. "We had a plan!"

"Maybe you'd better explain what you're talking about," the sergeant said.

"First I've got to check out the girl," Jericho said. He held out his hand to Greg Tobias. "Help me up, will you?"

For a moment the world spun around as he stood, and then it seemed to settle on an even keel.

"Dizzy?" the doctor asked.

"For a minute. It's okay now. I'd better get to my place and the telephone."

"You can use my phone," the doctor said. "It's just across the way. I can keep an eye on you. Come on, put your hand on my shoulder."

Walking was unsteady for a bit. No one seemed inclined to let him alone. Greg Tobias, along with Mrs. Greenbaum and the police sergeant, trooped after him and Dr. Holland.

In the doctor's office, Jericho called Sue Collins' home number. No answer. He looked up the number of the high school in the phonebook and called it, explaining to the woman who answered that it was an emergency. She told him he would be connected with the attendant in the women's locker room. Another woman with a pleasant young voice answered.

"Locker room."

"I have an urgent message for Sue Collins," Jericho said. "Has she come back from her morning jogging?"

"I wouldn't know. Hold on a minute." He waited. Dr. Holland was putting something on the wound at the back of his head. It stung a little. Then the voice came back on the phone.

"Sue's street clothes are still in her locker. She hasn't come back yet."

Jericho thanked her and stood for a minute, staring at the phone. Then he replaced the receiver and turned to Sergeant Mulloy. "That girl's in some kind of trouble," he said. He told the sergeant and the others about the man in the Nixon mask with the Dracula fangs who'd been bothering Sue Collins the last few mornings, and his plan to apprehend him. "The Collins girl was playing along. She was definitely going to follow her regular routine this morning."

"Greg tells me he went through the tunnel about six this morning on the way to the wholesale market," Sergent Mulloy said. "Did you see anyone hanging around, Greg?"

"No," Greg said. "If Mr. Jericho was there then, hidden behind that old sandbox, I didn't see him."

Mulloy said, "What beats me, Mr. Jericho, is how anyone got behind you to put the slug on you."

"There can be only one answer," Jericho said. "There's a door just behind that sandbox, covered over by a piece of rusty sheet metal. It must open from the inside. Whoever it was must have come from there."

"You'd have heard him open the door, wouldn't you?" Mulloy asked.

"Not with one of those big trucks crossing the overpass. It's like being in a thunderstorm. What's behind that door, do you know?"

It was old Mrs. Greenbaum who answered. "A long time ago there was an open sewer ran under the Mews. People who lived here could walk right out of their basements and dump garbage into the running water. Fifty years ago, just after I moved here, they put in a modern sewer pipe and nobody had any reason to go down there any more."

Dr. Holland looked at Greg Tobias. "But some people still used it, didn't they?"

Greg Tobias shrugged. "We kids used it. It was a place we could go to sneak a smoke without being caught, for one thing."

"What other things?" Mulloy asked.

"Sometimes we persuaded a girl to go there with us."

"Can we get to that door in the tunnel from anywhere in the Mews now?" Jericho asked.

"Sure. Right from my basement if you want," Dr. Holland said.

"Let's have a look, Sergeant," Jericho said. "Sue Collins didn't come through the tunnel. She could have been dragged through that door when I was knocked out."

"Let me get you a flashlight," Dr. Holland said. "It's pitch dark down there."

Mrs. Greenbaum stayed behind as the doctor produced a flashlight and led the others down into his basement. He had some trouble opening the door that led into the abandoned sewer. "It's been years since this was opened," he said as he finally managed to free the door from caked-on dust and dirt.

Mulloy shone the flashlight into the void beyond. A large pipe ran down the center of the underground passage. There were stone ledges on either side of it, like narrow sidewalks. Directly across from where they stood was a flight of stone steps leading to the door behind the sandbox in the tunnel. Jericho, Mulloy, and Greg Tobias crossed the ledges over the sewer pipe and up the stairs. The door had a doorknob and a slide bolt that held it in place. Mulloy slid open the bolt, tried the knob, and the door opened inward, almost noiselessly. Mulloy directed the flashlight down.

"The hinges have been oiled," he said. "It looks like someone's been using this door regularly."

Jericho bent down and picked up a two-foot length of iron pipe. He held it under Mulloy's flashlight.

"Bloodstains," he said.

"Looks like what your friend used to slug you," the sergeant said.

"You suppose he dragged Miss Collins out through here somewhere?"

"Let's ask him," Jericho said, turning and taking the lapel of Greg Tobias's jacket gently in his big hand. "What would you say happened, Greg?"

"What are you talking about?" Greg said.

"I'm saying I know perfectly well you never went through that tunnel out there at six o'clock. I saw everyone who went through. You didn't.

"You must have dozed off."

"No. I was watching like a hawk. Now, be quick about it—where did you take Sue Collins?"

"Why would I take her anywhere?" Greg asked nervously.

"Because you admittedly kind of took notice of her," Jericho said.

"You're wrong, Jericho."

Jericho showed him his powerful fist. "Every minute you delay you're asking for it," he said. "Now take me to her or else!" His hand moved from Greg's lapel to the back of his collar.

"You can't—"

"If we have to, we can search every basement in the Mews," Mulloy said.

"It might make sense to begin with the Tobias store," Jericho said. "What about it, Greg?"

They went back down the stairs to the old sewer under the Mews, Jericho forcing Greg Tobias ahead of him, his right arm twisted behind his back.

"It should be the last door on the right-hand side," Jericho told Mulloy. They crossed over to the ledge on the right side of the pipe. "Hold it." The sergeant had stopped. A sliver of light showed under the door that led into the Tobias cellar. "Someone's in there." He took his police special out of its holster.

Greg Tobias pulled halfheartedly against Jericho's grip on his collar and muttered.

As if on some cue, the door to the Tobias basement opened inward and Sue Collins, looking pale as death, stood facing them. Behind her, someone wearing the absurd mask she had described to Jericho looked taken by surprise. Mulloy raised his gun.

"No, for God sake!" Greg Tobias shouted, wrenching away from Jericho.

Jericho reached out, took Sue Collins' wrist, and pulled her around behind him. He lunged forward and ripped the mask off the man's head.

Looking up at him, angry and defiant, grey hair tousled, was Tom Tobias. "Why don't you mind your own business, Mr. Jericho?" he asked.

Sergent Mulloy stepped into the cellar and began slapping the old man over for a weapon. Jericho turned to Sue Collins.

"Are you hurt?"

She shook her head. "But I feel a little dirty," she said. Her voice was unsteady.

"He roughed you up?"

She closed her eyes. "He gave me a lecture."

"I told her to stay out of this neighborhood," Tobias said. "Flaunting her sex like a whore, tempting the young men—"

"I came through the tunnel as we planned," Sue told Jericho. "You were stretched over that sandbox, blood on your head. He was there. He told me if I didn't go with him he'd finish you off. He took me through that door behind the box and brought me down here. He told me what he had to say and I think he was just about to take me back up to the tunnel and let me go."

"I didn't harm her," old Tom said.

"How about Jericho?" Mulloy asked. "Did you harm him?"

"Meddling in other people's business," Tom Tobias muttered.

"Assault with a deadly weapon ought to keep you locked up for a while," Mulloy said. "Abduction . . ."

Jericho turned to Greg Tobias. "I guess I owe you, Greg," he said. "But you didn't go through the tunnel at six like you said."

"But I did," Greg said. "I've been thinking about that. I caught up with the Buffaloes before I got to the tunnel—you know, those construction guys. They like to fool around. One of them put his hardhat on me. You must have seen them and probably thought I was one of them. I found you, like I said, on my way back. It wasn't until you described the man in the mask to Sergeant Mulloy in Doc Holland's office that I knew it must be my old man."

"How did you know that?"

"Back when Richard Nixon was President, my father picked up that mask somewhere. I don't know why but it amused him. For years afterward, when kids came to the door on Halloween he'd put on that mask to scare them. I came along with you and Mulloy because I wanted to protect him if I could."

"So I read you wrong," Jericho said.

"Look, Mr. Jericho. You're not so badly hurt. Could you let him off the hook? That would square things with me. I promise I'll keep him in line after this."

Jericho looked at Sergeant Mulloy. "Let's talk about it," he said. He felt a cold hand on his and looked down at Sue Collins.

"Could we go somewhere out into the sunshine?" she asked.

Frances Davis

Rings on Her Fingers

She was seated just to the left of me in the group of students of which I was, at that moment, such a reluctant member. That was when I first noticed her hands. She wore four rings on her left hand, three on her right. They were large elborate rings, with a great deal of silver and several flat green stones. Her fingernails were carefully manicured. She had three bracelets on one arm, one bracelet and watch on the other. And her hands and wrists were busily engaged.

We were doing a writing exercise on the mystery story, and I couldn't think of a thing to say. I kept looking around at the others, enviously, irritably, wondering what they had found to write about. The course had been interesting and informative, but this was the final day of a week's intensive study and my imagination was at an all-time low. But the others in the class seemed to be full of ideas, their pages filling with the purposeful handwriting of women who knew exactly what they were doing.

But of all of them, it was the young woman with the jewelry that kept me most enthralled. Her pen was purple, I noticed, while the ink that flowed from it was bright-green. Her face was sallow, her hair mousy, and her body unattractively thin. But everything about her hands was arresting and dramatic. I couldn't keep my eyes off her.

Then all at once her left hand snaked off the desk, disappeared from sight for a fraction of a second, then reemerged. But now it was not quite the same. It took me a moment to register the difference. There were five rings on it now, and one of them was mine.

I blinked once, looked away, then examined her hand again. Yes, it was my engaement ring, the opals set high around a single pearl! I had taken it off at lunch, afraid the pearl was working loose again, and dropped it into my tote bag. And my tote bag had been sitting on the floor beside me for the past half hour. I leaned over and rummaged about in it now. But the ring wasn't there.

"Most of you seem to be slowing down now," Sylvia Rogers said. "Let's stop and listen to some of these beginnings." She had been a tactful and helpful workshop leader. It must have been uphill work at times—we were, to say the least, a mixed lot, though we all secretly considered ourselves budding Agatha Christies and P. D. Jameses.

And now one of us was clearly a thief, and another frozen with panic at the thought of explaining to an angry husband the loss of a thousand-dollar ring.

Sylvia turned cheerfully to her left and asked the woman with the orange hair and the purple pantsuit to begin. Good, I thought numbly. That meant she would go clockwise around the dozen of us in the circle,

175

leaving the thief and me to the last. Surely by that time I would be able to think of something to do.

But the fact of the matter was that I couldn't think at all. My heart raced and my temperature rose and fell in waves. I remembered Bill's bright expectant eyes as I opened the ring box fifteen years ago. I remembered the black fury in the same eyes when I lost the diamond wedding band down the garbage disposal last winter. At least we found that one again—though the bill for dismantling the system was more than half the value of the ring.

I tried to look as if I was listening to the story openings of the other workshop members. According to Sylvia, most of them showed some kind of promise. She listened, asked for comments and suggestions about development, and then moved inexorably on. I glanced at my watch. There were only twenty minutes of the workshop left. What was I going to do? If I couldn't find a way to stop her, my bejeweled classmate would walk away with the remnants of my married bliss.

It was from my friend Rachel, sitting to my right, that I finally got the first inklings of a plan.

"I couldn't think of much," she admitted frankly when it came her turn to read. She held up her short fat fingers (one wedding ring, plain gold band) as if to display her emptiness. "I'd like to write a really simple kind of story where there's a problem that can be solved with an ordinary brain. You know what I mean? Interesting but ordinary, not grand larceny or murder or anything like that. The trouble is," she laughed, "I can't get the idea going."

"Maybe somebody else can help you," said Sylvia Rogers, smiling around at the rest of us encouragingly.

"Here's one," I said, my voice thick and hoarse. My lips were dry and I clasped my trembling hands together in my lap, snatching a quick glance to my left. My ring was gone from her hand now—she must have found someplace to hide it. My heart sank. I had only ten minutes to accomplish my purpose. I took a deep breath and began.

"Suppose a student was sitting in a classroom taking an exam and she took her ring off because it was bothering her." I smiled what I knew to be a perfectly ghastly smile. "She was sitting there, scribbling away, when she looked up and saw the ring was gone from the corner of the desk where she'd placed it." The class gave a nice appreciative little murmur. The thief beside me was unnaturally still. I addressed Rachel. "Pretend you're this student. You look around you—at me, for instance." I smiled my ghastly smile again. "And you see the ring on my hand." A nice murmur again, this time unmistakably from Sylvia. I took heart and cleared my throat. "There's the problem. What are you going to do?"

There was a little pause. Then the woman with the orange hair spoke up derisively, as was her wont. "That's not a mystery. All she has to do is tell you to give it back."

"What if I refuse?"

"We're all witnesses. You'd never dare."

"Witnesses of what? Nobody saw me take the ring."

"But maybe she could prove it's hers."

"Maybe it has initials," someone else suggested helpfully.

"Suppose it hasn't, though? Most rings don't."

"Someone would have noticed how many rings you were wearing when you came in," said Orange Hair. Her need to simplify and dismiss complications had irritated me all week. Now I was delighted to have her there. She was feeding me all the right lines.

"Suppose I slipped it into my purse the moment after she saw it. She can't even prove I've got it, let alone that it's hers." I was almost enjoying myself now. The stillness to the left of me was uncanny.

Sylvia Rogers broke the silence. "What would a detective do?"

"A detective would search everyone in the classroom," said Rachel, "but nobody in this hypothetical classroom has that kind of authority. So the student would have to use some kind of trick—or a game."

I glanced at my watch. Five minutes.

"If you came right out with your suspicion that *someone*, not naming any names, had stolen your ring," Caroline, a sweet older woman with tinted glasses, suggested to Rachel, "and asked the others in the classroom to show you their pockets and handbags and so on, I bet the innocent ones might not like it but they'd do it."

"Because they'd want to prove I was wrong to suspect them, wouldn't they?" said Rachel. "Or would they?"

"Why don't you ask?" I suggested, trying to keep my voice steady. "Ask us to show you our handbags now."

"Okay." She grinned broadly. "Handbags, everybody." I held my breath. "Well?" said Rachel.

"Here," said Sylvia Rogers, getting up and marching over, holding out her bag. The one after another, the rest of the class went to her, turning out their pockets and shaking out the corners of even the deepest, fullest shoulder bags. Everyone but the thief, of course.

"What a fascinating exercise," said Sylvia Rogers over the buzz of conversation and the general movement in the room. "But I think we're running out of time. Now where's my watch? It was sitting right here—"

There was a swift movement to the left of me and my target was on her feet, but Rachel, for all her bulk, was faster and blocked her way. "Then I'd do this," she said, smiling benevolently. "I'd stand in the doorway like this and ask you why you haven't shown me your bag."

The mousy young woman gave a sharp cry and snatched her bag back as Rachel reached for it. The clasp gave, and out fell the contents: my ring, a half dozen watches, a handful of charms . . .

When the police arrived, Sylvia and I made our complaints. The rest of the jewelry seemed to fit the list of items reported as mising by other students attending summer session at the college. The girl remained stubbornly silent throughout and never once met my eyes.

After the wretched little creature had been driven away in the patrol car, five of us took Sylvia out for a drink.

"What made you get up the way you did, Rachel?" she asked.

"I knew there was something wrong," Rachel replied. "My friend Frances here was as hoarse as a bullfrog the whole time and I know she never loses her voice unless she's scared out of her wits. Besides, her smile was absolutely sick."

"Didn't I know it," I commented.

"And the workshop had really got me into thinking that way," Rachel went on. "I mean, it's a whole mental attitude, isn't it?"

Sylvia nodded. "Being sharp, observant—suspicious even."

"Do you think what happened would be a good idea for a story?" Rachel asked her.

"Not enough action," said Orange Hair.

Barbara Callahan
Out of the Maze

As soon as I entered the women's room of Scarlet and Rhett's Single Bar two weeks ago and saw my face in the mirror, I knew I had to make a statement. With a red magic marker, I wrote my manifesto on the cold white tiles over the sinks.

"In a singles bar, survival depends on mastering the art of friendly disdain. One must somehow appear receptive to the stranger weaving his way through the crowd toward her while at the same time conveying an air of indifference in case he has staked a claim on the woman beside her. The unchosen one whose face transmits pain and not disdain in this cruel game of selection is relegated to the status of cheese. The cheese stands alone, as all of you who as children played 'The Farmer in the Dell' know. I am almost never chosen, and remain the cheese because of a face full of pain and not disdain. Don't tease the cheese, please, she is dying by degrees."

I could have written more, but I sensed that I was no longer alone. A small circle of women were solemnly reading the message on the tiles.

"The handwriting on the wall," someone murmured.

"She's a prophet," said another.

"She's a lunatic," muttered Diane, my friend and partner in the singles scene, a she clamped my arm and used me as a wedge to part the crowd. After propelling me back to the bar through a maze of Jordache and Sassoon, she led me out to the parking lot.

"This is the last time I'll ever go anywhere with you, Amy," she said as she slid into the driver's seat. "You really must see a psychiatrist."

On the way home, I tried to think of a way to explain why I had acted so strangely on each of the three nights we'd gone to singles bars together. My mind drifted back to the first time at the Go For It tavern when two men joined us to watch mud-wrestling. Diane and the men cheered wildly for the female contestants, but the sight of the two bodies covered with slime made me burst into tears.

As the men shifted uncomfortably in their chairs, Diane told them I had been under a great deal of pressure in my job. I'm a high school home-economics teacher. "There are boys in her classes now," Diane explained. "Bachelor Living, it's called. She's trying hard to adjust."

"It's not my classes, Diane," I objected, "it's this mud-wrestling. Human beings shouldn't be returning to the slime. I mean, all the centuries of evolution count for nothing if we're so willing to slide back into the mire. And with everyone applauding and—"

Diane pulled me from my seat and marched me to her car.

Several weeks passed before I approached her in the teachers' lounge and asked if I could go with her to a singles bar again. As my thirtieth birthday drew near, my need to meet someone and start a lasting relationship had become more intense. Diane frowned. "Okay," she agreed, "but we'll have to be careful to avoid places that don't suit your sensibilities."

She selected the Quaintly Naughty Victorian Lounge, a haven of flocked wallpaper and ornate gilt mirrors. Within minutes, I knew I shouldn't have come. Gaslights on the wall flickered over faces scanning faces for signs of consent to one-night stands. In the first half hour, I counted five couples who left together for the motel located conveniently next door. And from the negative swish of her long hair, I could tell that Diane had received a motel offer on the dance floor.

During a medley of Rolling Stones hits, a fortyish man appropriated Diane's bar stool and offered to buy me a drink. Startled, I thought for a moment that he was my Uncle Bernard from Scranton, Pennsylvania, but the man was simply a blown-dry, racquet-club version of my uncle. Accepting my silence as acquiescence, Uncle Bernard's döppelganger ordered me a glass of Chablis.

"You're a white wine drinker," he said complacently, "I can always tell."

As I sipped the wine, he recited the details of his divorce from Vanessa, his wife of twenty years, his leather-and-leopard-skin condo only a few miles away, and his vasectomy. It was quite obvious that I had just received a résumé from an applicant for a one-night stand. Excusing myself, I went to the chalkboard that advertised the sandwich specials and removed the chalk. Angrily, I returned to Vanessa's ex and drew a straight line down the sleeve of his burgundy-colored shirt.

"Hey, what are you doing?" he sputtered. "This shirt cost seventy-five dollars."

Still gripping the chalk, I headed for Diane's partner, who was not very subtly trying to dance her over to the door. Quickly, I hackd a long white line down the back of his black-silk shirt.

"What the hell!" he exlaimed as his hand flew to his back.

"You've been branded with the Number One," I said. "You're a one-night stander just like the other man I branded at the bar."

Since we were so close to the door, Diane had no trouble removing me that time.

As Diane drove us home from Scarlet and Rhett's, I felt terrible about the times I had embarrassed her. She had agreed to go out with me a third time only because I had lied and told her I was seeing a therapist who thought I had progressed to the point where I could once more attempt the singles scene. As I frantically groped for words to explain the compulsions that came over me in singles bars, I remembered images from a recent dream. In it, I was rescuing young men and women from death by pulling them away from the mythical minotaur.

Seizing on the dream, I said, "I wrote on the wall tonight, Diane, and did the other strange things because I want to save young adults from the minotaur. You remember the minotaur, don't you?"

Icily she answered, "As the teacher of honors English classes, I am quite familiar with the half man-half beast who lived in a labyrinth and devoured the young people of Athens."

"Then you'll understand my metaphor. Young adults are being devoured by the minotaur of consumerism, Diane. We're throwaways in a throwaway culture. After we've been devoured, there will be no replacements for us because we're not sufficiently reproducing our-selves. My actions might seem strange to you, but I'm trying to lead my contemporaries out of the labyrinth, like Ariadne did when she gave Theseus a thread to follow out of the maze. Tonight my message had an impact. You heard. Someone called me a prophet."

Diane drove on in silence. When she dropped me off at my apartment, she said, "Please continue seeing your therapist."

My sadness over Diane's lack of understanding lifted momentarily when I entered my apartment. To clear my mind of the jagged images of the singles scene, I glanced around the living room, the room I had furnished with solid pieces from my parents' home. Mother, Father, and I had enjoyed such a happy life until the minotaur of technology, as my father put it, changed our lives. But these mementos of an era when men and women made long-term investments in each other reminded me once again that someone should be with me to enjoy a real home.

Wearily, I sat down and flipped through *Urban Weekly*, a newspaper that carried classified personal ads—Love Ads, they were sometimes called, that were written by men and women who had tired of singles bars. Occasionally, I had considered running an ad but resisted after mentioning the idea to Diane. She had commented, "Those ads are the last resorts of losers. If the advertisers were as great as they describe themselves to be, why are they hiding behind box numbers in a newspaper?"

"Well, at least they'd know that the respondents can read," I had answered sarcastically.

She said, "I think running an ad like that satisfies the need for the rejected to become the rejector. Receiving responses and discarding those that aren't appealing must compensate for the times the advertiser was passed over and couldn't do anything about it. You don't need an ad, Amy. You're intelligent and you're pretty. But you're too intense. You scare men off because you wear your desire for marriage and kids like an aura."

Listening to her opinions had gotten me nowhere. I knew there had to be someone out there looking for me, someone who had felt the hot breath of the minotaur and needed me to lead him out of the maze. I read through the personal ads for help in composing one to reach that someone.

But the ads depressed me. Most of the advertisers identified themselves by their marital status or sexual preferences, as if they were items waiting to be ordered from a mail-order catalog. The texts showed a terrible sameness or cuteness about what the advertisers liked to do: sitting beside roaring fireplaces, taking long rambling walks in the woods, frivolously skipping through public fountains, reading poetry aloud on stormy nights, watching late-night movies in bed, listening to classical music in a speedboat. Nobody mentioned important basic things like making a home and starting a family.

Reading on, I discovered that the style of the ads was mostly alliterative: "Warm, wild, wacky woman seeks wonderful weight-lifting wizard for whoozy woo in waterbed." Thinly disguised practitioners of aberrant sex beckoned to their counterparts: "An incurable prisoner of love, manacled to his mania, seeks to link himself with a male or female keeper of the keys."

I threw the paper on the floor in disgust. Going for a pad and pencil, I sat back down and wrote, "Single woman, tired of singles bars, seeks single man, equally weary, who wants to spend quiet evenings in a real home." Too dull, I thought, reading it over. After a moment, I tried to get somewhat into the style of the published ads: "Single artichoke-loving Aries, crazy about James Joyce and Agatha Christie, seeks single man who doesn't skip through fountains and isn't opposed to reproducing himself eventually in lawful wedlock." Mentally, I submitted this one to Diane, who rejected it for its "cute intensity."

The ad needed to be subtle, but it also *had* to let my Theseus know that I would lead him out of the labyrinth. After several more tries, I finally composed the perfect ad, one that would be instantly recognized by the man I wanted to reach: "Theseus, I will lead you out of the maze. Ariadne."

On Sunday, I mailed the ad to *Urban Weekly*," then cleaned my apartment until it sparkled. I would lead Theseus out of the squalor of the city into a spotless home where I'd serve him homemade meals. I'd lead him to the sofa where our conversation would be set to the music of Glenn Miller and Tommy Dorsey, recording artists my partents loved.

In the teachers' lounge on Monday morning I told Diane I had placed a Love Ad.

"Oh, good grief," she cried, "you'll be contacted by weirdos."

"No, Diane," I protested. "No weirdos will answer my ad. It's so artfully composed that only someone in perfect harmony with me will answer it."

"What did you write?" she asked suspiciously.

"I wrote, 'Theseus, I will lead you out of the maze.' I signed it 'Ariadne'."

She stiffened. "Amy, the only similarity between you and Ariadne is that you're becoming unraveled like that thread she gave Theseus to follow. You're in no state to lead anyone anywhere."

Very coldly I replied, "You couldn't possibly understand. Your sensibilities have been anesthetized by too many trips to singles bars."

She frowned, then delivered her cruelest blow. "You know who'll answer the ad, don't you? A passive type who wants to be led by the hand—a mama's boy or a parasite who doesn't want to work. Or an ex-con who can't make it on the outside."

I left the lounge, unwilling to reveal my deep hurt. It would have been wonderful to share this adventure with Diane, but she had become too jaded by encounters with the minotaur.

For the three days before the ad appeared, neither of us spoke. Her eyes merely widened when she noticed the preparations I was making for my new life: the soft curly hairstyle like the one worn by Ariadne in Hamilton's *Mythology*, the classically simple tunic dresses I had sewn, the new serenity with which I faced the chaos of lunchroom and hall duties.

On Thursday, I left school at lunchtime to buy *Urban Weekly* at the news agency. The simplicity of my ad made a startling contrast to the convoluted verbiage of the others—I was delighted with it and with the thought that at that very moment someone might be reading my words and rejoicing in his imminent deliverance.

Back at school, I noticed Diane leaning over her desk, studying *Urban Weekly*. I stood outside her classroom until she saw me and rushed out.

"Listen, Amy," she said, "I've found a new singles place that's run by a church group. There's no drinking, just dancing and conversation. How about going with me tomorrow night?"

"No, thank you."

She gripped my arm. "You're going to be strangled by your own thread, Ariadne."

I laughed. "Nothing can harm you when you cooperate with the Fates, Cassandra."

"You're not cooperating, you're manipulating, Pandora," she warned and walked away.

I stood and meditated away Diane's negativism. Instead of her hostile form, I saw the figure of Theseus confidently weaving his way through the streets of the city to answer my ad at the post office. That image carried me through Friday and into the weekend. I cleaned my apartment again and baked up some wholesome food.

On Monday, I struggled through my morning classes, sustained only by visualizing myself picking up my response from Theseus. That image had become so strong that I was shocked when the clerk at *Urban Weekly* handed me five letters. The first two envelopes contained ads from Armand's Escort Service and Thelma's Tarot Readings. I threw them away impatiently. The third envelope contained a printed invitation to the Delta Psi Orgy on the following weekend at Henderson College. It ended with the handwritten words, "Wooden you like to horse around with some real Trojans?"

The fourth bore the letterhead of Dr. Virgil H. Croydon, Chairman of Classical Studies, Corinth College. Scanning the page, I soon realized that the writer thought he was being contacted by his deceased wife. "How like you, beloved," he wrote, "to sign yourself Ariadne, the name I gave you because of the many times you led me out of the maze of world-weariness! How often have I begged Rufus Dirksen of the Parapsychology Department to help me contact you, and how often he has refused, unwilling to raise my hopes. You can appreciate how my spirits soared when I perused the personal ads, while waiting in the doctor's office in the hope that reading of the loneliness of others might strengthen me in my own, and saw your message beckoning to me. Answer me, Ariadne, and tell me where to meet you!"

On my free period that afternoon, I answered Dr. Croydon's letter and expressed my sorrow at his misinterpretation of my ad, a task made doubly painful since the last response brought me hope that I wished the professor could share. The letter read: "Ariadne, I will follow you out of the maze. Please meet me at 7 P.M. on Monday night at the Fountain of the Two Dolphins in McMichael Park. We shall know each other without prearranged signs. Gratefully, Theseus."

How quickly the letter from Theseus dispelled the vulgarity of the first three responses and the despair of the fourth. Not even Diane's crude comment about my looking manic that afternoon dampened my joy. I rushed home from school and carefully prepared for the evening, taking special pains with my makeup and finishing a dress I was making of silk the color of the Aegean Sea.

A soft May breeze ruffled my hair as I stood by the Fountain of the Two Dolphins at ten of seven, studying the faces of everyone who strolled through the maze of hedges leading to the fountain, a beautifully symbolic choice of meeting place. At seven, I began to worry that he wouldn't come. Only three lone young men had passed through the maze and none of them had glanced at me. When I saw a blonde head bobbing through the hedges, I wondered if Diane had answered my ad and come to the fountain to savor my disappointment, but the woman rushed toward a man and two small children. Chagrined, I turned away—and saw a man about thirty, almost the same height as I, standing opposite me, smiling. In his hand he held a sprig of laurel, the classical symbol of victory, which he extended to me, saying, "Ariadne, I presume?"

"Oh, yes." I stared into pale-blue eyes set under a thatch of red hair, thinking, Theseus as conceived by Norman Rockwell. The All-American Theseus studied me, waiting, I thought, for signs of disappointment, but I gave him none because his wholesome looks were a portent, I believed, of a commitment to old-fashioned values.

His name was Theodore Mannion. He asked me to call him Theo and gestured toward the entrance to the maze. I responded to his cue by walking ahead to lead him through the labyrinth out to the expanse of grass flanked by benches. The symbolism completed, we laughed and sat down. "As you can see, I'm not the stuff of which Greek heroes are made," he said. "But I'm willing to expand my horizons in a heroic way."

His eyes twinkled a I proclaimed my allegiance to the spirit of the classics and not its statuary. His good humor released all the agony within me and I soon found myself describing my painful odyssey through the singles scene. He listened intently, nodding occasionally, indicating that he, too, had been close to the minotaur.

After I finished relating my misadventures, we sat watching as faint stars appeared on the horizon. At first neither of us noticed the approach of a teenaged boy who asked us menacingly for money.

Reverting instinctively to my role of teacher, I said, "Young man, get out of here and leave us alone." Startled, he skulked off into the night. Theo stared at me. "The minotaur doesn't frighten you at all."

"I meet that kind every day at school. He's the punk offspring of our culture. What I do fear is the monster of consumerism that shapes and controls our lives."

"I fear him, too."

"I can help you escape from him, Theo."

"Yes, I think you can," he said.

"Come with me," I said, offering him my hand.

He accepted my hand and walked with me out of the park. On the sidewalk, he suddenly looked at his watch. "I've got to go now," he said.

"Oh, but you can't, Theo," I cried. "You'll be devoured."

"You're right," he laughed. "My muse will make minced meat of me if I don't leave now. I promised her four hours' work tonight. I'm a poet."

"What about tomorrow?" I said.

"Tomorrow night is yours from six to nine," he promised.

After giving him my address, I drove home and replayed each detail of our meeting in my mind until I slept.

In the morning, I felt energized by the anticipation of the night to come. When I went to the teachers' lounge, Diane appraised me and said, "You're glowing like a convention of fireflies. So you've met your Theseus and he's a perfect ten?"

"Yes, I've met Theo," I answered happily.

"Theo?" she echoed. "Short for Theseus, I suppose."

"No, for Theodore."

"Ah, as in Roosevelt. Does your Theodore walk softly, carry a big stick, and storm hills?"

"No, he's a poet."

"A poet!" she shrieked, puncturing my serenity.

"Shut up!" I said.

Diane giggled and said, "I'm sorry, Amy, but a poet is exactly the kind of dependent person I warned you about. In today's economy, they're about as much in demand as shepherds and blacksmiths."

"Dependent? Theo dependent?" I said. "How absurd. Theo is independently wealthy, an heir to a great fortune."

Diane frowned. "So what's he doing reading Love Ads?"

I sighed. "Theo read my ad just to pass the time while he was waiting in his doctor's office. My ad reminded him of his young wife who died tragically in an accident. Ironically, Theo used to call her Ariadne because she led him out of the maze of world weariness he was experiencing from managing his vast holdings."

"I'm sorry, Amy," Diane whispered.

I allowed myself a moment to gloat before sending a silent apology to the sad professor for borrowing some of his story. Diane's cynicism did, however, chip away at my joy and raise some unsettling questions. Was Theo reading *Urban Weekly* in the hope of finding someone to support his poetry habit? Did he abruptly end our meeting because I didn't seem sufficiently affluent? Could the muse he had referred to be a jealous wife?

Doubts plagued me even after I got home, almost ruining my concentration in preparing the chicken casserole I'd planned for our first dinner together. But when the doorbell rang at six and I saw Theo on the threshold with a bouquet of daisies, my doubts disappeared. As I arranged the flowers in a vase, I studied Theo's reaction to my home. He walked slowly around the living room before patting the sofa and commenting, "They sure built these babies to last. Not like the junk that's made today."

"That's so true, Theo," I commented. "Everything was so much more substantial years ago."

Throughout dinner, he praised everything, from the carefully laundered damask tablecloth to the texture of the perfectly cooked rice. An attentive guest, he centered the conversation on me. My rather prosaic existence seemed to fascinate him, as if he were an archaeologist delighted at finding a shard of ordinary pottery from an ancient race. After hearing my answers to his questions about my cooking, sewing, and wood-finishing, he said, "I think I've landed on another planet."

"No, Theo, you've simply been led to a better part of your own."

"And I'd love to stay in this part, Amy, but my martinet of a muse—"

"I understand," I said. "Can you come back tomorrow?"

"Not tomorrow. I have a heavy day at work."

"I could pick you up," I offered.

He flushed. "I don't think that could be arranged," he answered, gripping the doorknob tightly.

Perceiving that he had a job that embarrassed him, I said quickly, "Come whenever it's convenient."

He squeezed my hand. "I'll be in touch soon."

I stood at the window and watched him cut through the parking lot.

It didn't matter to me that he had no car or a job he could be proud of. I loved him for being Theo, an appreciator of life outside the labyrinth. For the rest of the evening, I planned dinners and outings that would help him to withstand the tedium of his job and the demands of his muse. Before bed, I rubbed cream on my hands, lingering over the hand Theo had touched. I pressed it to my lips and sent a telepathic caress to Theo's hand, to support it in its labors toward greatness.

On Thursday, he returned and we shared another beautiful evening. We had dinner and then danced to the records my parents loved. At quarter to nine, Theo gazed wistfully around the apartment and said, "Leaving here is like returning to an army barracks after a home furlough. But the muse is an exacting warden."

I touched his face and asked, "Do I provide some solace for you in your lonely quest for greatness?"

"Yes," he answered. "You sing me songs of home and hearth that strengthen my resolve."

I closed the door and pictured him alone in a bleak room in a shabby boarding house, the only place he could afford on his salary in whatever menially demanding job he had taken to free his mind for its evening's labors. Suddenly inspired, I decided I'd rearrange the furniture in the living room and prepare a work space for him in the alcove next to the window. I'd surprise him with his poet's corner the next time he came to dinner.

But Theo never returned for dinner. On Saturday he insisted on taking me to a nearby family restaurant. The cooking was mediocre, but I pretended to enjoy it. Theo saw through my shamming, however, and said, "I was crazy to think I could find a place nearly as nice as yours."

Using his praise for my home as a lead-in to the poet's alcove, I invited him to share my apartment. For a moment he looked so stunned that I assured him I intended only to be Beatrice to his Dante, thinking he'd understand that I'd make no demands on him. But Theo chewed his lip in what became an obvious effort to suppress nervous laughter. Humiliated, I suggested we leave.

Back at my place, I stammered out a hurt apology, but Theo ignored me and pulled out an album from a shopping bag he had left by the front door when he had come to pick me up. When I saw the cover of the album, I gasped. It could only have been conceived in hell. Four androgenous creatures cavorted on the cover, the lead singer holding an electric guitar as if it were a phallic extension of himself. The singer had curled his lips into a pout and grimaced under a canopy of pink-and-green spiked hair. Each member of the group wore tight leather pants, T-shirts sliding off their shoulders, and wide leather bands dotted with metal studs on their wrists—bracelets suitable for the guardians of torture chambers. The name of the album was *Vomit* and its authors looked as if they had been spewed up by the River Styx.

Aghast, I watched as Theo placed the record on the stereo and the screams and curses of the damned raged through my living room. To exorcise my home of the demons, I ripped the album from the turntable and threw it across the room. The disk crashed against the bookcase and shattered. Shaking, I turned to Theo, whose eyes registered a curious detachment.

"Never bring that filth here again!" I screamed.

Theo quickly shed his impassive expression and reached for my hand. "You cut your finger on the stylus," he said solicitously.

"I pulled away from him. "Leave. Right now."

"I'm sorry," he said. "I brought the record because a friend gave it to me and I thought we'd be so far from the minotaur here we could be aware of what's out there without being threatened by it." He looked so contrite I regretted my outburst and apologized. He shrugged and said, "You're just tired. I'll leave now and call you soon."

"Please do," I sobbed, squeezing my cut finger.

After he left, I lay on my bed and tried to meditate the evening away, but my mind replayed the scene of Theo coolly observing me as if I were a rat trapped in a maze and he a researcher taking notes. He's written me off, I thought miserably before slipping into a series of exhausting dreams where Theo continued to write me off on the early-dismissal forms we use at school.

In the morning, I felt ill but couldn't bear to stay home in my contaminated apartment. When Diane saw me in the corridor, she said, "You look terrible, Amy. Hath thou and thy poet splitteth?"

"No," I answered quickly—too quickly, because she added, "With your poky hair and pasty skin you look as if you posed for the cover of *Vomit*."

I grabbed her arm and pulled her into the empty Home Ec lab.

"What do you know about Theo?" I demanded.

"Nothing!" she answered, her eyes darting to the door.

"Then why did you mention that album? Theo has a copy."

"Everyone has a copy," she bleated. "It's at the top of the charts."

Were you the friend who gave him the album? Are you two in this together? Did you tell him to answer my ad?"

"No, Amy, no," she whimpered.

Convinced by her palpable fear that she hadn't set me up, I let her go. But she must have spread vicious rumors about me after that because so many of the teachers offered to cover my classes if I wanted to see a doctor. I thought of going home but I couldn't face being alone. When the closing bell rang, I started wearily out the door—and met Theo coming up the steps.

Without preamble he said, "It's a great day for a picnic."

Taking my arm, he escorted me to a car I had never seen.

As we drove to McMichael Park, I rested my head on his shoulder and murmured, "Dear Theo, I'm so glad to see you." When we reached and park, he hauled a picnic basket and blanket to a spot opposite the

maze. He spread the blanket and lifted a foil-wrapped package of bar-
becued chicken from the basket. He poured me a cup of iced tea from a
thermos and intercepted my attempt to apologize for the night before.
Accepting his unspoken forgiveness, I ate contentedly.

After a dessert of cheese and fruit, I slid down on the blanket and lay
my head on Theo's lap. I watched puffy white clouds floating across the
sky and pressed the scene into my book of memories. Closing my eyes, I
thought, It is possible to escape the minotaur. Wanting to share the
moment more closely with Theo, I reached for his arm—and knocked
a sweet-smelling cigarette onto the blanket. Shocked, I sat up as Theo
picked up the hand-rolled cigarette and brushed the ash away. After
inhaling deeply, he removed the vile thing from his mouth and offered it
to me. "It will heighten and extend the moment," he said.

I pushed his arm away and ran from the blanket. Out on the
sidewalk, I searched for a cab to drive me back to my car at school but
couldn't find one. I was pacing up and down with agitation when Theo
reached me, mumbled an apology, and offered to drive me back to
school. Disoriented by the abrupt shift the picnic had taken, I let him
lead me to his car.

When we reached the parking lot at school, I grabbed my jacket from
the front seat and hurried away without saying goodbye. At home, I
walked like an automaton to the closet to hang up my jacket when a
beige cardigan fell with a thud to the floor. I had inadvertently picked up
Theo's sweater along with my jacket.

But why would a sweater fall with a thud? Could there be a gun in the
pocket? Cautiously, I reached into the pocket—and pulled out a small
tape recorder. I removed a tape inside and read: *Notes for the book*. After
rewinding the tape, I pressed the play button and heard Theo's voice.

In the resonant tones of a TV announcer, he said, "Good evening,
this is your star reporter on his way to the big time, the Big Book that's
going to change him from a hack on a local paper to a big-league journalist pulling down megabucks."

Then, resuming his normal voice, he said, "Um. Okay now, this tape
is going to cover my fourth stint as an undercover investigative reporter
gathering material for a book on answering Love Ads. I thought three
stories would be fine, but Oliver the Agent decided I need another one.
Man, Oliver should try working full-time at the *Chronicle*, eliminating
meeting the ordinary people who answer these ads, setting up dates
with the weird ones, parking the car blocks away to protect his identity,
participating in the Love Advertisers' strange repertoires, begging off
gracefully, dictating notes on the way home, transcribing them, and
falling asleep at the typewriter."

Numbly I listened to another voice—Oliver's, I supposed: "Ted, you
have the humorous element in the character you call Amelia Airhead,
the gal who had you pretend to be her co-pilot on a trip around the
world. Her geographical blunders are hilarious. Your experiences with
Batty Billy, the sixty-year-old CPA who wore a Batman costume and had

you dress up like Robin, are pathetic in the best sense. That part about Billy losing his job because he bumped into his boss at a bar when he was suited up as the Caped Crusader is very moving. Your eerie activities with Nick Nercrophilios, the mortician-school dropout who likes to prowl cemeteries at night, is right on target. But there's a missing element, Ted. We need a dangerous segment to make the book really fly. Find someone who's involved in something dangerous or has the capacity for violence. Then we'll have a winner."

Ted's voice took over. "Since Oliver's got a string of money makers in his stable of writers, I'll follow his advice. I'm going to answer an ad that's intriguing: 'Theseus, I will lead you out of the maze.' Sounds like a code from somebody involved in hard drugs. This Ariadne must want to lead someone out of the maze of consciousness into the depths of the unconscious. And how else to do that but with drugs? She could even be a drug-pusher. Plenty of potential for danger here. I'll set up a meeting in McMichael Park, the favorite place for dopers, to let Ariadne know I've broken the code."

I sat down on the floor and listened to more of the tape. Treacherous excerpts still thunder through my mind: "I recognized Ariadne instantly. She had the glistening eye of a fanatic. I almost backed off, but, remembering Oliver, I handed her a sprig of laurel, a green gift of the earth, one of nature's psychedelic goodies, to let her know I was hip. I told her I wanted to expand my horizons. I thought that'd tip her off, but she started raving about the singles scene and a minotaur. She isn't into drugs, she's hooked on nostalgia. She's a looney, all right, but could she be dangerous? Man, yes, I think she could. She scared that kid in the park away. Her mood swings are awesome. I'll play along for a while and act like a grownup Beaver Cleaver, but then I'll switch to hard guy and freak her out."

I switched off the recorder and paced the floor, returning many times to the alcove I had chosen for Theo's work space. As I stared at the spot, a minotaur materialized. Pawing impatiently on the carpet, he muttered "Feed me, feed me, feed me." The sight of him strengthened me for more of the tape so I patted his head and said, "Later, pet, later."

The next portioin of the tape detailed Theo's utter boredom with the "tedious domesticity" I had subjected him to when he came for dinner: "Nora Nostalgia's place is driving me crazy. I think I'll take her out . . . Another awesome mood swing from Nora. She invited me to move in. she looked so vulnerable I decided to gauge her capacity for violence by playing *Vomit*. She was marvelously demented. But I'll have to think of something stronger for tomorrow—a mere broken record isn't going to satisfy Oliver's appetite for violence . . ."

The tape whirred along as Theo pondered more treachery. "Feed me, feed me," chanted the minotaur in the corner.

"I've got it! I'll offer her marijuana at a picnic. Grass on the grass—oh, man, what a wonderful way to rattle her cage!"

I turned off the recorder and went to sit next to the minotaur. Together we waited for Theo to reclaim his electronic diary and experience the danger I didn't provide him with at the park.

I smiled and handed him his sweater. He felt it.

"There was something in the pocket that might have fallen out," he said, glancing nervously around the room. I lifted the recorder off the table and said, "Could this be it?"

"That's it!" He smiled. "My tape recorder. I use it to dictate some of my poetry."

"If you want it, Theo, follow us."

As he turned to see who was with me, the minotaur charged past him and followed me out of the building. We waited in my car until Theo followed us outside. I turned on the ignition and called out the window, "Follow us. We'll wait for you."

When Theo's car pulled up behind us, we set out into traffic. At each intersection, I slowed down so Theo wouldn't lose us.

It was a lovely evening drive to the old Breuer Watchworks, so reminiscent of the times Mother, Father, and I drove to the factory Father owned until the minotaur of technology consumed the fine timepieces that were crafted under his guidance. After the bankruptcy, Father wrote a short note apologizing to Mother and me before he put the gun to his head. Time stopped then for Father and for Mother, too. She had to go to that terrible place where people sit in chairs and stare at the walls and day and night have no meaning. All during the years I lived with Grandmother I prmoised myself I'd have the lovely life Mother and Father had before the minotaur of technology shattered the fine mechanism of Father's mind.

When we reached the Watchworks, I let my imagination transform the boarded-up builiding into the thriving workplace it used to be. When Theo pulled up behind us in back where several old cars have stood abandoned for over a year,I picked up the tape recorder and took a flashlight and the old set of keys from the glove compartment and went into the building.

The minotaur snorted angrily, but obeyed my command to wait in Father's office. Carefully, I climbed the first level of stairs, avoiding the fissures in the concrete steps, steadying myself against the flaking wall. On the landing, I paused and flashed the light down at Theo as he stood in the doorway. Shielding his eyes, he advanced tentatively toward the stairs, then stopped suddenly and sucked in his breath. A large rat had darted across his foot. Unnerved, he staggered back and groped for the handhold. Finding none, he thudded against the front door. Anxious that he not run from the building, I called, "Follow me, Theo. My father owned this company and there are treasures up here I'd love to share with you."

"Okay," he agreed, "but keep that damned light out of my eyes."

Directing the beam to the floor, I forged a golden path up the crumbling staircase, then into the workroom on the second floor. I stepped over a small chasm created by rain from a leak in the roof, but Theo wasn't so agile. His foot slipped into the hole, his heel banging loudly against an exposed metal girder. I waited patiently as he worked his foot out.

"Whatever's up here better be good," he muttered.

"Oh, it is, Theo, it is."

I flashed the light around the empty workroom and Theo watched the beam skip over the walls and come to rest on a padlocked closet.

"That's where the treasures are, Theo."

As he limped toward the closet, I said, "But the key's outside hanging on a hook next to the door. I'll get it."

I flashed the light away from the closet back toward the entrance to the room and followed its beam out to the landing. Before slamming the door shut and sliding the bolt across it, I flashed the light into Theo's face and captured his dawning awareness of what was about to happen. It was a sight I'll always treasure.

As he banged his fists against the door and screamed for me to let him out, I pulled his tape out of the recorder. With manicure scissors, I clipped the tape and released it from its plastic housing. Graciously, I unraveled the tape and let it flow down the stairs behind me to become a thread for Theo to follow out of the dark labyrinth of the old Breuer Watchworks.

Malcolm McClintick
Fish Out of Water

I'd been there before.

It was one of those cheap night spots down on Jackson Street, where after dark the doors open and spill garish music and forced laughter onto the grimy sidewalks along with the reek of cheap wine. It was called the Tiger and you could get drunk in it while you watched girls dance. You could pay a little extra and dance with one of them, and rumor had it you could pay a little more and take her in the back room or out in the alley.

Someone had gone out in the alley with the dancer. She lay in a pool of blood, wearing her scanty dancing costume, her heavy makeup covering her face like a mask. She lit up in the flickering glare of the photographers' flashes while cops milled around and a plainclothesman named Harry Dunn scowled. You could hear the wail of the ambulance on its way.

I stayed back from the crowd. There wasn't room for me. Anyway, this part of it was for the cops. My name is Milo Malotti and I'm an investigator from the prosecuting attorney's felony task force. I carry a little gold badge that says I'm a task-force member, and since that doesn't always get me out of a tight spot I carry a snub-nosed .357 magnum in a shoulder holster.

Harry Dunn came over to where I stood smoking a cigarette. Dunn is pushing fifty, short but strong—he wears blue suits and a little plaid hat that always makes me have to swallow a laugh. He glared at me and said:

"Hello, Milo. You ever see this broad before?"

"I don't get here that often," I said. "Sometimes at lunch. They've got pretty good chili and their smoked sausage isn't too bad. Who is she?"

The ambulance rolled up and some attendants jumped out to hurry over to the body. The red emergency lights flashed against the rear of the building and were reflected in the water and blood running in the alley.

"Broad named Maris," Dunn said. "We don't have a last name on her yet, but some of the guys are inside checking the other employees and whatever customers haven't already beat it out the front."

"Dancer, right?"

"Uh huh, that's one name for it. She waited tables and danced, you know the bit. And took guys to the back for something extra." He leered. "I suppose you didn't know about that."

"Yeah, I knew about it."

Dunn nodded. "I suppose now the mayor'll decide to crack down again. Four months away from an election. You and your task force'll be busy again. You should've been a cop, Milo. Then you'd be busy all the time instead of having to stand around doing nothing for weeks at a time."

I had a rejoinder for that, but a uniformed cop came from inside and spoke to Dunn. "Lieutenant, her name is Maris Talbott. Her boy friend's Big Vic."

"You know Big Vic?" Harry Dunn asked me.

"Sure. Big Vic Lambert. One of the local hoods. Into drugs, prostitution, probably runs a protection racket. She was his?"

Dunn looked at the cop. "Where's Lambert?"

"Nobody's seen him in here tonight, Lieutenant. They say he hasn't been in all day."

"Well, check it out. I want to know where he is, and where he's been."

"Right, Lieutenant." The cop went away. Dunn turned back to me. "Between your boss and my boss, Milo, we ought to be able to clean up this street. Jackson Street's been this way since I was at the police academy. It was like this when you were in law school. What the hell's wrong with this city?"

"Politics," I said. "And you know it."

Dunn nodded. One of the ambulance attendants came over, a young dark-haired woman in a blue jumpsuit.

"The victim's dead, Lieutenant. She was stabbed several times in the throat and chest."

"Okay," Dunn told her. "You can take her as soon as the coroner's through."

The young woman wandered back toward the group clustered around the body and Dunn and I leaned against the cold bricks of the building and watched. Reporters milled around and a few sensation-seekers were being held back by uniformed cops. I was formulating procedure. Harry Dunn and the homicide boys would do the routine stuff. It looked like it was going to be Vic Lambert, though why he'd suddenly decide to cut up his girl friend in a back alley was puzzling.

I'd met Lambert a few times. He was in and out of the prosecutor's office twice a year or so for questioning and, occasionally, an arraignment. Lambert was a tough professional hood, and careful. Even if he wanted somebody out of the way he never did it himself, and the people he hired either got away clean or we found them face down in the river. Lambert stayed high and dry. I couldn't see him dragging this Maris Talbott into the alley and sticking her with a knife.

"Hey, Lieutenant." Another uniformed cop approached Dunn. "We found the knife in a trash can. They're checking it for prints."

I let my cigarette drop to the bricks and hiss out in a puddle of something dark, and pushed myself away from the wall. "I'll see you around, Harry."

"Where you off to?"

"To find Big Vic."

Harry Dunn chuckled. "Lotsa luck, Milo."

"Yeah."

As I left the alley for my car, it was starting to rain. It was about 7:45 P.M.

I found Vic Lambert an hour later in a place ten blocks away, a beer and pool parlor called Eddie's. Nobody in the place answered to the name Eddie, but that was the name on the red neon sign over the door. A narrow front room with a bar along the left side and booths opposite led to a dingy back room containing three pool tables. As I pushed open the connecting door and stepped into the back, I saw two surly-looking men squinting through a haze of cigar smoke at a tall fat man in a black suit, white shirt, and black tie—he had a black derby on his huge round head.

"Four ball in the side," the fat man said without looking up, and shot. The four ball came off one wall at an impossible angle and spun neatly into the side pocket. Then he looked up at me, and his thick black brows knotted over h is bulging nose. "This is a private game. What the hell do you want?"

"You know me, Vic," I said. "I just want a word or two in private."

"I'll finish the game first."

I shrugged and leaned against the wall. The other two ignored me. Lambert had five balls left on the table. He ran them all, quickly and efficiently, then racked his stick and glared.

"Come on," he growled, "I'll buy you a drink."

"Okay." I followed him back into the front room and slid into a booth opposite him. The bartender glanced over and I said, "Bourbon and water on the rocks."

"Make it two," Lambert said. He was smoking a fat cigar and he was sweating. "So what is it? I ain't got all night."

"Where were you an hour or so ago?"

"Who wants to know?"

"I do."

"Listen, Malotti, you got a warrant or anything? You're a lawyer, you know my rights. You trying to get me mixed up in something?"

"You go to The Tiger a lot, Lambert. You've got a girl there, a dancer." I watched his eyes for anything, but they were black slits. The bartender brought over the drinks and went away.

"That's right. Her name's Maris. So what?"

"You get along with her?"

"What kind of question is that? Sure, I get along with her. She gets out of line, I smack her around. She does what she's supposed to, I buy her things."

"Does she ever object to your smacking her around?"

He puffed hard at the cigar and a bluish cloud of toxic smoke wrapped itself around us. "Of course she doesn't object. If she's got it coming, she knows it. I wouldn't waste my time with her otherwise. What the hell's this all about, anyway? Don't make me mad, Malotti."

"Did you go to The Tiger tonight?"

"I was nowhere near the place tonight. I've been on the other side of town and I've been here. You going to tell me what this is about or not?" His hands became huge fists. Lambert would hit me even if I did work for the felony task force. If he was mad enough, he'd hit me even if I was pointing my .357 at him and getting ready to pull the trigger. I wondered if he'd been mad enough at Maris Talbott.

"It's about murder," I said quietly. "Somebody stuck a knife in Maris tonight." I tensed, watching for a reaction. Lambert had hit me once before, during an interrogation in my office. I'm a pretty sturdy guy and I keep in shape, but he knocked me on my tail and it took three men to get him off me. I waited.

His nostrils flared and his eyes opened wide, then he seemed to control himself with an effort. His eyes narrowed again and when he spoke his voice was low and hard. "Who did it?"

"We were wondering if you could tell us."

"No." Lambert picked up his glass and drank down the bourbon all at once, banged the glass down on the table, and said: "I wasn't there tonight. How did it happen?"

I told him, briefly.

"I'll tell you something, Malotti."

"Okay."

"You listen good. I didn't do it. I said just now I smacked her around when she got out of line, and I was telling the truth. But I never hurt her. You ask anybody. You ask'em at The Tiger. I'll tell you something else. I'm going to find out who stuck her. You can look, and those dumb cop friends of yours can look, but I'm going to find the guy who did it, Malotti. And when I find him—" He puffed at his cigar, then shoved it into his empty bourbon glass so that it hissed against the ice. "I'm going to get him, Malotti."

There was nothing else to say. I slid out of the booth and reached for my wallet. "I'll be talking to you, Lambert."

"Put that away. I said I'd pay."

"See you."

I left the place. Out on the street it was dark and cold. An old man in a ragged cost shuffled out from a doorway and opened his mouth. He had no teeth and he needed a shave. "You got any change, sir, for something to eat? I ain't eaten all day, sir."

"Here." I gave him a couple of dollars and went away.

At 9:30 I was back inside The Tiger. You couldn't have told that anything had happened, especially not that one of their dancers had been stabbed to death in the alley only a couple of hours earlier. Music blared from the jukebox. Young girls with skimpy costumes and too much eyeshadow served drinks or danced in a little fenced-off area they all referred to as the jungle. The bouncer, a 250-pound blimp named Don, gave me a nod and I sat down at a small wooden table whose surface was wet. A slightly plump blonde waitress came over, wiped off the table, and asked what I'd like. She had the vacant look in her eyes that most of them had, the look that meant she was there physically but mentally she was somewhere far away.

"I'd like a bourbon and water on the rocks," I said, "and some information."

"Bourbon rocks," she said. "I don't talk to the customers unless they dance with me."

I brought out my gold task-force badge and showed it to her. "Felony task force, prosecutor's office," I told her.

She glanced at it and shrugged her soft pale shoulders. "Dollar a dance," she said, and trotted away on spiked heels.

I lit a cigarette and waited. When she brought the drink she set it down, showing a lot of cleavage. "Two bucks for the drink."

I gave her two dollars, then took her wrist in one hand and gripped it hard. She tried to pull away but I held her and spoke in a low voice:

"You can have it one of two ways. I can have you arrested for obstructing justice, failing to cooperate with an investigating officer, and withholding information in a homicide investigation. Or you can sit down for a couple of minutes and answer a few simple questions and be on your way. I might even give you a tip."

"You big—"

"Okay, I'll go call for the cops," I said, letting go of her wrist. "You may as well tell your boss you're leaving."

Her eyes snapped. She wanted to hit me, and she wanted to run away. But she knew I was serious about the cops. She thought for a few seconds, then sat down in the chair across from me and glared, trying to look haughty. "I'll talk to you for two minutes. After that you can stuff it."

"Who was Maris seeing?"

"Maris who?"

"If I don't like your answers I'll take you downtown and ask 'em again. Who was she seeing?"

"I thought we had a Constitution and some rights. Okay, okay. She was seeing Big Vic, is that what you wanted to know? Look, I'm not trying to give you a hard time. You ask anybody in this joint. Big Vic don't like it when we talk about Maris."

"She's dead now, so it doesn't matter what he likes."

"Well, I'm not as brave as you. I don't have some fancy badge. Have you ever seen him get mad? I just don't want to cross him, that's all."

I nodded and tried to look sympathetic. "I understand. Look, somebody took Maris outside tonight and put a knife in her chest a

few times. I'm just doing my job. I won't mention your name and Vic
Lambert won't know you said anything to me. I never saw you. I just
want to know what happened. Did Maris date anybody else? Have any
problems with anybody? You know of anybody who's argued with her
or had any kind of a run-in with her lately?"

The girl glanced around quickly, as if looking for someone. Then she
leaned across the table and said, "You don't know where you heard
this, okay? You got to swear."

"I swear."

"Okay. I believe you. Listen, some guy was trying to get Maris for
himself, okay? Nobody ever told Vic because they were afraid of what
he'd do to the person who told him. But this guy was after her—some
guy who came in here on and off starting about three weeks ago."

"Tell me about him," I said.

"A weirdo. Not the kind of guy you ever see in here. One of those
square guys, real straight, high class. He used big words. But he was
real shy—like a fish out of water, know what I mean? Stood out in here
like a girl in the boys' john. He had a thing for Maris, bought her drinks
all the time, danced with her."

"What about Maris?" I asked. "What'd she think about this guy?"

"Maris? She wouldn't give him the time of day. I mean, she'd let him
buy her a drink and she'd dance with him so long as he paid, but other
than that she ignored him. When we'd go to the girls' room or out back
to cool off, she'd talk about what a nerd he was, how he claimed to be
falling for her, like in some movie. He wanted to take her away to
someplace nice."

"So she laughed at him."

"Yeah. At first. But then it got sort of weird. He started, you know,
bugging her, and she tried to avoid him. Called him a meatball, and
Freddy the Freak. That's his name, Fred something or other. Then she
wouldn't dance with him any more, wouldn't even wait on him."

I was interested. This changed things. "Fred's his name? You don't
have a last name?"

She shook her head. "Naw. We called him Mr. Nice Guy. You know,
as a joke. But I never knew his last name."

"Was he in here today anytime, or tonight?"

"I've been here since four this afternoon. I never saw him. Nobody
did. We figured he must've given it up." Suddenly her eyes widened
and she jumped up. "I've got to go, I can't talk any more—" She trotted
off to the bar.

Turning, I peered at the front, expecting to see Big Vic Lambert
coming through the door, but instead I saw a tall thin guy, frail, mousy,
with little pink cheeks, horn-rims, short hair, a dark suit and tie. If he
wasn't Mr. Nice Guy, the world was flat.

He scanned the room, which was crowded with customers and
dancers, and made his way over to a table against one wall. A cute girl

with long dark hair went over and took his order and went away. I stood and went over to his table, looking down at him. When he glanced up at me there was fear in his eyes, magnified by the thickness of his glasses.

"Your name Fred?" I asked him.

"Yes." He spoke in a high, almost hoarse voice. "Fred McDaniels."

"Hello, Fred." I took out the gold badge and held it in front of his glasses. "Milo Malotti prosecutor's felony task force. Mind if I ask you a few questions, Fred?"

"I suppose not." He swallowed hard and his eyes got bigger.

"Good." I sat down. The brunette brought him something that resembled a whiskey sour, or maybe it was a daiquiri.

"Did you want something?" she asked, smiling at me.

"Bourbon and water on the rocks."

She nodded. "Anything else?"

"I'll let you know." I turned back to Fred, who was nervously stirring his drink. "Tell me about Maris Talbott," I said.

He went pale. "Maris? Who's—?"

"Don't give me any bull, Fred. I know you knew her. I know you bought her drinks and danced with her. What about it? Were you hot for her, or was it true love?" I was trying to make him mad, to get his reaction. These shy backward types can be good at conning you, but if you can make them lose their tempers they sometimes blurt things out.

"I resent this," he said, his voice up another notch. "I resent this interrogation, and your crude innuendos."

"Where were you when she was killed, Fred?"

He stared into his drink for a long time, as if searching for something in its depths, something to help him answer. Finally he sighed and looked at me with eyes that were wide and sincere.

"Mr.—"

"Malotti."

"Mr. Malotti, I'm going to tell you the truth. I met Maris Talbott in this place three weeks ago. I'm not a confident man. It's difficult for me to meet women. I found that I could talk to Maris, and I developed strong feelings for her. You might call feelings lust, or love, or something else, but I wanted to be with her, I wanted to make her leave this place so that I could take care of her. I wanted to marry her." He paused, swallowed some of his drink, and continued: "Unfortunately, she had another man, someone who I believe is a criminal. I believe his name is Lambert. I gave it up. She saw nothing in me, I wasn't her type. I came here tonight, just now, to tell her that I'm leaving, that I won't be bothering her again."

"Where were you about two hours ago, Fred?"

He straightened his tie and looked indignant. "I was with Judge Lawrence Baxter until half an hour ago, Mr. Malotti. You may have heard of him. He's the chief judge of the court of appeals for this district. I believe he will corroborate my whereabouts."

I did know Judge Baxter. One of the more reputable appellate judges in the state. If he said Fred McDaniels was with him, then he was. I stood up. "I'll see you around, Fred." I started away, then turned and added, "I'm sorry about Maris."

"Yes," he said, giving me a curious look. "So am I."

Just as I got to the door the cute brunette trotted up to me. "Hey, don't you want this?" She was holding my bourbon.

"I forgot about it." I took it from her, drank it down, and returned the empty glass to her tray. "How much?"

"Two bucks."

"Here." I gave her a five. "Keep the change. Maybe I'll use part of it next time I'm in here."

She smiled, a big warm smile. "I'll be looking for you."

I nodded at Don and walked outside. The cold night air hit me like a bag of ice. I'd had too much bourbon and inhaled too much of everyone else's cheap cigar smoke. Down the street on a dimly lit corner was a pay phone. Heading for it, I thought how Fred had said he hadn't been in The Tiger earlier, but he hadn't been surprised when I mentioned Maris's death. I stepped into the booth and punched some numbers, remembered to deposit a quarter, and punched them again. It rang and was picked up.

"Milo Malotti," I said. "Is Lieutenant Dunn there?"

"Minute."

A few clicks, then Dunn said: "What is it, Milo?"

"What'd you get on that knife they found in the trash?"

"The knife. Yeah, here it is. No prints. Somebody wiped it clean. It had her blood on it. Belongs to the kitchen."

"Okay, thanks." I glanced at my watch. "It's after ten. You working all night tonight?"

"What's it to you?"

"Nothing. See you later." I hung up, got another quarter out, and punched another number. This one I had to look up first. On the third ring, a woman answered and without asking who she was I identified myself and asked if I could speak to the judge. I could. He came on the line a moment later.

"This is Milo Malotti, your honor. Sorry to bother you this late, but I'm investigating a murder and you might be able to help."

"Quite all right, Mr. Malotti. What can I do for you?"

"Do you know a Fred McDaniels?"

"McDaniels. Yes, I believe I do. A banker, if I recall correctly. I met him a couple of months ago. What's the problem, Mr. Malotti?"

"Was he with you at any time tonight, your honor?"

"Tonight? Mr. Malotti, I haven't seen Fred McDaniels in over a week."

My pulse shot up. I pressed the receiver hard against my ear, wondering if I'd heard correctly. "You haven't seen him tonight at all?"

"Not at all."

"Thanks, your honor. I'm sorry I disturbed you."

"Have a good evening, Mr. Malotti."

I pressed the hook down, dug out another quarter, and dialed the first number again. "This is Malotti," I said when Dunn came on. "Get an address for Fred McDaniels and get over to his house on the double. I'll meet you there. Step on it!"

I hung up and flipped through the tattered directory till I found an address for McDaniels, Fred. He'd known she was dead, he'd lied about being with Judge Baxter. Mr. Nice Guy, the fish out of water. I had to admire his nerve, going back to The Tiger a couple of hours afterward, but I didn't think much of his intelligence. He must have known I'd check his alibi.

Once I got to my car it took me twenty minutes to find his house. Two marked cruisers roared up to the curb as I got out. A black Cadillac was parked out front, a few feet from the drive, and somebody was hunched behind the wheel. I pulled my .357 and trotted toward the Caddy but its engine was already running and the driver burned rubber, taking off down the street.

"Who was that?" one of the cops asked, running up to me.

"Somebody's driver. Let's go in. And be careful—he knows we're on to him."

"Lieutenant Dunn's on his way," said the cop. "He wants us to wait for him."

"No. We go in now. A couple of you get around to the back in case he tries to leave that way."

"Sir—"

"Look, I'll take the responsibility. Let's go."

They exchanged glances and drew their revolvers. Two went silently toward the back of the house, the other two followed me up to McDaniels' front door. I tried the handle. It was unlocked. I thought I heard voices inside. Opening the door an inch or two, I called out: "McDaniels!"

"For God's sake," came his cry, "help me!"

"Come on!" I rushed in, .357 cocked, and ran down a short hall into a brightly lit room. Big Vic Lambert was down on his knees with both hands around Fred McDaniels' throat. McDaniels was on the floor, his head bent at an odd angle. Lambert's big face was red with rage. I leveled the .357 at him. "Get off him, Lambert! Get off him *now*!"

Lambert seemed to sag, then he straightened and sat back on his haunches. Slowly, leaning on the arm of a chair, he got to his feet and stood gazing at me, dazed.

One of the policemen rushed over to the unmoving McDaniels and knelt by him, probing and listening. "He's alive, but just barely. Call an ambulance," he told his partner.

"Lambert." I shook my head.

"I told you I'd get him, Malotti." Lambert took a deep breath, almost a sob, and let it out. "He told me just before you got here. He argued with her tonight in the alley behind the bar. He waited out there for her, till she went out for her break. When she laughed in his face, he hit her. She pulled the knife she carried out in the alley with her for protection, and he took it away from her. He stabbed her with it before he realized what he was doing. He killed Maris. He was packing to leave—his clothes and a suitcase are in there on his bed."

"How'd you know it was him?"

"I knew about him. Maris told me all about him."

"Let's hope you didn't kill him, Lambert. Let's hope we got here in time."

The front door banged and Harry Dunn charged into the room. "I don't believe this," he said.

Fred McDaniels stood trial for the murder of Maris Talbott and he was convicted. He's got various appeals pending, but meantime he's doing a life sentence in the state pen. He'll be eligible for parole in a few years. If he survives. I understand he's a little out of his element there.

John F. Suter
The Third Possibility

In hot and in mild weather, the buffet luncheon at the Greenbrier, in White Sulphur Springs, is a delightful experience. The food is superb and it is eaten in a relaxed company at the Golf Club, in a large upper room, open and screened on two sides. The probability of encounter sometimes seems to equal the legend of Harry's Bar in Venice. However, this is secondary to giving one's attention to the green of the driving range in the immediate foreground and the towering backdrop of the forested mountain on the horizon.

Senator Franklin Lambert, a widower of eight months, liked the place for all of these reasons and came here as often as he could. But on this day, his thinking seemed not to be following the usual pattern. Dining alone, he had taken a place at a four-person table—seating himself to face the room, with his back to the view, as though he wanted to be noticed.

The waiter brought his meal and hovered. "Drink sir?"

The Senator stretched his wide mouth in a smile. "Bourbon and branch water, please." He studied the waiter's pale-chocolate face. "It's Fred, isn't it? How are you?" He extended a hand.

Fred took the wiry hand and shook it gravely. "Fine, Senator. A pleasure to see you again." He knew that Lambert wasn't currying votes. The Senator's home was several states distant.

When the waiter had gone for the drink, Lambert stroked his eyelids lightly with thumb and forefinger, then began to survey his food. He had hardly begun to eat when a pleasing contralto voice said, "Excuse me, but it *is* Senator Lambert, isn't it?"

He looked up and smiled. It was hardly necessary to put on hs public face. Graciousness to this woman was automatic, although she was a stranger. He could see the first hint of autumn in her auburn hair and the faint dusting of tiny freckles across her straight nose had begun to pale, but her skin was as firm as the lift of her chin and the green of her eyes was so arresting that it must have made her glance unmeetable years before.

He started to rise, but she checked him with a nod. "Don't get up." She gestured with her plate. "May I join you?"

"Please."

Fred had returned with the Senator's drink and hastened to arrange a place for the woman at the table. When he had finished, she extended her check. "Bring me a martini, please."

Lambert raised a hand. "I'll take it, Fred."

She waved aside Fred's hesitation. "I can't accept, I'm sorry. Go ahead and put it on my check, please."

203

She directed her green eyes at Lambert. "I won't keep you at a disadvantage any longer, Senator. I'm Tamara Reade. You won't have heard of me. I'm not a public figure of any sort, and my importance to you is only potential."

Lambert was relaxing again, but his posture was still ramrod straight. "Tamara Reade. Miss or Mrs.?"

"Miss." There was faint amusement in her tone. "You're uncomfortable with Ms.?"

He nodded, dismissing it. "And you are potentially important to me?"

She bypassed the question. "I find it strange that you can sit there so calmly—your broad back is so inviting to whoever might be out there looking for that exact target." She gestured in the direction of the mid-September sunshine behind him.

The Senator did not move. He sipped at his drink. "Are you a journalist, Miss Reade?" His tone was meditative, concealing the impact her remark had made.

"No."

"Then you're very imaginative. Why should I be a target for anything except criticism from my constituents or the opposition?"

Nothing but candor showed on her face. "It's not many months until the first primaries, is it, Senator?"

He seemed to brush the remark aside. "You're being taken in by the idle speculations of the press, my dear. After all, I'm single once again, and it's less than a year since—"

She interrupted. "And it's a race she wanted you to enter. That's one reason you intend to do it—campaign all the way to the top. You just haven't published that yet."

Lambert was a good poker player, but surprise caught him with his guard down. His bushy eyebrows went up, and his grey eyes widened. "How did—" he began, then stopped. "You wouldn't tell me, anyway. I suspect that there's more, so get on with it."

Her cocktail arrived and she tasted it. "There is more, but not much. I can give you a skeleton of your organization that you'll use in the primaries, beginning with Alan Winter. Shall I?"

Lambert contemplated the table before him. "You'd think I'd have learned something in fifty-four years. If you've turned up Alan, you have a good source. Damned good." He sighed. "Perhaps your remark about my back as a target is not so fanciful, after all."

She smiled in sympathy. "Perhaps not."

"Then it wasn't just to get my attention." He leaned forward. "Do you know something specific?"

"No, not a thing."

"Then, why—?"

"Just this, Senator. Why should you suppose that the present-day madmen would wait until you or anybody else made it to Inauguration

Day? How do you know who has been alienated—or thinks he has?"

The Senator was frowning—his "mien of outrage," as one comment-ator had labeled the look. "This is hardly a time to be discussing such a topic. It will spoil lunch for both of us. Suppose we drop it for now and get on with pleasanter things?"

The green pool of her eyes seemed sunlit. "Nothing would please me more."

Conversation during the meal was the lighest fluff. Senator Lambert learned nothing except that Tamara Reade was called Miss only because she had reverted to her maiden name after a very bad marriage. Beneath a veneer of polite talk, his busy mind was already constructing several scenarios from this and from her earlier remarks.

When they finished the last of the incomparable peaches and whip-ped cream, he dabbed his lips with his napkin. He saw that there was no way he could quietly annex her luncheon check, so he decided to let it go. She was either trying to impress him or asserting her indepen-dence. He pushed back his chair. "Shall we resume the conversation outside?"

She was already rising gracefully from her own chair. "Yes. Some of what I have to say will have little meaning for you, but it's very personal for me."

Lambert rose without awkwardness. Secretly, he was pleased to be seen with this woman. At the same time, if she had planned just that, he was on guard.

When they stepped outside on the upper level, he said, "I must apologize. I came from the hotel in the shuttle. I can't offer you a ride."

"Don't apologize. I came here the same way."

She had not been on the same shuttle with him. Lambert made a quick estimate of the time she had arrived at his table. She had probably come earlier and waited. He pointed out the obvious. "We'll have to wait for the return trip. Do you care to sit?" He indicated some vacant deck chairs.

"No, thank you," she replied, turning her attentioin to the large low building to their left where the indoor tennis court swere housed. Lambert followed her glance up the long gentle ravine where the white springhouse stood. A glint of light reflected from somewhere among the crafts cottages on the left slope momentarily irritated him.

Tamara gestured to the tennis building. "Have you seen the indoor courts?"

"No."

"Let's go over there."

The interior of the building was pleasantly cool. Numerous dark-green courts ran from the back wall to the viewing area along the front. There were several small clusters of tables and chairs in white and pleasant patels scattered through the spectators' area. Just inside the main entrance, counters dispensed equipment and light snacks. An abundance of windows let in ample illumination. Few lights were on, except for some overheads shining on one of the courts, where a player was practicing serves and another was throwing the balls back.

"Isn't that—?" Lambert started to ask.

"Gerulaitis? It's quite possible. I think he's doing an exhibition here tomorrow."

"I must try to see that." The Senator steered them to a table. No other visitors were in sight. He reflected on this as they sat down. Without a crowd, they had no anonymity. Worse, both of them were dressed completely, conspicuously in white.

"Now," he said, finally coming to grips with the enigmas she had raised. "Suppose you tell me what you want of me. No more indirection."

Tamara laughed. "I want to work for you."

The Senator felt a letdown. A job-seeker. He wondered if she thought there was a debt she could call in. He couldn't think of any. "I'm afraid," he said with a rueful chuckle, " I have no opening that even a charming person like you could fill. I have an efficient secretary, a well staffed office, some very astute public-relatioins people—"

"But no lifeguard."

Lambert's response was one of incredulity. "A lifeguard? But I'm a good swimmer. It's one way I keep fit. Besides, there's always someone on hand whenever I swim. You'd be a strange luxury."

Tamara glanced down at her hands. "I'm afraid I didn't put that very well." She looked up again. "It really has nothing to do with swimming."

Lambert was not given to patronizing. He decided to listen without interruption.

She began again. "What I want is for you to realize that every word I'm going to say is true, however incredible it might sound." She hesitated. "I had better begin with my marriage to Roger Gray, because that's when it started. Up to the time of our honeymoon, I had thought he was the most charming, most loving person on earth. I thought that landing him was the greatest good fortune. Every woman I knew envied me, I was sure.

"It didn't last long. I found out in a hurry that Roger was of the same opinion: that I was incredibly lucky that he had condescended to marry me. Further, he was the kind of person who believes that a household ruled by fear is the only one that holds together. I won't go into details. If you've read anything about battered wives, you'll know what I went through."

Lambert was confident now of what she wanted. He let his mind stray to a recent telephone conversation.

("You sure that's what you want now, Senator?"

"It's what I want. Does the money cover eveything?"

"Sure, it's fine. But let's go over one thing again. You'll get a close miss, if that's what you want and that's what the situation permits. But if it takes a flesh wound to make it more convincing, you'll still go for it?"

"I'd rather not, of course, but if your expert says it has to be that way, yes, I'll go along."

"All right, sir. We have your daily schedule for the next three weeks. Will there be any changes?"

"No. Can you tell me when and where?"

"You wouldn't want that. You want this to be convincing.")

The Senator caught himself as Tamara was finishing a description of some of her marital indignities.

"I think I understand, my dear," he said. "You have some legislation pertaining to abused wives. You want me to be a sponsor, is that it?"

A glint of anger came into her eyes. "No, that is *not* what I want!"

A smattering of indistinct dialogue from the practice court drifted into the momentary silence between them.

"I'm sorry," Lambert said. "I misunderstood."

She accepted the offering. "I'm sorry, too. You must be approached by many people who want to use you. I'll get to the point as quickly as I can."

Her tone became intense. "For years before I married, I'd often had vague premonitions when I was near anyone malign. My experience with Roger focused all of that into a mental talent I wish I didn't possess. I now know when I am within a small radius of someone who actually intends to kill another person."

Over the years, Lambert had learned not to heap ridicule or scorn on anyone who had not fully demonstrated that it was deserved. Although he was feeling apprehension, he wanted to hear her out. "Would you elaborate, please?" he said.

"The realization came to me in the last confrontation I had with Roger. By then I had learned not to let myself get to a place where he could prevent my escape. That time I tricked him into thinking I was hiding in my bedroom closet. When he went inside, I slammed the door and propped a chair under the knob. And *then* my mind caught it: the full force of his naked mind. It was more than the fury and emotion of the moment. He had a complete plan for killing me. I got out of here as fast as I could and filed for divorce the next day. I had no trouble. Too many witnesses knew how he'd treated me."

She stopped and was silent, looking into her private hell. The only sound was the impact of another tennis ball being served.

"At the hearing," she went on, "he was his old charming self, but my mind caught it again: he planned to kill me someday. I've managed to keep on the move, under different names, wearing different wigs and eyeglasses and so on. Luckily, I have money from my father's estate. My mother never knows where I am."

"What does Roger do for a living?" Lambert asked.

"He's a painter. An artist."

"He clearly has an overdose of temperament." Lambert stroked his chin. "Is this all of it, then—you have a murderous husband whose intentions you can divine, and you want to work for me as protection?"

"Not as protection for me. Protection for *you*."

At his stupefied look, she went on. "It only started with Roger. Since then I've picked up on dozens of minds who have revealed these same characteristics. I've not often clearly identified the intended victims. Except one. I was in California when that woman tried to shoot President Ford. I was only a few feet away from her in the crowd when I caught it, and it ws evident who her target was. If I had been quicker, I might have been able to prevent her."

"You're saying that you can read minds. If that's so, what am I thinking now?"

She looked at him earnestly. "I'm not saying I can read all minds. I have a talent, a special talent, and it might save someone's life. Maybe yours."

Lord deliver me from the kooks and crazies, Lambert thought. "This is something out of science fiction," he said.

"Stephen King. Yes, I know. That doesn't make it any less true."

"And you want to work as my bodyguard?"

She corrected him. "Not as a bodyguard. They're big and tough and trained to shoot. I'm none of those. Call it a lifeguard."

"Which means?"

She made an exasperated gesture. "I do my best to guard your life. When I pick up an enemy, I tell you at once, and you take some action to save yourself."

He wondered if she could pick up the bogus attempt against himself he had contracted. Probably not. No malice was involved, only a sort of public-relations job.

"You must admit it's rather fantastic," he said gently. "I'll have to give it careful consideration."

The corners of Tamara's mouth lifted in a rueful smile. "I suppose that means no. I was hoping my research into your plans might impress you enough to tip the scales in my favor. Whether you believe it or not, I've told you the truth."

"I haven't turned you down yet," the Senator answered.

"No, but—"

Someone from the practice court said, "Let's call it a day."

"A good idea," Lambert remarked, rising. "I'll walk you back to the hotel, if you like. Would you want to go by the craft houses? The Presidents' Cottage?"

She got to her feet and extended her hand. "No, thank you, I think I'll walk over and catch the shuttle. May I call you in the morning?"

"Certainly. Make it about—"

A look of horror crossed her face. *"No!"* she screamed.

The main door from the outside opened, letting in a long shaft of sunlight. The Senator's back was to the door.

He saw the horror on her face deepen. She stepped forward and gave him a violent push to the side. As he fell, two shots rang out. The door closed abruptly and he heard the sound of running feet. As he got to his knees, he saw her on the floor beside him. Two holes showed in the left of her white blouse, which was turning red at an alarming rate. Her body was very still.

Suddenly there were others around. Where they had come from, he had no idea. A man was examining her and another ran for the telephone on one of the equipment counters.

The tennis player helped him to his feet, saying, "I saw part of it. It looks like she might have saved your life."

"Who was it?" the Senator asked.

The man shrugged.

Lambert turned away and tried to clear his brain.

He had bought a false assassination attempt as a device to attract sympathetic attention. Had it misfired and claimed an innocent victim?

Had Tamara's vengeful ex-husband found her and finally carried out his intention?

With overwhelming sadness, the Senator heard the man putting in the call to have Tamara Reade taken on a futile ride to the clinic adjoining the hotel. If only her motive had been to try to fill the empty spot in my life, he thought. If only she had not come here.

He began to review the sequence of her final moments, beginning with when she had first screamed.

Then the third possibility entered his mind, and he saw that its probability was the strongest of all. From then on, he would seldom relax, and his life would never be the same.

Robert Edward Eckels
The Benefit of the Doubt

The address Coburn had been given turned out to be one of the older stone-fronted buildings just off Michigan a block or two north of the Water Tower. There was no lobby to speak of and, of course, no directory, but a small brass plate fastened to the elevator wall beside the control panel announced that at least part of the seventeenth floor was given over to the Smallwood Galleries.

Despite himself, Coburn was impressed. Farther south in the Loop proper—which was as far as Coburn's business usually took him—a location that far above street would have marked Smallwood as one of the marginal and desperate, but here amid the condos, hotels, and smart shops of what its promoters modestly proclaimed "the magnificent mile," it only served to highlight his exlusivity—as did the understated showroom itself, with its modicum of discreetly lit and selected paintings placed around the walls as if primarily part of the furnishings and only incidentally for sale.

The room was empty when Coburn entered. No bell sounded, but he decided some kind of silent alert had to be attached to the door, because he barely had time to take out a cigarette and tap it against the back of his hand when a slender, youngish woman with dark-blonde hair worn 1960s style, long and uncut so that it reached almost to the small of her back, appeared in an arched doorway leading from the rear. "Yes?" she said, her voice carefully neutral, as was her small even-featured face.

Coburn grinned, seeing himself as she must: a tall, narrow-chested man with small beady eyes set close to a long thin nose in an acne-scarred face, wearing a suit that while not new was still a shade too sharp for the setting—although, he realized, "flashy" and "ambience" would have been her words.

"J. C. Coburn," he said. "Mr. Smallwood sent for me."

"Of course." There was a barely discernible change in the woman's voice, not a lightening exactly but at least a hint that she was willing to grant him a reason for existence. "This way." She turned abruptly and, still grinning, Coburn followed her back down a short hallway to a smaller room furnished as an office. It was windowless and lit only by a single lamp on the old-fashioned wooden desk.

"You may sit there," the woman said, indicating an uncomfortable-looking armchair only partially lit by the circle of light. Still not looking at Coburn, she sat down behind the desk and pressed an intercom button.

"Mr. Smallwood," she said, "the man is here."

She sat back, folded her hands on top of the desk, and gave a good imitation of preparing herself to suffer in silence for however long it might take. As it was, a good two minutes passed. Then a door at the opposite end of the room from which they'd entered opened and Smallwood bustled in. He was a stocky man in his early-to-mid sixties, made to seem even stockier by a large leonine head set down almost without benefit of neck on a pair of heavy, slightly rounded shoulders.

The long-haired woman started to rise, but Smallwood waved her back into her seat and came around to perch on the edge of the desk facing Coburn.

"Mr. Coburn," he said, "it was good of you to come. I'm Owen Smallwood. I see you've already met my associate, Miss Olliver."

Coburn glanced quickly at the woman, thinking he had detected a slight wince at the "Miss," but she had already resumed her passionless study of the opposite wall. Coburn grinned. "I guess you could say that," he said.

Smallwood shifted uneasily on the desk and cleared his throat. There was a slight dusting of dandruff around his collar, Coburn noted. It made him feel more at home.

"As you might realize," Smallwood said, "I've never had occasion to use a person of your profession before. A private detective. I doubt many people have—people of my sort, that is—in my position. I'm going to assume, though, that your time is as valuable as my own and get right to the point. You know, of course, about the unpleasantness we had here recently."

Coburn reflected wryly that for a supposedly intelligent man, Smallwood was doing a lot of assuming, but he was right on one point at least. Coburn had read about the "unpleasantness" when the story had first broken and then had looked it up again after Smallwood—or rather Miss Olliver on Smallwood's behalf—had called to set up this meeting. Thieves had broken into the gallery and taken five of the most valuable paintings—or at least what Smallwood had reported on his insurance claim were among his most valuable paintings. What Coburn wasn't sure about was how this concerned him, since the last he had read indicated that the property had been recovered. He said as much now.

Smallwood smiled bitterly. "Oh, yes," he said, "my insurance company paid a reward to the 'finder.' Actually, that's a euphemism. What they really did was ransom the paintings back from the thieves who stole them. Not that I have any moral objections. My problem is that only five paintings were returned. Six were taken."

Coburn shrugged. "Maybe your man had a wall he needed to cover," he said. "Maybe something else. Whatever, though, you ought to be able to work it out with your insurance."

"Ordinarily yes," Smallwood said. "Unfortunately, this particular painting wasn't on the insurance schedule. I realize that in the normal course of things the insurance company would have negotiated for its return as part of the whole with subsequent reimbursement from me for expenses over and above those covered by the policy. But that would have meant publicly reporting the loss and that, unfortunately again, was just what I couldn't afford to do."

Coburn looked at him curiously, beginning to be interested now for the first time.

"No," Smallwood said, interpreting the look correctly and shaking his head, "it was mine—at least as much as great art can be said to be any one person's. I bought and paid for it, anyway. As you may or may not be aware, however, many countries now have laws forbidding the export of art objects classed as national treasures. A short-sighted, chauvinistic attitude to be sure, but a fact of life nonetheless. Another unfortunate fact is that in recent years the policy of the U.S. government has been more and more to accede to demands for the return of, shall we call them, *unofficially* exported items." He sighed. "Even when return is not mandated, the litigation surrounding the matter can drag on for years, making a profitable resale impossible."

"I assume you wouldn't be telling me all this," Coburn said, "if that wasn't what we are talking about now—an unofficially exported item."

Smallwood nodded. "Van der Laan's *Burghers of Leyden*," he said. "No doubt you're familiar with it."

Coburn shook his head.

Smallwood smiled wryly. "I'm sorry. Like many another enthusiast, I have a tendency to suppose the whole world is as expert as I am. Or should be. Actually, though, the painting is quite well known. It was painted in 1629 by a man many critics consider at least the technical equal of Rembrandt for one of the town's more prominent mercantile families. It says something for our times, I suppose, that the same family retained possession until 1940, when the then owner bartered it to Goering in return for safe passage to England." Smallwood's smile deepened. "Not that it did him any good. He was subsequently killed in the Blitz along with the rest of his family. As for the painting itself, no trace of it was found after the war and it was generally assumed that like so much else it had been destroyed."

"Until you found it," Coburn said.

"Until it was brought to me," Smallwood corrected him. "I suppose you might argue I had a moral obligation to report the fact of its existence, but it's a fine legal point as to who really owns it now. Goering's heirs?" He paused and looked at Coburn shrewdly. "Do you have any idea what a painting like that's worth today?" he said.

Coburn shrugged. "A lot, I would guess."

"A lot indeed," Smallwood said. "Five years ago a van der Laan was auctioned in London for two and a half million. It would bring half again as much now. Obviously, I couldn't realize as much on mine, but there are countries where the governments' hearts bleed less openly than ours and consortiums of investors—speculators, if you will—are able to wait the long term. Even with a clouded title and a private sale, a million dollars isn't out of the question. Think about that, Coburn. One million dollars—more than enough finally to let me quit this rat race where most of what I earn is ploughed back into the next big deal, and the next after that, and start to live the way people are meant to." He laughed. "I could even buy back some things—really precious things—I've been forced to sell to ignorant clods who see them only as so much status on their walls. Do you honestly think I'd let some legal quibble stand between me and that?"

Coburn shook his head. "Not me," he said. "Only you just better hope your thief doesn't feel the same way and decide he can sell this masterpiece unofficially just as easily as you can."

"If he did," Smallwood said, "he'd soon find out otherwise. He has the painting, but I have the documentation that proves it authentic and it's worthless without that. In fact, a long as I remain silent he can't even prove he stole it from me." He shrugged. "It's a moot point now, in any case. The thief has been in touch with me." He nodded to Miss Olliver, who half rose to hand him a sheet of notepaper which he passed on to Coburn. On it words and letters cut from a newspaper had been pasted to spell out: For rest of consignment call 784-3206.

"Needless to say," Smallwood said, "I called the number. The price for return of the painting is one hundred thousand dollars. That's more than was paid for the other five altogether. But—" he shrugged again "—the man obviously knows the value of his cards."

"You're sure this is genuine, then?" asked Coburn.

"I don't see how it could *not* be," Smallwood said. "Aside from Miss Olliver and myself, and now you, the thief is the only one to know there was even a theft."

"The way I see it then," Coburn said, "you've got two options. You can pay the money or try to run him down by tracing the phone back to its location."

"I've already traced the phone. It's can accommodation drop on South Wabash. When I called, I was told I would be called back. Which I was—from, I'm sure, a second phone which would prove equally unhelpful if traced. Not that it really matters. All I want is the painting back in the safest, surest way possible. And if that means paying ransom—well, I have the money and I'm prepared to spend it. However—" his eyes slid over to Miss Olliver and it seemed to Coburn that his voice lost some of its assurance "—I'm not what you would call a man of action. I—ah—feel it would be better if the actual transfer were handled by someone more accustomed to this sort of thing."

"Like me," Coburn said.

Smallwood nodded. "Your name was mentioned as a possible intermediary during the earlier negotiations with the insurance company. It never came to anything because the company was able to carry it off alone. Still, they were very positive about your successes in similar cases in the past."

"Positive," Coburn said. "That was nice of them. Did they tell you my fee, too?"

"I believe someone mentioned something about a percent of the ransom amount."

"Ten percent, to be exact. Usually that's split between the parties, but since you did all the negotiating I'll settle for half that. Five thousand dollars."

Smallwood wet his lips. "That's a lot of money for a couple of minutes' work," Miss Olliver said quietly when he didn't speak.

Coburn shrugged. "Maybe," he said. But usually when I walk into one of these things I know exactly who I'm dealing with and just what's going to happen. This time I don't. Neither do you or you'd be doing it yourselves. That's what makes it worth five thousand. But it's your choice."

Smallwood hesitated, then nodded. "You're right," he said. "And with so much at stake, it would be foolish to quibble over pennies. The transfer is to be made tonight. There's a motel west of town, The Hideaway. You're to ask for Mr. van der Laan's room. The man there will either have the painting or tell you where it can be picked up. I don't anticipate any problems since it's in the thief's interest as much as my own to have the transfer go smoothly. Still—"

"Like I say," Coburn said, "that's what you're paying me for."

"Yes." Smallwood pushed himself off the edge of the desk. "Well, it's settled then."

"Just one other thing," Coburn said. "How will I know the painting I get back is the right one?"

Smallwood hesitated, and before he could speak Miss Olliver cut in smoothly. "I have photographs. Plus a description of some distinctive markings on the back of the canvas. That should be sufficient for your purposes."

Smallwood beamed. "What I don't think of, Barbara does. Well, I'll leave the two of you to work out the details." He turned to his assistant and added in a brisker tone: "I'll see you in my office when you've finished." With an equally brusque nod to Coburn, he left through the same door he had entered.

For a moment, Barbara Olliver sat at her desk, unmoving. Then, sighing heavily, as if reconciling herself to an unpleasant but necessary task, she brought out a large manila envelope from a desk drawer and pushed it across to Coburn.

He grinned at her. "You like Barbara better than Miss Olliver?"

She looked at him coldly. "What does that matter to you?"

Coburn shrugged. "Just curious. Occupational hazard, I guess. Is Smallwood your boy friend?"

The ice in her eyes turned to anger and Coburn quickly held up a placating hand. "Sorry," he said. "I should have asked if you were his girl friend. There's a difference and it's always polite to give the lady the benefit of the doubt."

Barbara Olliver stared at him for another long moment, then she nodded at the envelope still lying on the desk. "Is that sufficient?"

"Oh, sure," Coburn said, picking up the envelope without bothering to look inside. "What about the money?"

"You'll get that tonight. Do you know where the motel is?"

"I can find it."

"Take the expressway to Highway 38, then straight west on 38. The motel will be on your left just beyond St. Charles. I'll meet you there shortly after eight."

Coburn looked at her blankly. "You'll *meet* me there?"

"Don't worry," she said. "I'm not going to interfere with your exchange. But the insurance people made no secret of the fact they felt your successes were due primarily to your being tied in with the mob that did the stealing."

"Professional jealousy." Coburn said.

"Maybe. But a hundred thousand dollars is still a lot of money. I don't want you deciding the airport's a lot closer than we are and taking off with it."

Coburn grinned at her. "Frankly," he said, "the idea never occurred to me."

Barbara smiled back, the first smile Coburn had seen on her neat-featured face. "Good," she said. "Now we don't have to worry about it occurring to you later, either, do we?"

There was a coffee shop half a block from Smallwood's building, and Coburn sat in it, letting his coffee cool while he went through the material Barbara Olliver had given him. There wasn't all that much: two black-and-white photographs and a color print that was still mostly blacks and whites of a painting that showed a group of men dressed like the Pilgrim Fathers seated along one side of a small table, facing out. The prints were all too small for any detail to stand out, but at least, Coburn decided, he wouldn't be taken in if the thief tried to pass off a pastel of fauns splashing in a brook. Not that he cared, of course—unless it meant he wouldn't be able to collect his five thousand. The description of distinctive markings he put aside unread, but a note neatly taped to the back of one of the black-and-whites indicated the painting itself was oil on canvas and 24" by 36" unframed, which meant it would be easy enough to fit it into a medium-sized suitcase.

He looked up to find the waitress craning to peer over his shoulder.

"They look kinda like those cigar-box guys," she said.

"Yeah, they do, don't they?" Coburn said. He put the photos and papers back into the envelope, then went back to use the public phone just outside the washrooms.

There was no answer from the first number he dialed, but the second was picked up on the third ring.

"It's me," he said. "Coburn."

"Yeah? What's happening?"

"That's what I called to find out," Coburn said. "You're the one everybody says is supposed to know."

"Everybody oughtn't to talk so much," the man on the other end said. "You got something specific in mind?"

"Art theft," Coburn said. "Maybe a month ago. Smallwood Galleries."

"What's the matter?" the man said. "You upset you got left out?"

"Not me," Coburn told him. "I got to pass 'em up every now and then anyway or I'd end up in too high a tax bracket. That was Artie Melbourn pulled that job, wasn't it?"

"Why ask if you already know?"

"Where's Artie now?"

"Where would you be if you had that kind of money? Florida or one of the islands. Beaches all day, dog track all night. It's a great life. You ought to try it sometime."

"Maybe I will," Coburn murmured and range off, looking thoughtful.

He had no difficulty finding the motel, even though it was well after dark when he pulled into the parking lot. Apparently The Hideaway didn't do much midweek business, because the vacancy sign was still lit and there was plenty of parking space. Coburn picked a spot at the far end of the building, just outside the circle of light from the sign over the entrance.

The lobby was larger than he'd expected, with a waist-high reception desk along one wall, an unmanned and darkened souvenir boutique, and an archway opposite the desk that, judging from the sounds coming from it, led to a bar/restaurant.

An elderly lemon-faced man watched Coburn disinterestedly from behind the desk. Coburn winked at him to make his day and went through the archway to the bar.

Like the motel itself, it wasn't very full, and he easily spotted Barbara Olliver sitting alone at the booth farthest from the bar and went over to join her.

"You're late," she said.

He wasn't really, but why argue? "Traffic."

"Are you armed?"

Coburn patted the left side of his chest to indicate the shoulder holster under his arm with the .38. He didn't mention the .25 caliber in a sleeve holster he'd strapped to his forearm as insurance in case the thief decided a frisk was in order.

"Give it to me."

"What?"

"Give me your gun."

"You got to be kidding," Coburn said. "You think I'm going to walk blind into a motel room carrying a cool hundred thousand cash without—"

"I know what you're not walking in there *with*," Barbara said, "and that's a gun. Mr. Smallwood wants this transfer to go smoothly, and that means no violence—or provocation to violence. Take it or leave it. That's it."

Coburn held her eyes for a long moment, then his mouth twisted down into a disgusted curve. "Pass over your purse," he said.

Barbara frowned at him.

"God damn it," Coburn said, "give me your purse. Or do you want me to just hand the gun over in front of God and everybody?"

Barbara pushed her purse across the table. Coburn put it down on the seat beside him, slipped the gun into it, and then passed it back. For half a second he thought she was going to open it to check, but the added weight apparently satisfied her. She set the purse to one side and in return moved a slim leather attaché case over to Coburn's side of the table.

"Your man's in Room 246," she said. "That's the southwest side of the building, second floor. If you go out the other side of the bar, there's a doorway that takes you directly to the stairs."

"Like Smallwood said, the perfect assistant," Coburn mocked. "I'm surprised he didn't just let you handle the whole thing and save himself five thou."

She looked at him expressionlessly. Coburn grinned. "Ego wouldn't let him, would it?" he said. "He wasn't man enough, so you couldn't be, either." He rose and picked up the attaché case. "Wish me luck," he said.

"Just do as you're told. That's all the luck you need."

"Sure," Coburn said and went out through the doorway she had indicated.

The stairs were at the end of a short corridor. Coburn took them up to the second-floor landing, then followed the small signs indicating that even numbers ran to the left and rear, odd to the right and front.

Music from someone's overloud radio filled the corridor, growing louder the closer Coburn came to 246. He hesitated long enough to assure himself it wasn't coming *from* 246, then rapped on the door. Nothing happened. Coburn rapped again, more sharply, and this time the door opened as far as the length of security chain would allow. A single eye peered out through the crack. Coburn stepped back far enough to let it take in the attaché case.

"Swap time," he said. "You've been expecting me."

"Smallwood?"

Coburn nodded. The door closed for the chain to be removed, then opened again, this time fully. A tall plumpish man with thinning hair and a pale apprehensive face stood beside it, holding it open.

Coburn shook his head. "After you," he said. "I get nervous when people stand behind me."

The plumpish man hesitated, then walked into the room. Coburn stepped inside, leaving the door open behind him. It was a standard motel room: a short entry leading to the room proper, no closet but a rack with hangers and a shelf above it running the length of the entry. A door to Coburn's right just inside the door led to the bath. A quick glance convinced Coburn it was empty and he moved forward cautiously to check the blind spot where the bathroom wall right-angled with the entry. No one there, either.

"Satisfied?" the man said.

Coburn winked at him. "As my old mother said, better safe than sorry." He went back to push the door closed with his foot. The music was muted now, but the heavy rock beat still reverberated through the walls. "Some neighbors you got."

The plumpish man shrugged. "They won't bother us much longer. You have the money?"

"Right here." Coburn indicated the attaché case, then pulled it back as the man reached for it. "Uh uh," Coburn said. "First I see what you've got."

"Of course," the man said apologetically. He knelt and pulled a suitcase from beneath the farther of two double beds. As he straightened to rise with it, Coburn shot him twice with the sleeve gun, aiming for the center of the chest where he'd be sure to hit a lung if he missed the heart.

The .25 had no stopping power, but the man was enough off balance that the bullets sent him toppling over backward. He lay sprawled on his back, staring empty-eyed at the ceiling.

Sure the man was dead, Coburn stood motionless for a moment, alert for any sounds of excitement or confusion from outside or next door. There were none, but the .25 made scarcely more noise than a door slamming and the loud music had blunted even that. He wiped his palm across the gun to smear any prints the smooth surface might have taken, then tossed it down on top of the dead man. Unlike the .38 he'd left with the Olliver woman, it wasn't registered and couldn't be traced to him.

He picked up the suitcase, set it on the bed, and opened it, thinking that it would be a good joke on both of them if he'd guessed wrong. But he hadn't. The stolid group of Dutchmen who'd looked out at him from the photographs in the coffee shop stared up at him now. Coburn reclosed the case and took one last look around. What had he touched? Nothing. Good. Picking up both the suitcase and the attaché case, he left the room, using a handkerchief to mask his prints from the doorknobs inside and out, and making sure the door latched behind him.

The hallway was as empty as it had been when he'd come up, but instead of returning the way he had come Coburn went down to the end of the corridor, took a second set of stairs down to the lower level, then cut right and went out into the parking lot just beyond where he had left the car. A departing car passed him, but that didn't bother him. A man with a suitcase wasn't that unusual a sight in a motel parking lot.

Coburn continued to his car, threw the attché case with the ransom into the trunk, locked it, then, still carrying the suitcase with the painting, went back into the motel.

Barbara Olliver was still sitting in the booth where he'd left her. Coburn set the suitcase down beside her, but made no move to sit down himself.

"Did everything go all right?" she asked him.

"Like clockwork," Coburn said.

"Good."

"That's what I thought." He made a slight motion with his hand. "I don't suppose you'd like to go someplace else and have a couple of drinks to celebrate."

Her eyes met and held his. She shook her head. "No."

Coburn shrugged. "Can't blame a guy for trying," he said. "Well, don't let anybody tell you it hasn't been fun." He turned away.

"Coburn."

Coburn turned back quickly. Barbara's eyes were amused. She held an envelope out to him. "You forgot your money."

Coburn laughed. "That's right, I did, didn't I?"

It wasn't until after he'd left her that the empty shoulder holster reminded him he'd forgotten the .38, too. But all in all, he decided, it hadn't been a bad exchange.

The next morning Coburn stopped by his bank shortly after it opened. He hadn't bothered to count the money in the attache casé before, but as he stuffed it into his safety-deposit box, he realized there was only $25,000.

His first reaction was fury, but then he began to laugh—so loudly and so long, in fact, that the vault attendant rapped on the door to ask if he was all right.

At 10:35 that same morning, Emerald Sanchez let herself into Room 246 of the Hideaway Motel to clean the room for the day. When she first noticed the body, she thought the man was sleeping or drunk. Then she saw the red stain on his chest.

The story broke too late to make the morning papers but the afternoon editions were full of it, and Channel 7 sent a small camera crew out to the motel. Coburn watched the results from a stool in a small bar in Old Town. No particular sigificance was attached to the name van der Laan, probably because the painter wasn't as popularly known as some of his contemporaries.

When he got back to his apartment afterward, the phone was ringing

—and continued to ring with the same drawn-out insistence until he finally picked it up.

It was Barbara Olliver. "Mr. Smallwood wants to see you," she said. "Right now."

Relaxed, maybe even slightly drunk, Coburn settled back to enjoy himself. "About what?" he said.

"Don't get cute with me, Coburn," Barbara said. "You saw the news tonight. You know what about. You murdered that man."

"So what?"

"So—?" Her voice was shocked and Coburn grinned, glad he'd finally gotten to her. "You *admit* it?"

"Admit what?" Coburn said. "How could I kill anybody? You took my gun, remember? But what if I did—just for the sake of argument? What's that to Smallwood? You heard him say just as clearly as I did that all he wanted was his painting back. Well, he got it, didn't he? And didn't pay a cent more than he was prepared to, either. But if his conscience bothers him, all he's got to do is go to the cops and blow everything—including his million-dollar deal."

There was a moment of silence from the other end. Then Barbara said: "You've got it all figured out, haven't you?"

"You better believe it," Coburn said. "I even figured out that the reason you insisted on bringing the money to the motel yourself was so you could skim off your share without Smallwood catching on. So if you're a smart little girl, you'll go back to your boss and tell him there's nothing for us to talk about. Nothing at all."

"That doesn't mean you and *I* don't have something to talk about."

"Unh-unh, baby," Coburn said. "You're in the same boat with the rest of us. You try to sink it, you get wet, too."

"I know," Barbara said. "But in all your figuring you made just one small miscalculation. Smallwood wasn't the only one to hire a substitute. You killed the wrong man, Coburn, and the right one isn't at all happy about it."

Coburn wasn't entirely sure he believed her, and he was certain as hell he didn't trust her, but he agreed to meet her the following morning at the coffee shop near the gallery. Again, she was there ahead of him, looking cool and trim in a tailored suit. Conscious of his own comparative scruffiness, Coburn picked up a cup of coffee at the counter and carried it over to the table. It was a quiet time just after the morning rush and the place was deserted except for the two of them and a waitress killing time with a crossword puzzle near the cash register.

"It's your dime," Coburn said, sitting down. "You called this meeting. You start."

"Fair enough," Barbara said. She sighed. "I won't waste time denying what we both know to be true. There were two robberies. Someone actually did break in and steal five paintings. As usual, though, I was the first one there in the morning and I was the one to discover it. I hadn't planned anything, but now that the opportunity was there it was too good a chance to pass up. I hid the van der Laan in a storage room where I knew no one would look."

"And convinced Smallwood that he didn't dare mention it to the cops or his insurance people."

"Why not?" Barbara said angrily. "If work counted, that gallery would be mine, not Smallwood's. I've put a lot into that gallery these last seven years and what's to be my reward? Smallwood's turning it over to me when he finally retires with his millions. Sounds great, doesn't it? Well, maybe it would be if he hadn't bled it dry to pay for the van der Laan. All I'd really be getting would be the name, and that won't pay the rent, let alone finance the kind of purchases I'd have to make to restock.

"Anyway, it was easy enough once things had settled down to sneak the painting out to a safer place. Obviously, though, I couldn't handle the exchange myself. So I approached this man I knew."

"Boy friend?" Coburn said.

She met his eyes evenly. "Used to be."

Coburn nodded. "I'll buy that," he said. "If you two were still starry-eyed, you wouldn't have needed to take your cut off the top."

Barbara nodded. "Exactly. I had to do it that way because once he had the money there was nothing to stop him taking off with the whole thing and leaving me out in the cold. But he must have decided that if I didn't trust him he couldn't afford to trust me, either." She smiled rue-fully. "From the way things turned out, it seems his instincts weren't too far wrong."

Coburn shrugged. "Like you say, when an opportunity like this comes along it's too good to pass up. The solution's easy enough. Pay your boy friend his twenty-five grand. That cuts you down to fifty, but that's still a nice piece of change to restock your gallery with."

"I wish it was that easy," Barbara said. "But he wants the whole hundred thousand now."

"Or?"

"He goes to the police. He can do it, too. The worst thing they can charge him with is conspiracy to defraud, and he could probably bargain his way out of that in exchange for his testimony." She smiled at him grimly. "What can they charge you with, Coburn?"

Coburn studied her thoughtfully for a long time. "This guy got a name?"

"Arthur Ross," Barbara said. She took a photograh from her purse and slid it across the table. "This was taken a couple of years ago," she said, "but it's a good likeness."

Coburn made no move toward it. "You really came prepared, didn't you?"

Her eyes didn't waver. "He could take the money and still go to the police."

"Yeah, he could." Coburn picked up the photo, glanced at it briefly, then slipped it into his breast pocket. "It won't be easy," he said. "He's not going to agree to meet in any motel room or anyplace else there aren't lots of witnesses around—not if he's got any brains, and I assume he has."

"Correct," Barbara said. "But I told him I'd call him tonight at his apartment after I'd gotten the money from you to arrange the transfer."

"He knows about me!"

"Of course he knows about you," Barbara said with more than a flash of the old sharpness. "I had to tell him something, and after tonight it won't matter because he won't have witnesses with him while he waits for the call. He'll be there alone." Her eyes met his evenly. "The building's on North Lincoln. The 7800 block. You can't miss it."

"Highrise?"

Barbara nodded. "The front is open, but that just lets you into the lobby. There's a locked security door just in front of the elevators. You go in the rear through the parking garage." She put a key on the table between them. Coburn looked at it mistrustfully. "I told you we used to be friends," she said. "I just never gave it back. It'll get you through the security door *and* into the apartment."

Coburn picked up the key. "He park in the garage?"

She nodded.

"What kind of car?"

"Blue-greyish sports coupe with a stripe. You won't have any trouble picking it out if you need to. The parking stalls are numbered the same as the apartments. His is 23G."

Coburn nodded and put the key in his pocket. "You want me to call you when it's over?"

Barbara shook her head. "No. I'll call him at ten. When he doesn't answer, that'll tell me all I need to know."

"Yeah," Coburn said. He rose abruptly and went out, leaving his coffee still untasted.

Coburn drove past the building twice to get, he told himself, a lay of the land, then parked two blocks away and walked back. He hadn't brought a gun, but a heavy wrench was tucked into his waistband beneath the nondescript jacket he wore.

Once inside the garage, he checked to be sure Ross's car was in its place, then used Barbara's key to let himself into the building proper. A narrow corridor, half lit and deserted like the garage itself, led him down to an open doorway beyond which a short flight of stairs led in turn to the elevator landing. There was a house phone just Coburn's side of the doorway and he used it to call Ross's apartment.

"Mr. Ross?" he said when he had a response. "This is Johnson down in the garage. I hate to tell you this, but maybe you ought to come down here. The whole front of your car's smashed in."

What?"

"It looks like somebody's backed into it a couple of times at least. The fender's pushed back against the wheel and I'm not sure whether you can still drive it or not."

"Oh, Christ," Ross said, and Coburn could sense his indecision. "All right," he said finally. "I'll be right there."

Coburn put the phone back on the hook, half unzipped his jacket, and waited. After what seemed an eternity, the man whose picture Barbara had given him came down the stairs and through the doorway. He frowned when he saw Coburn. "You the one who called?"

Coburn nodded. "I saw the car when I was making my rounds. The condition it's in, I figured it had to have happened here."

"Hell," Ross said and started down the corridor. Coburn fell in behind him and as they neared the far end he pulled out the wrench and smashed it with all his strength into the back of Ross's skull. Ross lurched forward and fell full length. Coburn bent swiftly and struck twice more, then fled. He was halfway to his car when he realized he was still carrying the wrench. He threw it into an alley.

The first murder hadn't bothered him. It had been neat, almost surgically impersonal. This one had been messy and emotional. Very emotional. Coburn's hands were still trembling when he got home and it took half a bottle of scotch to calm them enough to let him sleep.

Coburn woke to a persistent pounding. The clock beside his bed read 10:00 and from the light filtering through the drawn blinds that meant ten in the morning. The pounding continued and he realized it was coming from the door and pulled himself together enough to go answer it.

Two men he instinctively recognized as police looked in at him.
'Coburn?"

"Yeah."

They showed him their badges. "Mind if we come in?"

"Yeah, sure," Coburn said. "I mean no, come on in." He stepped back to let them enter. Their eyes scanned the apartment quickly, weighing, judging, and finding wanting just as, Coburn realized apprehensively, they found him wanting, too. "You want to tell me what I owe this to?" he said.

"You know a man named Edwin Smallwood?" the taller of the two said.

"I've met him, yeah," Coburn said.

"Somebody killed him last night."

"Smallwood?"

The tall cop nodded. "His assistant says she heard loud voices in his office last night. She didn't go in because she figured it was better if she didn't get involved and it was almost time for her to go home anyway. Then this morning when she opened the place, she found Smallwood dead in his office with a gun on the floor beside him. He was shot twice, both times through the heart, so it wasn't suicide." He regarded Coburn steadily. "She says the other voice she heard was yours. The gun's yours, too—a .38 registered in your name."

Comprehension flooded through Coburn. Barbara! She wasn't content with just the $75,000 and the gallery when Smallwood retired. She was setting it up to take it all now—including the million-dollar deal for the van der Laan. He shook his head vigorously. "Oh, no," he said, "not me. I was nowhere near that gallery last night."

"Oh?" the tall cop said. "In that case, maybe you wouldn't mind telling us where you *were* then."

Coburn opened his mouth, then shut it again. For the first time in his life he had nothing to say.

H. R. F. Keating
Fonsy Noonan's Story

It was not until Fonsy Noonan overheard the lady with the genteel Rathmines accent offer to give Sean Boyle a pair of good leather gloves that he realized how much gloves were what he needed himself. He pictured the many times that the necessities of his profession might keep him hanging about at some wind-whistling corner or the nights he might be stuck on the look-out in a cold dank doorway, and he thought how much a decent pair of leather gloves would comfort him. A winter without chilblains. He might contrive that yet.

And now here was this motherly-looking soul, cozy and plump as a hen in a coop, asking Sean Boyle—Sean Boyle sitting there on his platform with the roller-skate wheels and his trouser legs wrapped under his stumps—whether he would like the pair of gloves she had by her at home, gloves he precious son had refused altogether to take across to England with him on the grounds that "no one there wears gloves, Mammy." And Sean had grunted out one of those grudging sounds of his that might have meant he was saying yes. So now the dear creature was promising to bring in her gift the very next ime she came shopping to Clery's.

An idea slipped into Fonsy's head, quick as a ferret.

He pushed the coarsely-printed American comic he had been reading for the ninth or tenth time into the pocket of his grease-stiffened striped brown suit. Then, sliding out of the sheltered nook in which he had been shrinking from a salt-laden Dublin wind, he eased himself into the slowly-moving afternoon crowd on the wide pavement. He nipped carefully behind Sean and his roller-skate platform, and in less than half a minute was at the kind old soul's side.

"Missus, missus," he said, putting a hand up to where his cap would have been.

The good creature began to amble along a little faster.

"Missus, one moment if ye will. I couldn't help hearing the grand offer you were making that poor fella just now. A grand offer, missus, a grand offer."

The old hen had slowed down a bit, thanks be to God. It was easy enough to get a biddy the like of her to see sense if only they'd listen at all. "Sure, an' I was thinking, missus, wouldn't it be altogether best if I was to step along wid you this minute and fetch them gloves for the poor fella now?"

She had come to a halt.

A vision of his hands snugly encased in find leather—a nice color of tan it would be—came into Fonsy's head. He saw himself waiting long hour after long hour while some conniving was going on, waiting till he had every last man at the meeting safely named, and a quid or two he might get out of Inspector Reagan for the information. Never mind that he would have put a decent stop to a criminal act. And to do it all staying warm. It'd be a different class of life altogether.

"You'll do no such thing, my man. D'you think I don't know what'd happen to my poor Brendan's gloves if I gave them into your keeping?"

Fonsy put an expression of deep hurt on his two-days unshaven features.

"Would I do a thing like that, missus? Isn't the fella there one o' me closest buddies? It's just than I'm thinking it's cruel sharp weather already and sure it's bound to get worse. An' yourself might to too busy wid your grand house beyond to remember to bring them gloves next time, an' the poor fella killed almost wid the cold."

"That's quite enough of that," the motherly soul replied tartly. "Go away now, or I'll call a guard."

The vision of the tan gloves grew brighter and brighter in Fonsy's mind as his chance of getting hold of them seemed moment by moment to recede. He knew there might be many a time in the months ahead when he would need to hide away somewhere in the bleakest part of the night spying out something or other, or there would be times when the necessity of earning an honest pound note would drive him to agree to acting as look-out man for some godforsaken devil like Bruiser Hegarty on one of his evil undertakings. Inside those fleecy-lined leather gloves —yes, they would be lined in babysoft pale yellow—his fingers would forever stay snug and supple.

"Ah, now, missus," he whined, "you can trust Fonsy Noonan the way you'd trust your own son. Where is it you live, missus? I'll be there wid you in a jiffy and—"

"Guard! Guard! This man is annoying me."

Jaysus, there was a guard there, too. Mick Clanagan—big as a wall, the great eejit. Why hadn't he remembered to keep an eye open for the likes of him?

He felt Garda Clanagan's heavy hand descend on his shoulder like a great lump of meat.

"It's you, Alphonsus Noonan, is it? And what were ye after trying, ye squirmy little louser?"

The motherly soul bobbed away in the direction of the bus for Rathmines, taking with her Fonsy's every last hope for warm hands in the bitter months to come.

Twisted 'round in the guard's massive grip, he did his best to produce some sort of explanation.

"Gloves, is it?" Garda Clanagan said when he had heard all. "Gloves for the like of Sean Boyle, an' him well able to buy himself forty dozen pairs o' leather gloves from all his thievin' an' receivin' o' stolen property."

"Ah, sure he's a warm man," Fonsy agreed as he gave a little wriggle in the hope of getting free of the guard's grasp. "A coldhearted bastard of a warm man. Since the day Tony Hegarty ran over his legs with that van when he helped himself out of Tony's political friends' collections he's been as black as the divil himself."

"He has so," agreed Garda Clanagan somberly. "Sure it was a pity entirely Bruiser Hegarty didn't make a decent job of it."

"An' how could he? With the engine o' that van comin' to a dead stop just when he'd reversed clean back onto Sean's prostrate body after he was knocking him down?"

Garda Clanagan shook his massive head sadly.

"He oughta have had him killed completely," he said. "Sure, an' Inspector Reagan would've bottled Bruiser nicely for murder then, the way he's never been able to pin him for anything else yet. An' that'd be one bucko the less on our backs now, an' another, too, with Sean Boyle outta the way."

Emboldened by this note of sentimental reminiscence, Fonsy finally slipped free of the guard's meaty grip. To venture on a touch of malice.

"An' why didn't your almighty The Rock Reagan get Bruiser for Grievous Bodily Harm?" he asked cheekily, though in fact he well knew the Inspector would never have obtained the evidence. "Sure wouldn't it have been murder itself as it was, only Michael Murphy come along and lifted the van?"

The flick of spite failed to penetrate the hazy goodwill still swirling in Garda Clanagan's huge head.

"Ah, sure," he said—was there a dampness welling in his marble-hard blue eyes—" sure Michael Murphy's the one. There isn't a man in Dublin else could've lifted up that van the way he did. A tower o' strength he is surely. An' nut-sweet as a babe in arms. He'd do a good turn to a tinker, so he would."

"An' why wouldn't he?" Fonsy asked cuttingly. "With himself touched in the head from the day he was born?"

But this extra bit of malice—of malice directed, too, against a young fellow regarded throughout the Coombe as so simple-minded as to be almost holy—did get through to Garda Clanagan's horse-and-cart mind.

"Gloves!" he exploded, switching back in his righteous indignation to the origin of the present encounter and with vigorously illogical fervor. "Gloves, is it? I tell yous this, Fonsy Noonan, if I so much as see a finger o' them gloves on Sean Boyle's dirty hands, it's you I'll have for un-licensed begging, so I will."

"Me?" Fonsy shrieked in outrage. "Is it me you'd be runing in?"

"It is so. Make no mistake about it."

"An' what harm have I done? What harm have I ever done? Is it me that's going to be give them gloves, me that's needing them more than any?"

Garda Clanagan regarded him squarely, his two huge hands planted at the belt of his uniform.

"Whatever the way of it," he pronounced with leaden and illogical finality, "I'm telling you this, Fonsy, me boyo. One sight o' them gloves on Sean Boyle's fists an' it's up before the court wid yous."

Rage almost made Fonsy inarticulate.

"An' why amn't yous dragging Sean Boyle up before the court, the lousy rotten bastard?" he stormed. "Him as is wearing the gloves that are life an' death to me? Why amn't yous charging him wid unlicensed begging, so?"

"Would I be dirtying me hands wid a fella the like o' him?" Garda Clanagan retorted.

And he turned and moved lumberingly off, the question he had offered to the world being so patently one that needed not the least vestige of a reply.

Fonsy, inwardly railing at fate, mooched back toward the out-of-the-wind nook where he had been happily perusing the mighty tale of *The Incredible Hulk Fights the Human Fly*. What was he going to do? That Rathmines biddy was sure to bring Sean Boyle the gloves. She had that determined do-good look all over her. And Garda Clanagan would see the gloves on Sean. He was bound to. He'd make a point of looking. And then ... then Fonsy Noonan up in court sure as eggs is eggs. And fined for unlicensed begging. And where the hell would the money to pay that fine come from? Wasn't he skint entirely already? He'd end up in jail—when he'd spent every last day of his life doing nothing but try to keep out of it. And trying to make sure, where he could in any sort of a decent way, that them that ought to be there behind bars were put so.

It wasn't fair, so it wasn't. It was surely to God unfair.

A hand like a thin-steel grab closed itself'round his right calf.

Sean Boyle. It was Sean Boyle reaching out from his roller-skate platform as he passed behind and holding him with a grip like the devil's.

"Is it yourself, Sean?" he inquired of the cripple, doing his best to get some sort of a smile onto his face.

"You're a rat, Fonsy Noonan," Sean Boyle said by way of answer, his steel fingers unmoving.

Fonsy could think of nothing to say to that. He tried easing the heel of his trapped leg off the pavement so as to be able to lever himself free. But those four digging fingers only dug the harder.

"You thought I didn't see yous." Sean Boyle said.

"See me? Sure I didn't see yourself at all, Sean."

"No?"

A swift jerk on his calf almost brought him tumbling to the ground.

The cripple's dark unshaven face, lined and drained by pain beneath the sharp standing bristles, looked up at him. "Don't you be thinking, Fonsy, I'm not knowing full well what you got in that nasty little head o' yours. Yous heard the silly bitch offer me them gloves. Yous thought you was going to cut in ahead o' me, didn't yous? Didn't yous?"

Each of these last questions was accompanied by a downward twist of the gripping hand. Pain went shooting through Fonsy's leg as if the very ligaments inside it were being torn from their moorings.

Nothing else to do but answer as he was bid.

"I did. I did, Sean. God forgive me."

The cripple grinned. A grin of cold triumph.

"So I'm warning yous, Fonsy," he said. "If them gloves are not on me hands this day week, you'll pay for it. I can catch yous, Fonsy Noonan. Mebbe I can't run like the scared rat you are. But I can wait for yous. An' I will. I'll wait till I catch yous wid these two hands o' mine an' then I'll break every rib in your chest."

The steel claw gave a sudden jerking push. Fonsy lunged forward, striving to keep his balance. Unsuccessfully.

No sooner was he sprawled face-down on the dirt-spattered paving stones, however, than he was scrabbling to his feet again. He was beyond the reach of Sean Boyle's powerful arms. He could run. And he did.

Being out of immediate danger was all that Fonsy had to congratulate himself on, however. Try as he might to comfort himself in a corner with the Incredible Hulk, or by investing money that should have gone for his rent in drink crouched up in Mulligan's snug, he could not push from his mind chaotic thoughts of the dilemma he had got himself into.

On the one hand, if Sean Boyle was seen with the old lady's gloves on his hands this day week, then Garda Clanagan would joyfully seize on him and haul him up as an unlicensed beggar and with whatever evidence produced against him bound to be believed, that would mean jail, no less. And on the other hand, if Sean Boyle did not get the old lady's gloves, then sooner or later the steel-clawed devil would catch hold of him and crack every rib in his chest. He would. He could. There was bound to come a time when forgetting himself for a moment he would let the cripple get near enough. And then . . .

He could almost feel the ribs going as he sat there. The sharp crack of them one by one. And the pain, the piercing inward pian. Sean Boyle would do it. He would do it to the last rib.

There was no way out. He was banjaxed. Banjaxed entirely.

All that night, it seemed to him, he tossed and turned in his bed, thinking of his terrible situation. And it was only when he woke next morning, jerking suddenly out of deep sleep, that he found he had the solution to it all there in his head.

It could be done. It could be done. Satisfy the devil on the one hand and the devil on the other.

The first thing was to find Sean Boyle, keep a quiet watch on him, and then, whenever the moment looked best, to act.

Only Sean Boyle was nowhere to be found. His wheeled platform was not jammed up against its usual lamppost where the lady from

Rathmines had found him the day before. It was not anywhere else in the city, it seemed. All day Fonsy went through the streets, peeking and peering to left and right. But never a sign did he see of the hunched figure and the dark pain-lined face.

And there, always at the back of his mind, were those two alternatives, inescapable unless he could twist luck enough to bring off the plan he had found in his head when he had wakened: Garda Clanagan, immovable as the brick wall his red-mottled face so much resembled, and Sean Boyle, black with hatred every day since Bruiser Hegarty had punished him so brutally on behalf of his political friends.

He had to find Sean. He had to see if his notion would work. But Sean was not to be found anywhere that day or the next. Perhaps he was busy about some piece of dirty business or other away in one of his hideyholes. Or was it that he was keeping out of sight on purpose? He was devil enough for that.

But then, on the very afternoon when the lady from Rathmines was due, Sean Boyle was there again, back at his old post, his platform jammed carefully up against the very same lamp-standard.

Fonsy was too impatient to wait and watch as he had intended in order to seize the very best moment to put his plan into operation. Instead he simply went sidling up and began the vital but hazardous process of ingratiating himself enough to be able to play on the cripple's terrible sense of pride.

"It's yourself Sean, is it?"

The cripple, of course, made no reply. But he did jerk his head in Fonsy's direction for an instant. Which emboldened Fonsy, until he registered the look of bleak contempt in those pain-stamped eyes.

"Sure, it's a grand day," he went on nevertheless. "A grand day but for the wet."

It was raining. Raining with steady persistence. And it was cold with it, too. Just the day to have a fine pair of leather gloves on your hands.

Fonsy gulped.

Now had come the moment when just that thought, of what a great gift those gloves would be, had to be put first of all into Sean's head. A preliminary altogether necessary if his plan were to succeed.

"Sure," he said, his voice suddenly rising high in his throat, "sure an' that pair o' fine gloves'll be suiting yous a treat, Sean, when the lady comes."

The innocent offering at least attracted the pike lurking in the green water. Sean Boyle turned his whole twisted body on his platform and, though he still said not a word, he grinned. A grin of cruel pleasure.

"Ah," Fonsy went on, struggling to get his voice somewhere near sounding natural, "it was no call at all I had to be tryin' to get me own hands on 'em. No call at all. Sure they're not for the likes o' me, leather gloves. Not at all. Not at all."

"They'd better be not," the cripple muttered. "Unless you've learnt to sing without your ribs, Fonsy Noonan."

Sean Boyle grinned again. Browny-yellow teeth showed, fanglike, in his jaw. "Mebbe she won't come at all, Fonsy me boy," he said. "Mebbe she's sitting there at home this minnit an' saying to herself, 'Sure, I can't go out at all today with the rain so bad and the cold I have on me certain to get worse.'"

Fonsy knew that to please Sean Boyle, as he must do if he was to gain his full confidence and thus pull off his plan, he should show every sign of panic at this. He had no difficulty in doing so. Wasn't it altogether likely that the old biddy hadn't ventured out on a day like today? And if she hadn't, then even if he contrived to bring this off now it would be no use at all. Sean would not take that for an excuse. It would be pain and torment then.

He thrust the thought aside. Events beyond his control must not be allowed to exist.

"Ah, sure to God," he said, "them gloves'll look a treat on you, Sean. A treat indeed. Sure I can see them on yous now. Tan gloves, like a gentleman or an officer in the Army itself."

For a moment the cripple's thin hands flexed and he extended the fingers that were usually curled in pain or hatred.

Fonsy let a silence grow, hoping the first seeds of his scheme had been well sown and might be blossoming slowly behind the cripple's tight-shut face.

He glanced at the street, busy with afternoon traffic. Was that a No. 14 bus coming, jerking and jostling its way in?

He cleared his throat with a rasping squeak.

"Ah, tan gloves," he said, "tan gloves. Just the job to keep the rain off. Just the job. And fleecy-lined inside, I dare say. Lined wid the warmest fleece. Sure there's not a blast o' wind this winter that'll disturb you at all." He fixed his eyes on the cripple's hands. Would he see them stretch out again like a contented cat's? Or were Sean's black thoughts elsewhere? Was he imagining himself grasping a helpless body and hearing the ribs in it cracking one after the other like a volley of gunfire above a grave?

The hands remained clenched as they had been ever since that single catlike gesture earlier on.

Fonsy racked his brains for a word of praise more for the gloves.

But, before even a glimmering of it had come, Sean Boyle suddenly brought his two hands together and rubbed them vigorously. You could almost see the picture of those fine smart gloves that had formed in his head.

"Ah, sure," Fonsy said, jumping in with his second stage, making proud Sean see the gift as something to be despised and rejected, "them's the gloves for you, Sean, me bucko. Sure if anything good's going you're the boy as deserves it."

For that he got a grin that was hearteningly complacent as well as cruel.

God, would it go wrong now? Would that damn bus come in before he had it all set? If the old biddy was to get off at the stop just now, she could be over with Sean in two minutes, and handing him the gloves with a terrible smile on the face of her. And then Sean would take them and keep them as a God-given right.

Which would mean that Garda Clanagan would be down on the two of them in less time than it took to tell.

He could feel that huge wrapping 'round his elbow and marching him away.

Frantically, he slapped at his thigh—it was at the level of Sean Boyle's face as he sat on his platform—in a gesture of thwacking jollity.

"Sure, if anything good's going—"

No, he had tried that already. If he was to be saved, he had to push it further than that.

"Sean, me boyo," he hastily began again, "if ever a man deserved charity, you're the one." Yes, this was the way of it. "If ever a man deserved to be given a fine pair o' cast-off gloves belonging to a young Rathmines lad as has gone over to England thinking no one wears gloves in that forsaken island, then it's Sean Boyle who should be getting them. Poor Sean Boyle without the use of his legs at all an' feeling the wind come whistling through his hands till he could cry out wid the pain."

And those hands were clenched now into two hard fists of hatred. Had he brought it off? Had he done enough?

A voice broke in on his intent poring over the cripple in front of him. A voice with a soft Rathmines accent.

"Ah, there you are, you poor fellow. And, see, I've brought you the gloves I promised. You thought I'd forget, now didn't you? But I remembered you every day of the week, you poor, dear man."

Fonsy looked up at the gently smiling face, the face that had taken on such an obdurate look when he had tried to wheedle the gloves away the week before. And he saw, too, behind the plump form of the lady the great red-faced wall that was Garda Clanagan.

What would happen now?

A noise, entirely inarticulate, came out of Sean Boyle's twisted mouth. But articulation was not needed. The dark-faced cripple made himself perfectly clear without a single word. He seized the proffered gloves—they were tan leather, a beautiful light shade of tan—in his claw of a right hand. For a moment it looked as if he was actually going to crush them to a mangled mess, so tightly did he grip them. But then with a single jerk of his powerful right arm he flung the two squelched, rejected objects, joined together by their buttons, far out into the heavy, jerking traffic in front of him.

And Fonsy darted like a squirming rat between a huge buff-colored bus coming one way and a battered old pick-up fresh from the country coming the other. His hand swooped downward. His fingers encounter-ed the gloves, hooked desperately, and scooped them up. A youth on a motorcycle on the far side of the pick-up came to a squealing halt, his machine canting wildly. Fonsy hurled himself forward again, wriggled and ran and gained the sanctuary of the opposite pavement.

'Round the nearest corner he stood at leisure and one by one pulled the gloves onto his hands. The linings were fleecy. Fleecy and yellow.

Before very long, however, Fonsy's prize was to prove a cat with a can at its tail.

The winter continued unusually cold over and past Christmas, and he had reason to bless again and again the gloves that were keeping the chilblains from his fingers. He wore them day and night, sleeping in them even, turning the pages of his cherished comics with scrabbling difficulty with them still on, not taking them off in the warmth of a bar when he was treating himself to a cautious jar or two, despite the sweat which made their fleecy lining unpleasantly clammy, so afraid was he that someone would feck them while his attention was elsewhere.

In only one set of circumstances did he take care to push his hardwon treasures deep into the side pockets of his suit. That was when anything took him anywhere near the vicinity of Sean Boyle. The reminder might well, he considered, give the malevolent cripple second thoughts about that moment of rage when he had flung the despised gloves into the streaming traffic.

But it was on New Year's Eve, 'round ten o'clock, when the streets were full of revelers swirling about, awaiting the magic midnight hour, that, in the daze and excitement of the moment, he made his mistake.

He was carefully spying 'round the edges of the crowd that had begun to gather at the big bonfire on waste ground beside Christchurch Cathedral (people at a time like this were terribly careless about the way they carried their money) when a pair of fiercely hard arms came shooting out of the dark of a doorway and clenched him 'round the waist.

In an instant he was lifted off his feet and swept back into the deeper darkness up against the cathedral wall. And then a voice spoke quietly in his ear.

"Fonsy Noonan. An' it's a grand pair o' gloves you have on yous tonight."

"Gloves? Gloves?" he jerked out, as much as he could with his feet off the ground and Sean Boyle's sinewy arms crushing the breath out of his body. "What gloves is it at all?"

"Them gloves I threw in the roadway when the old biddy tried to make me take her bloody charity."

Fonsy found that his left heel and touched the muddy ground beneath him. It slipped and slid about, but after a moment or two he managed to get his foot steady. "Sure these gloves I'm after wearing aren't at all—"

He thought better of the attempt. Trying to lie to Sean Boyle would only get him into trouble worse than he was in already.

He felt for the ground with his other foot. "Ah, Sean," he said, "I was only taking what you yourself discarded. The leavings from your table, Sean, the leavings ..."

"What I put in the roadway's to stay in the roadway."

"Ah, sure yes, Sean. I'll see to it, Sean. I'll see to it this very night, so help me. I'll take the rotten ole gloves an' throw them in the very path of all the traffic, so I will."

The next thing he knew he had been sat on the slimy ground with a thump that jarred him from the base of his spine to the top of his head. But the arms banding his body had not slackened by so much as a quarter of an inch.

"Not at all, not at all," Sean Boyle's voice cam quietly in the densely shadowed darkness, while not fifteen yards away the revelers 'round the bonfire laughed and shouted. "Sure there's no call at all to be putting them gloves in any roadway."

"No?" Fonsy squeaked in answer. The prospect of retaining the gloves, of snug fingers on chill nights, peeped up into his brain once more.

"Not at all," Sean Boyle grated on. "Not when they're going for a dip in the canal wid you inside them."

Fonsy felt the very center of his being shrink and shrivel away to nothingness. Getting into the water had always been a nightmare to him. Unlike almost every other boy he had known in his schooldays, he had never learnt to swim. It had been something he had been tormented over for the whole of his boyhood. And Sean Boyle must have got to know about it.

The canal, that sluggish stretch of browny water encircling the south side of inner Dublin like a fond arm with its burden of imperceptibly drifting dead cats and old motor tires, with its sudden dartings of swimming rats, with its patches of bright green, clinging weed: it had always held a special horror for him. He invariably took great pains to avoid the paths beside it which other Dubliners loved to lounge along, and he even walked at an extra rapid pace when he had to go over one of its humpbacked bridges. Had Sean Boyle somehow penetrated down to these innermost fears of his?

"Sean, no," he said, feeling sweat come up under his armpits. "For the love o' God. You wouldn't do that to me. Sean, if I was to go in the canal, I'd drown. Sean, I'd drown dead in a minnit. Sean, no."

"Yes," said Sean Boyle.

Fonsy felt himself heaved up again, suddenly reversed, and slammed down across the cripple's broad muscular shoulder. He felt the roller-skate platform underneath them begin to lurch forward.

"Sean! Sean, no! No, for God's sake—help! Help someone!"

But if anybody 'round the big leaping bonfire heard, they must have put those agonized shouts down to mere horseplay. Because no one, as the cripple's platform jerked and slid over the wet ground, did anything about coming to investigate.

"Sean." Fonsy breathed the word as a prayer. "Sean, I'll do anything. Anything."

The platform was gaining speed now as the cripple piloted it on to the start of the hill down from the cathedral.

And then it slewed to an abrupt halt.

Had its little wheels stuck in a pothole in the roadway? Would a shout now, a shout loud as lungs could make it, bring help after all?

"You'd do anything?"

Before Fonsy had taken breath for his shriek of distress, Sean Boyle's quiet, menacing voice had trickled into his ear.

"Sure, Sean," he gabbled in answer. "You know I'd do anything for you. Haven't I been a friend to you in time o' need? A friend through thick an' thin?"

"You've not. Neither you nor any man."

"Sean, honest to God, I—"

"No, not any man, and, begod, not any woman."

The cripple's voice was harsh in the darkness of the ill-lit street.

Fonsy thought that silence was his only course now. Hanging as he was,head down across Sean's well muscled shoulder, his face all too near the broken surface of the roadway, he felt that no notion his vividest imagination could conjure up would help him.

But Sean had brought to a halt that wild, jerking downhill race toward the distant canal and its cold, mud-bottomed waters. He must have had some reason.

"So you'd do anything?" the harsh voice brooded. "Then here's what you'll do for me, Fonsy Noonan."

Sean's shoulder heaved.

Fonsy felt his body tumbling over like a soft flail. He landed on his back on the ground' beside the platform with a thud that momentarily brought a total blackness. But it was momentary only. In a second he had come to his senses again—to feel one of Sean's hands gripping his wrist like a manacle.

"You'll fetch me a woman, Fonsy Noonan. That's what you'll do for me. You'll bring Nuala Murphy to me. Tonight, at half after midnight. She'll be about somewhere. Find her and bring her or, begod, I'll have you in the canal if I have to fetch you every yard o' the way from Clontarf or Dun Laoghaire."

Fonsy hardly heard these last words. What Sean Boyle had proposed had put even the thought of the cold waters of the canal out of his mind. Nuala Murphy. A whore all right, a girl happy enough to dispense her favors for money, but a girl he had often heard rejecting crippled Sean. She had said, said for everyone to hear, that if he was the only man on earth and had all the moeny there was on earth to pay her she would not so much as go near him. And she was Michael Murphy's sister.

Michael, that soft-headed giant, pride and favorite of the whole Coombe. Michael, with strength enough in his huge frame to have lifted up the van that Bruiser Hegarty had deliberately reversed onto Sean Boyle and saved his life. Michael, so softly gentle that children never hesitated to play with him, but who, as everybody knew, had one gap in his wide-spreading good nature: an attachment to brother and sister so strong that if either were harmed it would unleash in him the utmost violence.

If ever Michael learnt, so they said, who it was ten years before who had betrayed his brother to his murderers in the famous Bella Street Killing, when he had been hiding there after breaking with his political comrades, he had death awaiting him as surely as if he was standing under the tumbling rocks of a landslide. And it would be just the same, Fonsy knew, for anyone who betrayed Michael's beloved sister Nuala to a man she abhorred.

A sudden, terrible vision came into Fonsy's mind. It was of Michael's pavior's mallet—he was quite able to earn a living in a street-repair gang, biddably doing whatever the foreman asked—lifted high and about to descend with the calm inevitability of some act of nature. And of his own fixed-open eyes looking up at its shaggy wooden head made from a whole section of a tree-trunk.

"Sean," he pleaded, "I can't do it, Sean—I can't. You know she won't come to you, Sean. You know she's rejected every pound and penny you have. If Michael . . . Sean, you know."

"Never mind that eejit Michael," Sean Boyle said, his voice horribly clear in the darkness. "You bring Nuala to me. Don't you be telling her who she's to come to. You've pimped for her before often enough, she'll trust you, Fonsy, rat as you are. So just bring her to a cellar I have the use of beneath Peadar Donnell's place beyond. Bring her there at half after midnight sharp. An' after that you'll have no trouble from me at all."

"But, Sean, I can't."

"The canal, Fonsy. I won't change me mind another time."

"Listen, Sean, listen. You know how Michael feels about Nuala. You know she's the only—"

But Fonsy realized it was no use going on. Swiftly propelled by the cripple's ape-powerful arms, the low platform had gone rattling and banging down the hill out of sight in the darkness.

Fonsy sat where he was on the wet roadway, the misery of his situation washing into every corner of his mind.

It was hopeless. Hopeless. If he was to do what Sean Boyle wanted, there was bound to come the moment when Nuala found she had been tricked, when she entered this hideyhole of Sean's—one of several he had, and a well kept secret up till now—and those steel band arms closed 'round her. No doubt at all that Sean would get what he wanted then. Let yourself come within his reach and there was no gainsaying him. But after! After when Nuala told Michael how she had been trapped, it would be a question of hours only before his own blood would be soaking into the soft-wood fibers of Michael's mallet, all spongy from repeated beating on stone setts.

But if he ignored Sean's demand ... If he failed at the stroke of half-past midnight to bring Nuala to Peader Donnell's place (so that was one of Sean's hideyholes—who'd have thought it?) Nuala smelling of her perfume and her powder, holding onto his arm, from that hour on he would have to be on his guard for Sean Boyle. And he could not go on doing that forever and ever.

And then the canal.

How the devil did it happen that he kept getting into fixes the like of this? They were the very pattern of his life. From schooldays on, it had been the same. Caught between tagging along under threat in all sorts of mischief behind boys like Bruiser Hegarty and doing what the teachers and the nuns said you ought. And that had been the way of it ever since. Scared into helping Bruiser and his lot on the one hand, and on the other hand, still more scared, telling Inspector Reagan a scrap here and a scrap there about what was going on.

And Paddy Reagan had been every bit as bad when the three of them had been at school together, too. Every bit as ready to use his fists to make you say aloud the prayers he'd had you admit you'd forgotten that morning, down there on your knees on the asphalt of the playground with all the school ringing you 'round and jeering the hide off you.

Why couldn't they let him have some little nook of his own where he'd be happy and harm no one?

But this was the worst scrape of all. The worst far and away. There was death in it this time, not just a hiding. Not even jail. Death. Death either way. Death under that shaggy-headed mallet or death in the weed-clinging waters of the canal.

What could he do? He could run, he supposed. Go across to England. Even try to get to America, though where he'd get the fare money for that was way past and beyond him. And what would he do in England even? With everything strange all around him? It would be no life at all. There'd be no hope of a quiet time and a safe one in a jungle of a place like that. And America would be worse. Even Superman had a hell of a life of it there.

So what was he going to do? Was he really going to get hold of Nuala Murphy? it would be easy enough. Sean was right there. She wouldn't be going off with any fella now till after the midnight hour and its celebrations, and there'd be no trouble after that getting her to set out for a bit of business in the cellar Sean had beneath Peadar Donn ...

The cellar Sean had, so secretly, under Peadar Donnell's place. There was a way out of this after all. There was.

There could be no doubting that if Sean Boyle had taken good care no one else knew about the place, then it would be one of the stores he used for stolen stuff. It would be only because he had needed to spring his trap for Nuala Murphy, where no screaming and shouting of hers would bring people 'round his ears, that he had let out the secret.

But there the fella had played into his hands entirely. Surely, surely. Nothing easier now than to give Inspector Reagan, up in the Castle, this one piece of information and get him down to Peadar Donnell's at half midnight on the dot.

Nothing easier, if it could be done quick enough. It would mean breaking his rule of never showing his snout anywhere near the CID offices in the Castle. There wasn't time enough for the usual ta-ra-ra of giving The Rock Reagan a ring and arranging a meet. But with any luck the man himself would be there in the Castle. If he wasn't, it'd be a case of trusting someone else for once. Because it had to be done.

It could be, too, if there was any luck in it at all. A raid on that cellar beneath Peadar Donnell's and Sean would be safe away in Mountjoy for six or seven years to come, and himself not having antagonized soft-headed Michael with that almighty mallet of his one bit.

He picked himself up from the wet roadway and hurried off.

Inspector Reagan had turned out to be on duty at the Castle all right. But things were not going as easily as Fonsy had envisaged. Instead of getting straight in to see The Rock, he had been left to wait in a tall corrdior, its walls lined with the heavy black-bound volumes of old files.

And time was going by.

If The Rock left it much longer, half-past midnight would have come and gone. And if no one appeared at that cellar beneath Peadar Donnell's, before very long Sean Boyle would leave it. He might very likely set out there and then on the hunt for himself, with the thought of the black waters of the canal dancing all over his evil mind. And if Sean got to hear later that the guards had raided his cellar . . .

Every now and again a guard in uniform would come clumping, heavy-booted, along the corridor and Fonsy would try to pluck up courage to ask whether The Rock was still in his office or had he gone out somewhere. But he never did get the pitch of putting his question before the fellow had gone past.

It wasn't even as if he knew what o'clock it was. He certainly seemed to have been waiting a hell of a long time leaning against the long shelves of the thick black-bound files. But the sound of midnight striking had not come yet. The start of the new year. What sort of a year would that be for him? Disaster? Or a new lease of life, with Sean Boyle off his back, with no fears of Michael and his mallet, and with the prospect of some decent, quiet days in it at last?

But surely midnight could not be far off now.

So why wouldn't The Rock see him? Didn't he realize that this was urgent? The message he had sent into him had said so. And on the strength of it, he had been put to wait here.

Could he even take a glance at his comic? It would take his mind off his troubles, sure it would. He had *Fury of the Scorpion God* in his pocket, and not read more than twice. But somehow he didn't like to take it out. Not here inside the Castle. It would be like playing cards in church.

And then into the silence of the night there came the clear twelve strokes of Christchurch Cathedral and St. Patrick's, one on either side of the Castle, tolling out midnight. At once hooters and horns everywhere were blaring and blasting greetings to the brave new year.

A year of quiet and comfort, of going about the city in tan leather gloves snug and easy? Or a terribly short year in the life of Fonsy Noonan?

"Fonsy, c'm here."

The Rock was standing at the far end of the corridor, looking bigger than ever with his shock of rust-red hair, his great shoulders, and his huge fists—fists that he himself had seemed to have been at the wrong end of all his life long.

Fonsy scuttled down the corridor as he had been bid.

Once inside the office, he saw why there had been that long wait: the desk was littered with glasses and there was a three-quarters-empty bottle of Powers alongside them. The Rock planked himself down in his chair and tilted it comfortably back.

"So what brings Alphonsus Noonan to the Castle?" he said.

Fonsy tried a careless shrug.

"As I said in my note to yous," he began, "I've red-hot information."

"Red-hot information, such as it's been, never yet gave Fonsy Noonan the pluck to step inside these walls."

The statement was delivered with all The Rock's accustomed implacable confidence. Fonsy had known it and been cowed by it since they had both been no more than six years old.

"Sure," he stammered in answer now, "it's a case of extreme urgency, so it is. If Sean Boyle's not to throw me in—" He checked himself. No need to tell The Rock anything about his personal problems. He was there, as a good citizen, to inform the proper authorities where a large amount of stolen property could be found. That and no more.

"This is the way of it, Inspector," he began again, trying to achieve a businesslike and formal tone. "It has come to my knowledge this very night that certain goods believed to have been stolen—"

"Where's Sean Boyle going to throw you, Fonsy?"

"In the canal, God help me."

The words were said before he had the will power to stop them. The Inspector's punched-out question had breached a dam behind which all his fears had been precariously held.

And now The Rock was smiling, a wide grin showing all his fine white even teeth.

"The canal," he said. "Sean Boyle threatened to put you in the canal, did he? Sure he couldn't have hit on anything better. Don't I remember you on Merrion Strand when we were no more than a pair of chiselers, and you with your back stuck against the sea-wall, mortal fear all over your face and the sea calm as a looking-glass?"

"I wasn't feeling too good that day. I was after being terrible sick the night before."

"And what's Sean Boyle wanting you to do that he's going to put you in the canal if you don't?"

The question was inescapable, As inescapable as Paddy Reagan's big little fist back in the school playground.

"Nuala Murphy," Fonsy breathed.

"Nuala, is it? And Sean wanting to get his dirty hands on that one. Sure no wonder you come scuttling 'round to me trying to get him put away nice and safe in Mountjoy. If young Michael found you'd pimped Nuala to Sean Boyle he'd crucify you."

"His mallet," Fonsy replied simply. "It'd be that pavior's mallet of his."

"So it would. So it would."

It seemed to Fonsy that The Rock, tilted far back in his chair, was contemplating him and the fate that awaited him, the twin fates, with altogether too much prolonged consideration. Surely to God there was only one answer to be made.

At last it came. The chair banged forward onto all its four legs.

"Ah, well, sure we must see what we can do for you, Fonsy, me lad."

Immense relief flooded through Fonsy's whole small body. He would have preferred greatly not to have let The Rock see how much these words had meant to him, but the feeling that a lead sack of a burden had been lightly plucked off his shoulders made him suddenly so delighted that there was nothing he could do not to show it.

"And you, Fonsy Noonan, had better be seeing what you can do for me."

"Do for you, Paddy?" Fonsy was so surprised at The Rock's words that the old playground name slipped out without him even realizing.

But the Inspector did not seem put out by this piece of lese-majesté. "Ah, yes," he said softly. "There'd be a little thing I'd want you to do for me, Fonsy, before I do what you're wanting me to do for you."

"But as a citizen . ... But the man has stolen property . . ."

Fonsy gave up.

What is it?" he asked, knowing full well that whatever it was he was not going to like it in any way at all.

"Bruiser Hegarty," The Rock answered. "You're going to give him to me, Fonsy."

"Bruiser? But I can't. Jesus, Mary, and Joseph, I daren't."

The Rock smiled again. Except with his eyes. "I'm well knowing you daren't," he said. "Sure you never have dared or I'd have had the bastard this many a year. But this time you're going to do it. You're going to find out just what a fella from England was doing over here talking to Bruiser just before Christmas. And when you know all about whatever it is Bruiser has in mind, whatever bank it is he thinks he's going to clean out, whatever jeweler's, or whatever class of thing at all he's intending, then you're going to tell me every last bit about it, and well beforehand, too. And if you don't undertake that this minute, I'm not going to stir meself by one little finger to put Sean Boyle safely out of your way."

"But, Bruiser," said Fonsy. "Bruiser'd do to me what he did to Sean wid that van. Only there'd be no Michael Murphy to come along an' save the likes o' me."

"That's your problem, Fonsy, me lad. Your problem. But I tell you this. If this affair of Bruiser's goes ahead, and I'm not after hearing every last word about it, then I'm going to pull you in, me boy. I'm going to pull you in and see that you go down for eighteen months' hard. And before that ..."

The Rock leaned even farther forward across his drinks-cluttered desk. "Before that, I'm going to have a wee session with you meself, Fonsy. Just you and me, and perhaps Black Tommy, too, Just as a witness to say I never touched you. Now, do I get the lads out on their way to find Sean Boyle's stolen property or do I not? You were mentioning it was a matter of extreme urgency, Fonsy, me old buddy."

Fonsy had given the go-ahead to Inspector Reagan. He had known really from the first that there was nothing else he could do. If he had been pushed out of the Castle without having secured The Rock's agreement to pick up Sean Boyle, it would have been almost certainly too late to have got hold of Nuala Murphy. And even if he had managed to do that before half-past midnight, it would only have left the prospect before him of the gentle giant Michael and his huge great, shaggy-headed pavior's mallet.

But that night, in the little back-room in the decrepit tenement where he had his home until his arrears of rent caught up with him, he did not enjoy the quiet and contented rest he had seen himself as getting at last when the answer to Sean Boyle's ultimatum had sprung into his brain. Not even the knowledge that Sean had been safely arrested and would be out of circulation for many a day to come was a comfort to him. Indeed, he hardly slept at all, tossing and turning even more than he had done on the night when the plan to obtain the leather gloves had come to him.

But if he slept little, he thought a lot.

Bruiser Hegarty had never let him in on any of his plans yet, beyond telling him the little necessary for him to carry out whatever small part he had been given in one or another of them—a night on the watch somewhere, or a weekend spent making sure no unexpected person visited some jeweler's shop which the following weekend was to receive Bruiser's attentions.

So how was he to get to know all about whatever it was that Bruiser had in mind?

Damn it, he hadn't even known that Bruiser had some fella over from

England. Who would that be now? Some safe-blowing king? Or a thermic lance operator? Whoever it was, it certainly meant that something more than usually big was in the air, something very big indeed.

But how to get onto it?

And if he did, what a hell of a risk he would be taking. Bruiser had a short way with informers. He often boasted of what he would do to anyone who tried to shop him. And those who heard believed him. That was why The Rock had failed in all these years to get his hands on his old school fellow.

Yet something would have to be tried. Because if he did nothing, The Rock would put him inside without a moment's hesitation. He would create the evidence. It was a known thing that he had done that before, where a fella looked as if he was going to get away with something but had a weak spot in his past. One small chink like that had been enough for The Rock. He had taken advantage of it, had added a little something of his own, and had seen his victim happily into jail. He simply thought that such was his right. It had been the same even back at school when he suspected some chiseler was fecking things but didn't know just what. He had simply fecked something himself, put it in the fella's coat pocket, and then snitched on him. Or, more often, had made poor Fonsy do the snitching.

Begod, yes, something had to be tried now. Anything. Or it was jail for him surely. A shoplifting charge it would be, or a charge of taking lead pipes from an empty house. And he had gone looking for lead piping, that was a fact. Twice. So when it came to it, he'd be terribly disadvantaged in swearing he'd done nothing of the sort.

And, worse perhaps than jail, there was that threatened "session" with The Rock first. The fella knew ways of inflicting a fearful amount of damage and not leaving a mark. And Black Tommy in there with him, as witness that he'd never been touched—Black Tommy, a better hand at "touching" then even The Rock himself. If ever anyone had earned his nickname it was Black Tommy.

So he must get hold of Bruiser. And as soon as may be, too. If Bruiser had begun making his plans before Christmas when the English fella had been over, the date for the big job couldn't be all that far away. And up to this night, he himself had known nothing at all about it.

As soon as he could, he must put himself in Bruiser's way.

Perhaps he fell asleep for a little then. If he did, he dreamt of the school playground and himself up against the black-grimed brick wall of it once again and Bruiser's red fist measuring up to his eye. Or that may have been a waking thought. A waking nightmare.

Whichever it was, it frightened his whirling brain into hitting on a scheme at last.

He would take his courage in both hands and go up that very evening to Bruiser's place. It was at Foxrock. He knew just where, though he seldom ventured out to this smartest of Dublin suburbs. He would go to

Bruiser there, and he would tell him he had found out The Rock knew about the fella from England.

Lying in his twisted, grubby sheets, Fonsy was suddenly bathed in admiration for the notion that had come into his head. He would tell Bruiser that The Rock knew about the expert from England.

Surely to God, that would get him well and truly into Bruiser's good books. And surely, too, Bruiser would not, despite that he'd learn, give up a job as big as the one he was planning. He would only take extra precautions. But, if he himself was trusted by Bruiser, he would learn just what those precautions were. Then at the right time, taking every possible care, he could pass on the information to The Rock. So The Rock would get Bruiser and have him put away for fifteen years or twenty. And, if everything was done cleverly, Bruiser would never know how his plan had gone astray.

But, sitting on the top deck of the slow-chugging bus out to Foxrock that night, Fonsy felt less happy.

And, standing at last in the driveway of the big house with its picture windows below and its diamond-leaded ones above, with its garden sprouting urns and statues like so many warts and pimples on the face of a Henry Street harridan, with its carriage-lamp on the porch and its two-car garage at the side, he felt much worse.

He stood there for almost five minutes, unable to pluck up courage to go and ring at the front-door bell. It was only when he heard a car drawing up outside the next-door house that at last he made a quick rush to the porch and jabbed his leather-gloved finger onto the bell-push.

Ding-dong. Ding-dong. Melodious chimes from within. And then, with terrible swiftness, the carriage-lamp lit up and simultaneously the door jerked open and Bruiser Hegarty was there, framed in the light, big, black-haired, and standing, as he had always done even at six years of age, in a fighter's crouch.

He saw Fonsy.

"Yous," he said. "Round the back."

The door shut. The carriage-lamp clicked off. Fonsy stood there, feeling the thumping of his heart.

As soon as he had somewhat recovered, he hurried 'round the side of the house, past the big square oil tank for the central heating and on to what must be the kitchen door. It would never do to keep Bruiser waiting.

As he got to the door, it opened. "Yous can come in," Bruiser said, drawing back just far enough to allow him to step inside and close the door.

Over Bruiser's rounded boxer's shoulders, Fonsy gathered a vague impression of a kitchen in the sort of wood-tone laminates he had seen in the windows of Brown Thomas's and other big stores in the city center. But he had little time to look about him.

"What d'yous want?" Bruiser shot at him.

He gulped, felt for a desperate moment that he was not going to be able to find his voice at all, then at last managed to get out some part of the story he had gone over and over in his head as the Foxrock bus had chugged him toward his fate.

He must have succeeded in getting it all the right way 'round, he thought afterward, because as he had spoken a look of intense thoughtfulness had slowly settled on Bruiser's heavy black face.

For a long time after he had finished—it seemed to Fonsy as if hours had gone by—Bruiser had stood just where he was. But at last his eyes had come up and he had given Fonsy a quick, contemptuous, but not dismissive look.

"Yous. I'll likely need yous. Come tomorrow night at seven. No, hell, we've got a dinner party. Come the night after."

In the days that followed, Fonsy gradually got clear in his head most of the details about the big job that Bruiser Hegarty was planning. It was to be a raid on the Bank of Ireland—in College Green, no less. The man from England was a tunneler. He was going to show Bruiser's boys how a long underground passage could be dug from empty premises nearby into the vaults of the bank itself. The job was to be done over the long Easter weekend. It was going to lift Bruiser into the international class.

All Fonsy learnt could have easily gone straight to The Rock Reagan. There were times enough when he had been left to his own devices and could have used an out-of-the-way callbox to ring the Inspector's special number at the Castle. But there was one obstacle in the way of that. One terrible obstacle.

It had been put into Fonsy's path the second time he had gone up to the house in Foxrock. "There's one thing I must tell yous," Bruiser Hegarty had said. "An' listen well, Fonsy Noonan."

"Sure. Sure an' I will." Fonsy had peeled off his tan gloves, a gesture he felt somehow established the tremendous willingness with which he was going to listen to whatever Bruiser had to say.

"I know yous, Fonsy. You're a scut. I wouldn't trust yous one bloody inch. So I tell yous this. If anything goes wrong on this business—if we find the guards waitin' for us when we come outa where we're goin' in—then I'll get yous, Fonsy. It'll be the same for yous as it was for that gobshite Sean Boyle. Only this time there won't be any van engine comin' to a stop, an' no Michael Murphy to lift up any van afterwards. It'll be the end for you, Fonsy, an' a slow end, too. An' another thing. Yous know who I did that job on Sean Boyle for, don't yous?"

"It—it was the fellas that he took the money off, the—"

"Enough said, Fonsy. Enough said. But just yous remember this. They owe me for that job on Sean. They owe me, an' if be any chance I'm in Mountjoy itself I've only to send the word and them's the boys as'll repay that debt. On you, Fonsy Noonan."

It was stalemate. Stalemate between this threat of Bruiser's and the threat The Rock Reagan had delivered up in the Castle. Fonsy had known it at once.

So in the weeks coming up to Easter, as he was told more and more about the Bank of Ireland job, ironically he felt worse and worse. What good were all these details to him? What use was it to him that he could give The Rock enough information now for him to have guards all 'round the empty shop behind the bank they were going to tunnel from? Enough, too, to send Bruiser himself down for twenty solid years? When messengers like Garda Clanagan came up and told him out of the corner of their mouths that "himself up in the Castle" was getting impatient, he dared do no more than make a quick phonecall and pass on something vague about preparations for the affair seeming to be getting nearer and nearer completion.

It had happened to him once again, he reflected over and over. He was caught between two fires. Caught just as he had been at school when half the time he had reluctantly gone along with little Bruiser and fecked apples from shops, and the other half, almost as reluctantly, he had obeyed Paddy Reagan's orders to follow every last precept of the nuns and teachers or be pasted.

There was absolutely no way out. During long miserable nights he lay on his back going over and over the circumstances of the raid to come and finding no answer.

So it was going to be that "session" with The Rock and Black Tommy, a terrible hour or more that might well leave him hurt for the rest of his days, and an unthinkable eighteen months in Mountjoy after it. It would have to be. The prospect of Bruiser and his van, or his political friends and their van, was too appalling to consider.

But as the days coming up to Easter went by one by one, and more frequent and more urgent messages from The Rock were surreptitiously passed on by Garda Clanagan and others, he could not help succumbing a little to this opposite pressure. In one of his quick, careful phonecalls to the Castle, before in sheer desperation he slammed the receiver down, he did let out just what the raid's target was to be.

Afterward, trying not at all successfully to get immersed in the story of *The Incredible Hulk Versus the Mandarin*, he kept trying to convince himself that he had not exactly betrayed Bruiser. After all, he had avoided letting The Rock know the method Bruiser intended to employ to get into the bank and he had not given away the date for the raid, either.

Yet he could not disguise from himself the fact that The Rock now knew Bruiser was going to lead a raid on the Bank of Ireland in College Green, and The Rock could work out that the Easter weekend was the likeliest time as easily as the Incredible Hulk could work out how to foil evil beings like The Mandarin.

Oh, if only life was like the comics, if only the good were decently guaranteed that they would win in the end, how easy it would be to stay on the right side.

As it was, now that The Rock knew as much as he did, there were likely to be guards everywhere 'round the bank once the Easter weekend had set in and Bruiser and his boys might well be spotted when they left the empty premises just off Fleet Street that they were to use for the tunneling. Bruiser would be carrying a gun, too, and would be ready to shoot his way out of trouble and get away. He would know someone had given The Rock a tipoff, too. And he would be altogether convinced who that someone was.

Was there no way out? It seemed as the days passed that there was not. Then on the evening of the Thursday before Easter, the night the raid was to begin, Bruiser summoned Fonsy out to Fosxrock.

"Yous is coming wid me," he said.

"But—" said Fonsy.

"Get in the motor," Bruiser said.

Fonsy had seen a new car tucked away at the side of the driveway of Bruiser's house as he made his way 'round to the kitchen door. Now, without another word of protest, he made his way back to it, black depression settling like cold stout on his stomach, but with none of the latter's enlivening effect.

This put the final kibosh on it. In the bus on the way out he had almost made up his mind that as soon as he had heard whatever it was Bruiser wanted to say he would go straight back to whichever railway station came handiest and take a train to nowhere. He'd be altogether miserable in the country, sure enough—he couldn't tell one end of a pig from the other—but he'd be safe there. Tucked away in some little place with no more than a couple of bars in it, Bruiser and his friends would never find him. And The Rock himself might come to forget.

But now—now he was to go with Bruiser to the empty premises while the gang dug their tunnel all through the long Easter weekend and dragged the stuff out from the vaults all Monday. Jaysus, he might be made to dig down there, too. And never the skin of a chance of getting word to Inspector Reagan and doing his decent duty as a citizen.

And when it came ot Monday night and they used the new expensive transceiver Bruiser had bought to summon a truck to take away the money and valuables, then, perhaps there'd be The Rock with half the guards in Dublin 'round them and Bruiser with his gun behind him.

He put his gloved fingers on the handle of the car door and paused. Maybe Bruiser wouldn't see him in the darkness if he cut and ran for it this minute.

The front door of the house opened and Bruiser stepped out, carrying a large green-leather suitcase in the latest style. His wife behind him called a last word of farewell.

"An', Bruiser, don't you be forgettin'. You can get your Easter Mass down in Cork as well as anywhere else."

"Yes, yes," Bruiser shouted back.

He entered the car, into which Fonsy had already hastily scrambled, started the engine with a savage jerk of the ignition key, and sent it roaring off into the road. Fonsy thought that this was not quite the time to say he was not feeling fit and would be better off in bed.

Fonsy did not have to join the rest of the gang digging the lengthy tunnel into the bank, but this was the only drop of consolation he could wring out of the whole long fearful weekend. He was kept busy, it seemed to him, every waking minute of it. He hefted sacks of earth away from the tunnel mouth. He cooked rashers and eggs on a camping gas stove till he felt sick at the sight of the frying pan. He made so many cups of tea he thought he would never want to put one to his lips again.

The time passed with appalling speed. Soon he was set to wipe every surface in the shop clear of possible fingerprints and he realized that it wouldn't be long before the moment would come when they opened the door of the old place, went out into the little sidestreet, and loaded up the truck Bruiser would have summoned on his new transceiver from its distant waiting place. And that would be the moment when the guards The Rock might have surrounding the area would come crashing down on them from every side. If there were guards there at all.

The moment came sooner than Fonsy had expected.

"Yous," Bruiser said suddenly, turning away from the transceiver over which he had been attempting, with much "over and out," to get in contact with the driver of the truck waiting at the other side of O'Connell Bridge.

"Yis, Bruiser, yis?" Fonsy answered, desperately rubbing his gloved hands together in a parody of enthusiasm. He had kept the gloves fast on his hands all over the long miserable incarcerated weekend. Somehow they represented to him the possibility, mirage though it must be, of getting out of the place unscathed and finding afterward a way to live quiet and happy in comfortably familiar surroundings.

"The damn transceiver," Bruiser said. "It isn't operating at all. The walls here is killing the radio waves entirely. So out you step, me boy, an' call up Liam from out at the corner where's there's room for the thing to breathe. Tell him we'll be ready for him in ten minutes from this. An' watch how you go."

"Yis, Bruiser, yis. Sure I'll watch to left an' right an' right again."

Fonsy heaved up the matt-black, knob-covered machine and stagger-ed with it to the shop door. Once that was shut behind him his mind began to race.

What to do for the best? Was The Rock waiting somewhere near with half the guards in Dublin behind him? If he was, would there yet be time to tell him the whole size of Bruiser's enterprise? And if he did, would The Rock believe him when he said this was the first and only chance he'd had to do it? But then what if The Rock hadn't worked out when the raid was likely to take place and there were no guards near at all? Then, if he failed to transmit the message to Liam and the truck never came, Bruiser would hold that against him almost as much as if he thought he'd been informed on.

Fonsy's mind was by no means made up by the time he had stepped out of the narrow lane where the empty shop was and into Fleet Street. But just as he did so, from 'round the corner from College Green, a truck running without lights swung in to face him.

Liam. It could only be Liam. He must have realized the transceiver was not getting through and decided to come down without orders. So the problem was solved. Nothing for it now but to go back and tell Bruiser.

Fonsy tried to stop himself thinking any further.

Then, above the sound of Liam's cautiously chugging engine, there came another sound. A shrill whistle blast. The guards. They were here. Liam's arrival must have sent them into action.

There was a deep unused doorway of the electricity depot just behind where Fonsy stood. He darted into it and shrank back to its farthest rubbish-littered depths, his gloved hands pressing against a broken iron grille that protected the old door.

Everywhere outside there was the sound of heavily running, booted feet. There must be a hundred guards out there.

He saw a mass of them tear past his hiding place and turn into the lane. And then there came the sharp crack of a revolver shot. Bruiser. Bruiser out of the shop and shooting his way to freedom.

Another shot and a sharp cry of pain.

The guards who had run past came back the other way, scattering for cover. Suddenly it was as silent again as it had been before Liam's unfortunate lorry had come blundering onto the scene.

Fonsy waited and wondered.

At last he could no longer bear not knowing and edged his way to the outer limit of the doorway.

It was a mistake.

Sudden sharp footsteps rounded the corner. It was Bruiser.

"Fonsy," he said. "Yous take this and keep a hold of it." And into Fonsy's obediently held-out hand he thrust his gun. Fonsy felt through his glove that it was still hot from the shot that had hit the oncoming guard.

"Mother o' God," he muttered.

The sound of Bruiser's fast-retreating steps faded into the night as half a dozen guards broke cover and set off in pursuit.

As soon as they had gone, Fonsy shoved the hot gun behind the broken grille at his back. A fair amount of rubbish had collected there over the years and he pulled as much as he could over the fearful incriminating object.

Sure, he thought, I can find the damn thing there whenever I have to, so if Bruiser does get away an' is in the clear if he comes askin' for it later it'll be no trouble at all to get it for him. He flattened himself back up against the grille again. The last thing he needed now was to get picked up by the guards.

"Fonsy Noonan, I thought you'd be skulking not far away."

It was The Rock himself. His huge, square-shouldered form had materialized from the darkness and a powerful torch beam flicked 'round to illuminate the whole doorway.

Fonsy put a smile onto his face.

"Ah, it's yourself," he said, trying hard for cheerfulness. "Well, sure an' hasn't it all gone like a dream? Like a dream entirely."

"Not like any dream you dreamt, Fonsy, you scut," The Rock replied. "Sorry help I had from you."

"But, Inspector—But, Paddy—I told yous. I told yous every drop about it."

"You told me the littlest you could, and that I had to pull out of you like chewing-gum out of a carpet."

The square shoulders turned abruptly away, though the torch beam did not waver. The Rock called out something and almost at once a guard came up out of the dark.

"Here, take this one up to the Castle," The Rock said. "Put him in one of the cars, not in a truck with the rest of the boyos. And keep him somewhere out of the way till I've time to get to him."

"Right ye are, Inspector."

Fonsy was plucked from his hiding place, twirled 'round once with his feet off the ground, and marched away.

Once more Fonsy found himself in the same tall echoing, file-lined corridor in the Castle awaiting The Rock Reagan's pleasure. But, where before he had been fumingly anxious for the Inspector to see him, now he was scared to dropping point as he waited for the moment when The Rock would scuttle him down to some out-of-the-way cell and begin, with the aid of Black Tommy, to beat the bejaysus out of him.

Every now and again a guard would go clumping past, generally looking more than ordinarily pleased with himself. Once a pair of them came by, telling each other with glee that this was the best night the Dublin force had had in years.

And still The Rock made no appearance. Fonsy took off his gloves and with great care put one in each pocket of his suit. He had suddenly pictured to himself The Rock taking those precious objects and by way of a start tearing the fingers off them one by one.

His right-hand pocket, which also contained *Conan the Barbarian Faces the Scorpion God*, was bulged to straining-point now, and he extracted

the lurid comic and tucked it inside his jacket. He would have liked to
have sunk himself deep in its pages to blot out from his mind, if he
could, the thought of what was to come. But that would be an imper-
tinence he couldn't even contemplate.

At some bleak hour of the night he did get to hear one piece of good
news. Of a sort.

Two detectives he knew by sight turned into the far end of the corridor and, fearful they might remind The Rock of his presence, Fonsy
slid into a file-lined recess close by. So he heard, as perhaps the two
would not have wanted him to, the joke they had going between them.

"Black Tommy," said one, stifling a laugh.

"In the arse," said the other, muffling his laugh less successfully.

"An' it jammed deep in there, jammed solid," said the first, spluttering a little.

"Bruiser Hegarty's bullet jammed in the side o' Black Tommy's arse
like it was shot into a barrel o' sand," said the second. "Just ready for the
boys in the lab."

And he broke down completely, hardly to be sobered when his com-
panion added with abrupt moroseness. "If we ever catch the bugger to
pin the other end of the business on him."

The two of them disappeared at the far end of the corridor.

Fonsy felt a small surge of relief. At least Black Tommy would not be
available now in that out-of-the-way cell to witness that The Rock had
"never touched him," would not be there to add his own particular
brand of not touching to The Rock's.

But the moment of lightened fear was short-lived. Bruiser had got
away, and that meant that The Rock wouldn't lay his hands on him
again this time. Hadn't he himself wiped every last fingerprint off
everywhere in that shop? And none of the boyos the guards had caught
would talk, that was for sure. So even when he had finished his eighteen
dreaded months in Mountjoy, Bruiser would be out there. Sooner or
later he would come for him. With a van.

Already pressed against the very back of the file-lined recess, Fonsy
now in a new access of misery could not stop himself sinking into a
womblike crouch on the floor. And still he had to endure the slow, slow
passing of time.

Was that a glimmer of dawn coming in at the little window high
above his head? Or was it only the reflection of some street lamp?

He began to want to hear The Rock's voice calling for him. At least
it would end this fearful waiting.

Before much longer, he saw that in the little window there was a full,
cold light. It was day. It was tomorrow. But no hope in that for him.
Only that session with The Rock awaited him in it.

At last, driven frantic with fear-filled tedium, he actually reached out,
darting-eyed, and pulled from the row of black-bound files down near

the floor beside him the first volume his hand came to. It would be something to read, whatever it was. Surely he could find even in lists of names from long ago something to take his mind off what awaited him. And it wouldn't be as disrespectful as reading a comic. Dully he forced himself to pick out what was written, in a terrible class of hand, on the great stiff page in front of him.

Suddenly, he gave a start. The words he had been reading—"P. Reagan, Sergeant." It was The Rock. He was reading something The Rock himself had written years before when he had been no more than a sergeant.

He looked at the big volume more carefully.

This was what they called a Duty Book. Evidently every detective had to write down in it where he was going when he went out and what he intended doing. So here was The Rock's day on—Fonsy searched for the date—yes, on 24th June, ten years before. He had been out, it was written here in his own fist, "10 A.M. On inquiries, Bella Street."

Bella Street. It might be only a bit of a road up in the north side near Summerhill, but it was the place marked out in legend where, ten years before, on 24th June—a day ever since remembered—Christy Murphy, beloved brother of Michael, the gentle giant, had been brutally gunned down by men who thought he was going to go across to England to inform on them to the Special Branch there. Had been gunned down after his hiding place had been betrayed to his former political comrades by some informer.

And now it was clear, clear as could be given The Rock's customary way with anyone he disapproved of, just who that informer had been. The Rock himself. The Rock Reagan was the informer Michael Murphy would kill with one blow of that great pavior's mallet of his the moment he got to know about him. Would kill as surely as a stroke of God.

And, yes, The Rock would have given Christy to those people because it was after a bank raid that had gone wrong and resulted in the death of an innocent bystander that Christy was getting away to England. It would be just like The Rock to decide that Christy was the guilty party there, and that he himself had the right to administer justice whether the case against Christy was properly proved or not. He must have stumbled across Christy's hiding place when he had gone to Bella Street that day on some other business altogether. How he must have prayed after the shooting that no one would notice those two scrawled words "Bella Street" in the Duty Book. As they had not. Not for years and years. Not until now.

Fonsy raised himself to his feet. From the pockets of his old striped brown suit he drew out, one by one, his fine leather gloves and put them on his hands. He had no need at all now to fear The Rock Reagan tearing them to pieces nor doing anything else. Or he would not have when he had completed one sharp piece of business.

Quick as a flash, he reached up and yanked open the little window above his head. Then he took the heavy black-bound volume that recorded Sergeant Reagan's activities on that distant day ten years ago just before the Bella Street killing had taken place and he threw it neatly out into the new-born day. All he had to do now, when he was hauled away to see The Rock, was to tell him that he had seen what he had seen in the book, not just now, but at the time he had been in the Castle before, and that he had sneaked the volume out of the building while he was being kept waiting then and had it now in a safe place. After that he would be free from the attentions of The Rock Reagan for ever and ever. Amen.

Only there was still Bruiser Hegarty. Bruiser, who sooner or later would be waiting for him with the engine of a van running.

What would it feel like the moment those tires touched his prostrate side? Began to scrunch over him?

Oh, God, Bruiser was there dominating him still as he had dominated him from the very first time they had set eyes on each other in the asphalted school playground all those years ago.

He hardly wanted to bother now to transfer *Conan the Barbarian Faces the Scorpion God* from his inner pocket, where it had been awkwardly uncomfortable, back to the pocket from which he had just taken one of his gloves.

But dully performing the action with awkwardly fumbling gloved fingers triggered off a memory in his mind. It was a memory going back to not many hours before, though it seemed almost a lifetime away. It was of the feel of Bruiser Hegarty's hot gun through the leather of that same glove he now wore.

The gun that had been shoved from Bruiser's ungloved hand into his own gloved one.

The gun that would have Bruiser's prints on it, sealed in his own sweat. And the bullet from that self-same identical gun was at this moment lodged safely in Black Tommy's enormous arse—and bullets, as everyone knew, could be attached to the weapon that had fired them as surely as fingerprints could be attached to the hand that had made them. So, put the two things together, and there was proof, all the decent proof that any court could ask, that Bruiser had committed armed assault on a member of the Garda Siochana.

And where was the vital link in that chain of proof? Safely tucked away behind a broken old grating at the electricity depot in Fleet Street where only Fonsy Noonan knew about it.

He had Bruiser on toast, just as surely as he had The Rock on toast. He was safe. Free. Untouchable. Home. Home at last.

Fonsy Noonan in the middle and loving it.

Martin Russell
Kill Before Publication

In the ordinary way, thought Miles, her features would have been striking. But something had happened to distort them a little. Trouble emanated from her, like polluted steam.

"The Editor?" he repeated cautiously. "He's busy, right now. Can I do anything?"

The woman glanced along the counter. Four yards away, the small-ads girl was attending to a female customer. She spoke again on the same hushed note. "Is there someone else I can see?"

Miles quelled his irritation. The implication that he himself amounted to less than "someone else" was one that eleven months in the Beechway office of the *Gleaner* had taught him to be able to ignore. University, he now realized, had given him ideas above his station. A sensible fellow, he was willing to accept that it was up to him to make a fresh start in the real world, and cash in later. He knew he looked young for his age. This woman, whom he judged to be in the region of forty-five, could hardly be blamed for wanting somebody more blatantly mature.

"I'm from Editorial," he said patiently. "Maybe I can help."

"I was rather hoping to speak to—someone in authority."

Her figure was still trim. The merest hints of silver were beginning to touch her dark hair, softly waved about a face that, in Miles's estimation, had only recently commenced to sag just a little, to lose the confident elasticity of the first half of a lifetime. In her youth, she might well have been a knockout. He gave her a cheerful smile.

"If you could just outline to me what it's about, Mrs.—?"

"Stanhope." The name brust out as if under pressure. She hesitated, eyeing him. Her voice dropped lower. "It's concerning a—a police matter."

She glanced again at the customer, who was querying a wordcount. The only other person in the front office, an elderly man with facial blotches, was examining a rack of photographic prints and humming to himself.

"Criminal offense?" Miles inquired briskly. "Road-traffic problem? Neighborhood dispute?"

"A court appearance."

"Involving whom?"

"Actually, I was wondering—"

Miles waited. He was the kind of young fellow who always summoned a laugh at other people's jokes, especially when they weren't funny. Somebody had once told him he was too soft a touch to be a successful journalist. This was partly why he had taken up the challenge. There was, he knew, a vulnerable side of his nature. On the other hand, he did possess the sort of tenacity, the hatred of letting go of the rope, that distinguished the hack from the newshawk. In tandem, the traits had potential, although in a place like Beechway the scope for development of an investigative technique could hardly be said to be limitless.

A touch of defiance seeped into Mrs. Stanhope's attitude. "I really came in," she said, raising her chin at him, "to find out what the position is regarding— It was a shoplifting case, in fact."

"I see. When was it dealt with?"

"This morning. A fine was imposed."

"On yourself?"

Her eyes closed for an instant. "That's right."

"So now it's all over." He smiled at her.

Neither her eyes nor her lips responded. She reminded him of some dead creature being jerked around by electrical impulses deficient in voltage. "The court hearing is over. But you'd have had a reporter in court, wouldn't you?"

"We would, and so would the *Mercury*. Then there's the free-sheet, the *Advertiser*. They sometimes—"

"Yes, well. This is why it's so important that I should speak to the Editor."

Miles studied her with some compassion. "You'd like our report killed before publication?"

Hope sent the current surging into her. "Is that possible? It's terribly important to me. There needn't—"

"I'm sorry, Mrs. Stanhope. We report all cases. There can't be exceptions. That's the way it is."

She gazed past him at the mail pigeonholes behind the counter. Her lower lip, like a child's, was quivering. Unlike a child, she awaited the return of self-control before venturing on further utterance.

"Surely there must be flexibility? You can't possibly override every mitigating—"

"If we did it for one person," he explained, "what excuse would we have for refusing someone else? It's not for us to judge. The courts are held in public. Either the Press covers them or it doesn't."

She said hoarsely, "It seems a rather insensitive system."

"What's the alternative?"

Her fingernails, polished deep-pink, tapped the counter surface. Although she was watching them, she seemed unconscious of their activity, as if they were being powered by a remote substation of her nervous system while the main generator roared desperately to open gates elsewhere. Presently she looked up. "If I were to speak personally to the Editor—"

"You'd get the same answer from him, I'm afraid. It would just be a waste of your time, Mrs. Stanhope. I'm sorry."

"How about a doctor's certificate?"

"A medical certificate," Miles said guardedly. "To what effect?"

"It's my mother, you see. She's living with us, and she's elderly and not in good health. If she were to get to hear about this—"

"I don't honestly see how you can keep it from her. Whether it's published or not, she's bound to find out, isn't she?"

"Not if I don't tell her."

Miles rubbed his jaw. "I think, Mrs. Stanhope, you're being a little overoptimistic. I could be wrong, but it seems highly unlikely to me that she wouldn't get to hear of it sooner or later. And though initially it might come as a shock—"

To his alarm, Mrs. Stanhope slumped in tears across the counter. She did it quite silently. The sole giveaway was the slight heaving of her suede-clad shoulders. Barbara, the small-ads girl, however, had sharp eyes. Abandoning her customer, she came over. "Is the lady feeling ill?"

Miles made discreet signals. "She's a little upset. I'll take her into the interview room for a moment. Come along, Mrs. Stanhope."

The twin upright chairs inside the interview cubicle were of light, tubular-steel construction, enabling Miles to introduce one of them adroitly beneath the buckling form of his client while manipulating the other closely alongside so that he could bring physical as well as vocal succor to bear. The cubicle walls were mere chipboard partitions. Acutely aware of the pointed ears outside, he spoke quietly.

"If it would help at all, Mrs. Stanhope, I'll see if the Editor would be willing to talk to you for a moment. But you really mustn't expect anything from him. He'll tell you the same as I have. Like me to try?"

She nodded into her sleeve. Her voice was muffled. "You're very kind."

Raising his eyebrows in response to Barbara's inquisitive glance as he walked back through the front office, Miles went upstairs. The Editor, Bob Hartley, was on the telephone. Establishing himself in the doorway to his room, Miles waited without qualms. Despite an eight-year age gap and the gulf between their respective positions, he and Hartley were on terms of easy familiarity: to Miles, his nominal chief seemed no more than a likeable older brother, although Hartley's appointment to the top job at the age of thirty was said to have aroused a degree of resentment in certain of his more elderly subordinates in the newsroom. Even they could scarcely deny that he was smart, destined for greater things.

At the moment, however, Hartley looked anything but dynamic. His face had a bleached appearance and he was sagging sideways in his chair. Mumbling a few final words into the receiver, he dropped it with a clatter, picked up a galley-proof, and began marking it with limp strokes of a ballpen. Eyes blearily upon the task, he said. "Yes Milesy? Trouble?"

"Nothing wild." Miles advanced to the desk. "We've a shoplifter downstairs. Wants it kept out of the paper."

"You know the routine." Scoring through a line, Hartley scrawled a weary replacement in the margin.

"She's in a bit of a state. Weeping in the interview room. I said I'd see if you felt like talking to her."

"I don't feel like talking to her."

"I warned her you wouldn't." Miles made no move to leave. Immobilizing his pen, Hartley scowled at the facing wall.

"Menopausal syndrome?"

"Well, she's in her mid-forties, I'd say."

Hartley waggled the pen feebly. "Got to you, hasn't she, my son? Those tear-streaked jowls—"

"I'm only doing this," Miles said tolerantly, "in case she has hysterics all over Barbara's domain. I never promised her anything."

A sigh rose from the depths of the Editor. "What's her name?"

"Stanhope, Mrs."

From a wire basket on the desk, Hartley extracted a pile of folded copy paper covered with neat handwriting and sifted through the sheets. "Here we are," he announced presently. " 'Mrs. Syliva Stanhope (forty-six), housewife, of Lennard Gardens, South Beechway, fined forty pounds with seventeen-fifty costs for stealing from Jepson's Super-market three tins of red salmon, a tin of pork luncheon meat, five packets of soup, for boxes of processed cheese, and a can of creamed rice —total value seven pounds thirty-six.' "

"Didn't do things by halves, did she?"

"I expect she told the Bench they slipped into her pocket by mistake: 'an unaccountable lapse, she told the magistrates, which she now bitter-ly regretted . . . only explanation her mental state arising from domestic stress . . . dependent mother in poor health . . . worries about the chil-dren . . . estranged from husband, now living at another address with a former woman friend of the defendant."

Hartley peered up. "In her shoes, I wouldn't be sobbing my guts out in the front office of the *Gleaner*. I'd be clawing the other dame's eyes out in her front parlor. Maybe she's tried that. Well, Milesy, I'm sorry. Seems to me, Joe's turned in a factual report that need do her no harm at all, if somebody in a position to help sits up and takes notice. Which is obviously what she was after."

"I don't think she sees it that way, Bob."

"Go back down and explain it to her."

"I doubt if she'll take if from me. It's the top brass she's after."

Hartley's second sigh was of dinosaur proportions. "What do we pay you for? I'm up to my eyeballs, for God's sake. If I felt good, which I bloody don't, I'd still have no time to spare for neurotic females. What can I say to her that you can't?"

"It's not what's said. It's who says it."

Clambering out of his chair, Hartley grabbed his jacket. "Interview room? Give me a call there in two mintues, on the button. Say I'm wanted at the Town Hall. Leave it a second longer and you get the quarterly meeting of the Ratepayers' Federation tonight, and that's no threat: it's a pledge." Wobbling outside to the landing, he began clumping down the uncarpeted stairs. The building was old and it echoed. With a faint smile at his lips, Miles returned to the newsroom.

"What happened to you?" demanded Polly Chubb, who was Features. "You're supposed to be getting that pictures file for me."

"Sorry, Poll. Got involved with a female in flux."

"Try concentrating on one cookie at a time. Who was she?"

"Some housewife up on a supermarket rap. Wants the story killed."

"Wow, you don't say? Young, I take it? Good-looking?"

Miles pretended to cogitate. "A dish."

"I knew it. The only—"

"Twenty-five years ago, that is. Now slightly threadbare. Which isn't to say—"

"No, it's not, and don't. Get me that file."

When he emerged from the fileroom, Miles observed through the glazed upper section of the Editor's office door that Bob Hartley had company. It was Mrs. Stanhope. Installed in the deep-seated leather chair that Hartley found useful for placing his visitors at a disadvantage, she was gazing up at him from the humiliating half sprawl that its antique springs engendered, appearing to listen intently to what he was saying. He was gesturing emphatically, although beneath the surface activity there remained a lifeless manner untypical of him. Miles consulted his watch. Forty minutes had elapsed since he had first gone downstairs to attend to the woman. Handing Polly the file, he remarked, "She's certainly turning the screw. Bob's looking a little crushed."

"What are you on about?"

"That woman. The supermarket felon. She's been closeted with him for half an hour, and they're still at it."

"Give him a buzz on the intercom."

"I've done that. When they were downstairs."

"No result?"

"He just said, 'Yep, okay', and hung up."

"We can't do more."

Miles returned to a couple of stories that were toasting on his machine. Twenty minutes later he again had occasion to pass the Editor's door. This time he noticed that Mrs. Stanhope had left. Hartley was back on proof-correcting, hunched over the narrow sheets as if analyzing the paper's very texture for flaws. Idly, Miles wondered about the outcome of their confrontation. He hoped, in a way, that her objective had been gained. The idea of an elderly parent suffering from reflected odium troubled the pappier side of his nature.

He was unable to ask Hartley about it, because an hour later the

Editor went home, complaining of stomach pains and a sensation that six-inch nails were being forced through his scalp. Into his place leapt the chief reporter, Geoff Craddock, who deputized in emergencies. Craddock held traditional views on editorship. Policy issues, in his philosophy, were not up for discussion with staffjuniors. Apart from this, his departure from the newsroom threw an extra load on the others, and for the rest of the day Miles had no time to dwell on peripheral matters . . .

The following morning, it became known that Bob Hartley was down with gastric flu and would be absent for a week. Entrenched in the Editor's chair, Craddock became still less approachable. Miles forgot about the incident until Friday.

It was while he was scanning the new-minted columns of the Court Page that memory stirred.

Having given more careful attention to the headlines, he wandered across to Polly Chubb's littered desk. "Bob must be more jellycentered than we thought."

The Features Reporter peered up perspiringly. "Why?"

"He spiked that case. The shoplifter."

"The woman who came in?" Polly shrugged. "She must have produced a medical certificate."

Miles eyed her. "Ever known it to succeed before?"

"No, but there has to be a first time. Now leave me alone before I go bananas."

Miles mentioned the matter to a couple of the senior reporters. They showed scant interest. Yielding to a feeling of obstinacy, he went downstairs for a copy of the opposition. Although officially it hit the streets half a day later, the *Mercury* generally contrived to get itself on sale simultaneously with its main rival, and a bundle had already turned up. Careful inspection indicated that Mrs. Stanhope had been persuasive in more than one office. There was no mention of her conviction.

Returning upstairs, Miles poked his head around the Editor's door, to find the room empty. With the week's issue triumphantly behind him, Craddock had taken publication day off. Miles went back to his own desk, pondered briefly, lifted the phone.

"Hi, Sue. How's the prettiest girl on the town's second-best newspaper?"

"How's the ugliest guy on the town's third?" Although younger than he by a year, Sue Baxter had joined the *Mercury* direct from school; her practical experience thus outweighed his by a formidable margin, a fact which she rarely allowed him to forget. "I see your stuff went through the slaughterhouse again."

"My work isn't appreciated," he lamented. "Yet. Hey, Sue, on a serious note—"

"Who's joking?"

"Something I wanted to ask. There was a court case back in the week—a Mrs. Stanhope, shoplifting, fined. You don't seem to have carried it. Any idea why not?"

"Sid must have missed it." Sid Sullivan was the *Mercury's* resident court man." Want me to ask him?"

"Is he there?"

After a pause, a male voice came to the phone. "Morning, youthful Miles. What's this about a shopfitter?"

"Lifter," Miles explained.

"I could have missed it," Sid opined slowly, "but I believe not."

Miles was puzzled. "You mean, you don't recall writing the story?"

"On the contrary, I recall perfectly well that I didn't. It's news to me."

"You've no knowledge, then, of Mrs. Stanhope calling on you to ask for it to be kept out?"

"If I had," Sid replied logically, "I'd have known what you were babbling about. What's your interest?"

"Nothing special." Miles hesitated. "Thanks, Sid. If I could have another quick word with Sue—"

Having fixed a date with her for that evening, he put a call through to the *Advertiser*. Although a giveaway, it carried a substantial percentage of hard news and was particularly strong on court coverage. By chance, its court man, Ray Woods, was available and communicative.

"Sylvia Stanhope? Doesn't clang a bell. This week, you say?"

"Tuesday morning she came up. Called on us in the afternoon. It occurred to me she might have gone on to you that same day, or Wednesday?"

"Hold on, I'll check."

When Woods came back, he sounded mystified. "You're positive it was Tuesday?"

"That's what she told me. She should know."

"Well, I've no record of the case in my notes. What's more, the guvnor tells me he's had nobody of that name pestering him with an exclusion plea." After an interval, Woods added, "Why are you asking?"

"I wish I knew." Miles stared hard across the newsroom, seeing nothing that was in view. Presently, with a start, he said, " Sorry, Ray. Didn't mean to fade out on you. I think I must have my lines crossed. Forget I mentioned it."

"I shall, old boy, the moment you hang up. Did I miss a good yarn, by the way?"

"Hardly the scoop of the decade. Thanks for your trouble."

Ringing off, Miles reverted to his contemplation of space. Becoming aware of his vacant expression, Polly Chubb glanced over and said playfully, "When you make it onto a daily, you'll get this reaction six times a week. Think you can stand it?"

Giving her an absent look, Miles rose. "I'll be out for ten minutes," he announced to the room at large, and left.

The courtroom building was an easy canter from the *Gleaner's* premises. Miles had covered hearings only a few times, but he knew his way to the admin section and had been prudent enough to strike up a working acquaintanceship with one of the clerks, a spinster in her thirties with more than a soft spot for presentable Press trainees in their early twenties, especially those who came equipped with sympathetic eyes and a full complement of white teeth. Since the Bench never sat on Fridays, the building was relatively deserted and the clerk had time to spare. After a few moments of mandatory banter, Miles switched directly to the topic in hand. She wrinkled her somewhat oversized nose at him.

"*Gleaner* losing its grip? If the case was heard, your man Joe Wilkinson—"

"I know, Kathy, but I can't ask him. He's gone off for the weekend, as usual. Be an angel and look it up for me, huh?"

"You newshounds. You're all the same." She opened her ledger. "Incessantly on the cadge for priority treatment. Mrs. Sylvia Stanhope, Tuesday. —Sorry. No record of it here. You did say shoplifting?"

"No, but she did. Try Monday."

"At once, my lord." Presently she shook her head. "No one of that name. How about the previous week?"

"Go back to last Thursday," he suggested.

They drew a blank. The clerk eyed him quizzically. "Sure you didn't dream it? You didn't *imagine* she came into your office?"

Too preoccupied to deliver a comeback, Miles stood drumming the ledger with the blunt end of his ballpen. "This is the full court record?" he asked finally. "There's no subsidiary file for minor cases?"

Her headshake was conclusive. "It's all here. If your Mrs. Stanhope came up and was dealt with, she'd be down there in black and white. Black, anyway."

"So why isn't she?"

"Because she's a phantasm, that's why. Stick to flesh-and-blood, my lad, if you want to know what's good for you. Shall I go back any further?"

"No, Kathy. Thanks. I've wasted enough of your time. See you around."

"Only if you come looking," she retorted, smiling at the back of his head as he left.

Polly Chubb was once more alone in the newsroom, tapping drearily at her feature. Planting himself on her desk, Miles arrested the typewriter carriage. She scowled up.

"If you're that stuck for an occupation, how about fetching me some coffee?"

"You reckon Bob would object, Poll, if I phoned him at home?"

"Now? Unless he's made a miracle recovery, I'm certain he'd mind like hell. Is it urgent?''

Miles gazed past her left ear. ''Tell me something. Would you take me for a fanciful sort of guy?''

''I wouldn't take you on any terms.''

''I'm serious, Poll.''

''You're about as earthbound as an earwig. Satisfied? Now get off my machine.''

''I'm still baffled about that—''

The telephone bleeped. Polly snatched it up. ''Miles Repton? Hold on.'' She passed the receiver across. ''One of your harem,'' she said crossly, and blitzed a sentence out of the keyboard.

''Who?'' asked Miles. ''Oh—Kathy. Hi. Did I leave something behind?''

''Yes. A feeling that I hadn't been as helpful as I might.'' The court clerk sounded contrite. ''So I ploughed back another week or two, but there wasn't anything.''

''Thanks,'' he said blankly. ''Very good of you.''

''Then I had a look at last month's ledger. Guess what I found?''

Miles waited. On a deflated note she went on, ''April the ninth— that's five weeks back—there was an entry about a shoplifting case. Mrs. Sylvia Stanhope of Lennard Gardens. Is that the one?''

''Bullseye. Five *weeks*? That's incredible. She gave me to understand— Never mind. Kathy, you're a sleuth. What kind of chocolates do you like? Oh, I see. Buy you a Campari, then, sometime. Thanks again. 'Bye now.''

Cradling the receiver, he sat staring at the paper in Polly's machine as it rattled to and fro. She suspended operations to glare black. ''Now what?''

''That shoplifting case, Poll. It was over a month ago.''

She puffed her cheeks. ''You're getting obsessed. If it's back in the past, what does it matter now?''

''But it was only this week that she came in asking for the report to be kept out.''

''Maybe she's been in an extended trance. The shock and shame of it all. She finally came to her senses on Tuesday and though it had only just happened.''

Miles's forehead went into a dozen puckers. Without answering, he quit the desk and wandered over to the rack where back-numbers were kept for three months, pending their transference to microfilm. Withdrawing the issue of April 12, he spread it out on the working top.

His search took moments. On the extreme right of the Court Page, center column, an item was headed WOMAN STOLE. It related to Mrs. Sylvia Stanhope of 29 Lennard Gardens, fined for stealing groceries worth a total of— Miles read it three times. Then he carried the print over to Polly's desk. Resignedly, she stopped typing and leaned back, thrusting fingers wildly through her gingery hair.

"You've traced it. You still can't make it out. You want the benefit of my objective opinion. Shoot."

"If we carried this last month, Poll—how come we had a report of the identical case scheduled for this week?"

"Is it the identical case?"

"Down to the last detail."

Polly meditated. "It's what I figured," she said at last. "Mrs. Stanhope suffered a time-warp. She was five weeks late getting to us."

"You're missing the point. There was a four-slip report of the case from Joe Wilkinson in Bob's tray on Tuesday, waiting to be subbed. I saw it myself."

Polly sat in silence. Miles added, "If it were just the Stanhope woman's account, I'd feel you were right—she'd lost touch with events. But Joe's dependable, isn't he? He wouldn't be likely to resumbmit something more than a month after it took place."

"Unless," she said slowly, "that was an alternative version he wrote at the time. It would have got mislaid, then somehow mixed in with a batch of this week's copy."

"It's a feasible explanation, I suppose." Miles studied the news item a fourth time. "The only one that makes any kind of sense. But it still leaves questions." He scratched his neck. "You mean to tell me, Poll, the mislaid report turned up again on precisely the same day as Mrs. Stanhope happened to call in here, asking for it to be killed? That's more than coincidence. It's uncanny."

With a shrug, Polly impelled her chair clear of the desk and spun it a couple of times. Coming to rest, she said tentatively, "Maybe it waasn't Joe who mislaid it."

"What do you mean?"

"Bob found it, you say, in his in-tray. Perhaps it had been there all the time."

"Then how did this paragraph—" Miles thumped the newspaper "—get itself published five weeks ago?"

Polly took a breath. "Joe wrote two versions—right? The shorter one was subbed and published. The longer one went to the foot of the pile for some reason, and got overlooked."

Bobbing out of the chair, she marched over to the coffee machine and inserted ten pence. As a plastic beaker appeared obediently, she turned to him again with a long-suffering air. "Is any of this relevant any more? It's obvious what must have occurred. Bob checked on Tuesday with Joe, discovered the duplication, and sent Mrs. Stanhope off to get herself together. That's why nothing appeared this week."

Miles said nothing.

Claiming her tenpennyworth of foam, Polly returned to her chair and took a few sips, watching him closely. "Since it bothers you so much," she said presently, "why not take a flyer and call Bob at home, after all? He can only chew off your left ear."

"I just don't like being made to look a monkey," Miles murmured. He lifted the phone.

The voice that answered informed him that it belonged to Bob Hartley's mother-in-law. "He's very poorly, so I'm helping out with the children while my daughter looks after him. I'm afraid he's simply not up to talking to anyone. The flu's at its height."

"You couldn't ask him just a couple of simple— No, forget it. There's no urgency. I can have a word with him when he gets back. Hope he's soon on the mend."

"So do we, rather," the mother-in-law said devoutly. "The children are being quite a handful. You'll have to excuse me, I can hear breakages—"

"Thanks for your help," Miles said to the abandoned line. For several minutes, while Polly typed and sipped, he sat staring through the window. Suddenly she ripped out the sheet she was working on, crushed it into a ball, and hurled it across the room.

"You're making me fidgety," she announced. "For heaven's sake, can't you either do some work or go home?"

Smiling abstractedly in her direction, he sauntered to the door. "I'll be out for the next hour, you'll be relieved to know."

"It's Friday," she called after him. "Don't bother to come back."

South Beechway was the lower-middle-class end of the town, a region of dispiriting avenues and crescents, asphalted pavement verges, elderly terraced housing with half-tiled front elevations, and ragged garden hedges stuffed with discarded takeaway containers. Lennard Gardens, a not untypical specimen, was a cul-de-sac with more than its share of motionless metal parked at the curbside.

Leaving his Fiat Uno near the mouth of the junction, Miles proceeded on foot to the splayed gate of No. 29, a mid-terrace habitation whose window-frames had at some remote date received an application of dark-blue paint which was now taking a piecemeal departure. Someone had made a start on paving the front plot. Half a dozen irregular slabs had been bedded in concrete: the remainder of the fifteen square yards was occupied by more slabs in a drunken pile, a mound of ballast sprouting a range of succulent weed, and a platoon of garden gnomes on sentry-go in a corner, awaiting postings.

Eyeing the shambles, Miles clanked along the splintered quarry-tile path to the front door and applied a thumb to the bell-push. No sound resulted. While he was searching for a knocker, the door opened suddenly. The clamor of a radio, tuned to heavy rock, became audible. It seemed to come from upstairs.

"Saw yer through the glass. Thought you was the meter man." The woman who had appeared spoke with a certain good-humored disregard, as if resigned to making the best of what she had got in his place. Emerging onto the step, she gave him a narrower look. "Not, are you?"

Miles explained his identity. "I'm looking for Mrs. Stanhope. She lives here, I believe. Is it possible to see her?"

Glancing past him at the street, she focused briefly upon a parked motorcycle before inspecting him again, appraisingly this time. "I'm Mrs. Stanhope," she said.

"It's Mrs. *Sylvia* Stanhope I want."

"That's me." Folding her arms, she leaned back against the rotting doorpost. "You did say the *Gleaner*?" A wary note had edged into her voice. "What's it about? We take the *Mercury*."

"Obviously there's some mistake. The Mrs. Stanhope I want to speak to—" He paused. "You've a relative, perhaps, living with you? Or did have?"

"I'm the Mrs. Stanhope," she said forthrightly, "at this address. There's just me, my old man, and his dad. Then there's Beattie, our Jack Russell, and the cats. We ain't got no other relations. No room for 'em. What was it you was meaning to ask?" A look of faint intelligence dawned. "Survey, is it? One of them polls?"

Miles hesitated. With a sense of acute embarrassment he said, "This is going to sound peculiar, but I wonder if you'd mind telling me something? Did you by any chance appear recently at the magistrates' court?"

Her features tightened. "They said as I wouldn't hear no more about it. Paid me fine, I did. We've the receipt to prove it. We never—"

"Hold on a minute." To his amazement she stopped obediently. Irked by the abrupt transition to an officer/recruit relationship, he tried to moderate his approach, to address her informally. "Sorry, Mrs. Stanhope, if I'm confusing you, but there's something odd here. Was it, um, an offense involving goods in a store?"

"I did forget to pay, if that's what you mean. Never did it on purpose, but they wouldn't take *my* word for it. Oh, dear me no. All the papers— Half a bit." Heaving herself clear of the doorpost, she inclined forward to examine him in a new way. "Seeing as you're from the *Gleaner*, why d'you want to hear about it? You printed something at the time."

"I know that, Mrs. Stanhope. But the point is, you're not the same— Would you mind if I came in and tried to explain?"

"I'd mind if you didn't." Almost with eagerness, she bundled him into the house. The narrow hall was uncarpeted and smelt of damp wallpaper. From upstairs, the hammering beat of the radio music sent shock-waves through the ceiling. Slamming the front door shut at the third attempt, the woman stood with her back to it while Miles, at the top of his voice, did his best to acquaint her with the situation. Before he had finished, she interrupted.

"You'd best step into the back room. I'll fetch me father-in-law—I want him to hear this. He's just upstairs," she added informatively. "Go straight through. Mind Pluto, he's apt to get under your feet and if you tread on him, he'll spit. You'll find Beattie in there. If she barks, take no notice. She's all noise. Dad! You there, Dad? Can you come down a minute? It's somebody from the paper. He wants to know—"

Beattie the Jack Russell launched a series of shrill, ear-piercing yaps at Miles's appearance, and maintained the onslaught, despite verbal blandishments and outstretched fingers, until its mistress appeared, pursued by a small, purple, semi-inflated man of indeterminate years, garbed in a dirty beige-woollen waistcoat, cords, and leather slippers.

"Pipe down, Beattie," she ordered. Backing reluctantly into its rag-strewn corner, the dog lay smoldering, showing the whites of its eyes. Upstairs, the music thundered on. "Take a seat, Dad," advised the substitute Mrs. Stanhope, clearing a winged chair of magazines. "I'd like you to listen to what this gentleman has to say. It's about the Case. My little dust-up with Jepson's—you remember? Just you lend an ear. You're never going to believe this."

Miles went through it again. Fatigue was starting to steal up on him. Pluto, or some other cat, had gained entrance to the room and was clawing stealthily at his trouser-ankles, now and then penetrating to the flesh. With difficulty, Miles refrained from retaliatory violence. When the story had been retold, Mrs. Stanhope and her father-in-law sat in mute communion with one another while Miles waited hopefully. As time passed, and niether of them seemed disposed to carry matters forward, he said promptingly, "You've some idea, have you, what it's all about?"

The mouth of Mrs. Stanhope smacked shut like a steel grille. Re-opening it, she said grimly, "I've more'n a suspicion *who* it's about. What say, Dad?"

The old man indulged in a loud, prolonged sniff. "Got all the makings."

Abandoning the niceties, Miles demanded, "The makings of what?"

Mrs. Stanhope began jabbing a thumb. She did it in the direction of the rear garden, portions of which were visible to Miles through a battered french window with small, grime-encrusted panes featuring a crack or two. From what he could see, the fifty square yards at the back were in even worse shape than the fifteen at the front. Grass, shrubs, bushes, and trees had become indistinguishable from each other, entangled in a single unbridled mass from fence to fence, throttling the few rambler roses that had made feeble attempts to crawl clear of the wreckage. The fences themselves looked in dire need of replacement. Altogther, the outlook was one that seemed to demand the attentions of a mechanical earth-shifter and site leveler, prior to total rehabilitation.

Mrs. Stanhope, however, betrayed no diffidence at calling a visitor's attention to the scene. Manifestly, her own mind was fixed upon the immediate topic. "Her ladyship," she intoned significantly, perpetuating her digital pulsations.

"A neighbor?" Miles speculated.

A short bark erupted from Mrs. Stanhope. "Not much neighborly about *her*," she observed. "Eh, Dad? Suffered our ups and downs with *that* party, wouldn't you say?"

A repeat of the sniff indicated assent. "Downs, mostly."

"Downs, mostly." His daughter-in-law came in like an echo. "Nothing physical, mark you. We've not been chucking things. Not that I'm saying it mightn't come to that."

Miles craned his neck. "That house there, facing this one? You've had problems with the occupant?"

"You could say that."

"So you feel she may have had a hand in this?"

Mrs. Stanhope shrugged. "Can't think of nobody else. For one thing, she about fits your description. For another thing, it's got her trademark about it—right, Dad? Wouldn't put anything past our Viv, I wouldn't."

"Do you know her surname?"

"Kemp. Miss Vivien Eleanor Kemp. Told us that, didn't she, Dad, when we first come? Quite proud of her full title, she is. Thinks she's royalty, I reckon."

"But what would she hope to gain?" asked Miles. "The whole exercise seems pointless. If Miss Kemp wanted to get at you, surely she'd start a false rumor or something, not try to squash a factual report?"

Cogitation rendered Mrs. Stanhope momentarily cataleptic. "Dare say she just enjoyed talkin' about it to someone. Chew it over, like. Weird, she is. You never know where you are with her."

"How long have you been acquainted?"

Mrs. Stanhope consulted her father-in-law, who looked sage but remained dumb. "Five years, Dad, since we moved in? Six? I know it was the year Meg died. How old would she be now? Jimmy was just fifty, so she'd have been—"

"And Miss Kemp," Miles intervened gently, "was here when you arrived?"

"Lived here all her life. A fixture, she is. Reckons she owns the district."

"Friction right from the start, was there?"

"She seemed all right at first. Quite matey. Kept popping round with tinned meat for the dog, stuff for Dad to take—suffers with his asthma, Dad does—and she even put a present through the door at Easter. A box of soap, very nice it was. That's Easter the first year, I'm talkin' about. Then, not long after that—"

"Beattie," grunted old Mr. Stanhope, nodding at the Jack Russell.

"Took this sudden dislike to Beattie, she did. Said she was always yapping and getting into her garden. Then it was the cats. Why didn't we keep them in of a night? Always yowling under her window, according to her ladyship. After that—"

"Fences."

"That's right. When was we going to fill in the gaps? I said to her, that one at the end is yours as much as it's ours, why don't *you* stop it up? That did it. Public enemy number one we was, from then on. We've not spoken since."

"How does she get on," queried Miles, "with the other residents around here?"

"Search me." Mrs. Stanhope spoke with indifference. "We're not ones to go around gossipin'. Personally, I've other things to do with me time."

"Might I ask you something else, Mrs. Stanhope?" Miles sought a suitable arrangement of words. "Are you—still on friendly terms with your husband?"

She stared. "I was when he left here this mornin'."

"You've not split up, then?"

"If we have, he's not mentioned it. Is it on account of the Case, you're askin'?"

"Not directly, no. How about your children?" Miles went on recklessly. "Any problems with them?"

"There might be, if we 'ad any. Never wanted kids, Cyril, did he, Dad?"

"And you haven't a dependent mother?"

"Me? My mum's been dead eleven years. That's why we're able to have 'im." She nodded toward old Mr. Stanhope, who contrived to look simultaneously complacent and anxious, as if half fearful of the turn the conversation might take.

Shaking off the cat, Miles stood up. "I'm sorry to have been a nuisance. Just one other thing. If I were to go round and have a word with Miss Kemp myself, is there anything you'd like me to tell her?"

A hoot came from Mrs. Stanhope. "Got a week or two to spare, have you, love? No, don't you bother. Far as we're concerned, she don't exist no more. Not worth the hassle. Tell her that, if you like. Best of luck."

The houses in Oak Grove, parallel with those in Lennard Gardens, were a notch or two up on the social ratchet. Most were semi-detached, with Georgian-style windows and integral garages whose vividly painted up-and-over doors were connected to the street by ribbons of white-speckled asphalt in various states of disrepair. The driveway belonging to The Pines was an exception. It had been resurfaced with immaculately laid pink-and-grey flagstones, and flanked with conifers. The house itself had recently been touched up with a combination of cream and green paint. The porch tiles were a brilliant red. Treading gingerly so as not to leave footprints, Miles rapped twice with a door-knocker fashioned in the shape of a rampant buffalo. The sound it produced was something of an anticlimax. Before he could launch a second strike, however, the door opened smoothly to reveal a figure in blouse and slacks, with a pair of binoculars on a strap hung about her neck. Her tiny smile was enigmatic.

"I guessed," she said, "you might be heading this way. Do come in, won't you?"

Miles entered the thickly carpeted hall. The wallpaper was floral, and there were multiple mirrors. A contemporary coatrack and a pair of cane chairs with bright cushions constituted the furniture. There was a faint scent of perfume, but whether it had been sprayed about or came from Miss Kemp herself, Miles couldn't determine. Coming to a halt on the decorative doormat, he turned to face her as she blocked out the street. "You remember me, then?"

"Of course I do."

"I wasn't sure if you might. Last time we met, you were Mrs. Stanhope."

She blinked up at him, but said nothing. Swallowing his annoyance, Miles added, "As you've probably guessed, I'm here for an explanation, Miss Kemp. Why did you pose as your neighbor opposite?"

"Please come through to the lounge." She led the way, as if conducting royalty to the banqueting hall. "You've the right to an explanation, of course," she proclaimed, indicating a chintz-covered armchair by the picture-window, "since you seem to be still rather in the dark. I assumed you'd have been enlightened by now, but evidently I was wrong. What did the Stanhope have to say?"

Occupying the armchair, Miles regarded her steadily. "How did you know I'd been talking to them?"

The tiny smile reappeared as she seated herself on the tiled window-sill to face him. "An obvious move, wasn't it, on your part? Besides—" she tapped the binoculars "—with these, I can see most of what goes on over there. I've a clear view from my bedroom window."

"You spend your time spying on them?"

"Not *all* of it," she said, taking no offense. "I have to admit, though, I do like to keep track of events. That's why I keep the glasses handy, as you see. The Stanhopes intrigue me."

"Obsess you, more likely." Miles spoke with the candor of total pique.

She replied in a mild key. "There are two sides, you know, to everything."

"I'm quite willing to hear yours. But I'd prefer it to be straightforward. Maybe you've forgotten, Miss Kemp, but I'm the guy who had a pretty fantastic yarn spun to him when—"

"I haven't forgotten." She tilted her head to inspect him kindly.

"But you may not fully realize what you did. You came within a whisker of making us commit an offense."

"How, may I ask?"

"I'm not sure, to be honest. All I know is, we very nearly published two reports of the same court case five weeks apart. How it came about I can't guess, but if the second report—"

"Without my intervention," she agreed, "the *Gleaner* might well have gone ahead and published a second time."

Miles shook his head in perplexity. "I don't get it."

"Because it's not been explained to you, that's why." She spoke with the restrained patience of a primary-school mistress. "I expect you're wondering, for instance, where that second report could have sprung from?"

"The thought had occurred to me."

"There it was, on the desk of that very charming Editor of yours, Mr. Hartley. He had it in front of him. All written out in Joe Wilkinson's rather distinctive handwriting. He could so easily have taken it at face value."

"What stopped him?"

"I did, of course. That's what I came in for."

"But how could you have known he had it?"

"Because I had it sent in. I wrote it."

Miles sat forward, staring at her incredulously. "You did *what?*"

Miss Kemp remained placid. Turning her head a little, she scanned the garden, a small miracle of laundered turf and freshleafed foliage, marred only by the decrepit dividing fence at the far end. When she turned back, she was expressionless. Miles had the feeling that she had performed the same minor action many times already that morning, as well as on previous occasions too numerous and too unrewarding to recall.

"It's quite simple. I'm a criminologist, you see. Oh, nothing professional. I just like to take an amateur interest. For some while now, I've made a practice of attending the morning sessions at the magistrates' court, observing the proceedings. As a result, I've got to know the ropes."

"Ropes?"

"For example, I've made a study of the Press box. Your Joe Wilkinson, in particular. He has a method of his own. He invariably writes up the cases as he goes along. At the end of each morning he has a finished pile of copy—I believe that's the term?—which he then delivers personally to your office before going off to lunch."

"You're very observant."

"It's something I pride myself on," said Miss Kemp, accepting the compliment and disregarding the irony. "I'm also fairly deft. It wasn't too difficult for me to purloin a sample of Mr. Wilkinson's copy one morning—he often leaves it beside his notepad in the Press box while he goes out for his coffee break. All I had to do then was take it away for half an hour so that I could run off a photocopy."

"To enable you to study his handwriting?"

"At my leisure. Which I did. I've no special talent as a forger, but I had heaps of time. In the end, I could turn out quite a passable imitation of his style. Luckily he writes very clearly."

"You faked that report, then?" Miles thrust fingers through his hair. "It still doesn't explain how it got onto Bob Hartley's desk, inside a pile of other stories."

"If I could filch copy from the Press box," Miss Kemp explained reasonably, "I could put some back, couldn't I? The court supervision is absurdly lax. I had no trouble returning the piece I took, and still less in planting the phony item. I simply folded it the way Mr. Wilkinson does, then slipped it into the middle of his stack as I strolled past to the public benches. Nothing to it."

"It doesn't sound like nothing. It sounds like a lot of trouble to go to for a nil result. If you were going to have the piece kept out anyway."

"Aha!" Miss Kemp wagged an arch finger at him. "But I might not have. At that stage, I hadn't decided."

Coming away from the window, she crossed the room to a pinewood dresser on which stood a heavy orange-and-purple ceramic vase stuffed with dried flowers. Removing the strap from her neck, she deposited the binoculars carefully alongside the vase and gave them an almost affectionate tap. "You might say," she added, turning dramatically, "I was keeping my editorial options open."

Miles looked back at her stonily. "Why?"

Her face closed up. "I think that's my business, don't you?"

"Mine too, I suggest. You've wasted a good deal of my time, don't forget, with your slightly erratic behavior. You owe me more than half an explanation."

"Why can't we just forget it? No harm's been done."

Turning back to the dresser, she proceeded to dust its surface with a brown-paper napkin she extracted from a drawer. Collecting a few fallen specks of dried flower, she disposed of them inside a pocket of her slacks, administered a final polish to the woodwork, balled the napkin, and stood clutching it while she eyed the display of blue-and-white china on the shelves at the back. Miles felt that she itched to be giving it all a clean and shine. Presently she peeped across a shoulder.

"I'm afraid I don't know your name."

"Miles Repton."

"May we leave it at that, Mr. Repton? There seems no point, does there, in your squandering still more of your time? The matter's a trivial one as far as you're concerned. Why pursue it?"

"Because I'm a reporter, Miss Kemp, and you involved me, and I've rather a dislike of feeling exploited."

The air between them smoked for a few seconds. Presently she made a part-dismissive, part-resigned movement of her left hand, and supported herself on the dresser with her right elbow.

"To someone like yourself, I suppose it must all seem a little odd. When you've had more experience, you'll begin to appreciate the trials that can be heaped on people, in certain circumstances. The subtle degrees of torture—"

A gulp seemed to block her throat. Her eyes closed briefly. When they reopened, they were aimed at the window. Curious, Miles sat motionless, watching her.

"Have you ever," she resumed on an artificially bright note, "sat in a train compartment opposite someone gorging himself on chips out of newspaper, resting his feet on the seat next to you, and playing pop music loudly on a cassette when what you're aching to do, yourself, is sit quietly and look out at the scenery?"

Miles considered. "I can't say that I have."

"But you've got imagination. Suppose you did find yourself in such a position. What would you do?"

"If it bothered me, I'd go and find another compartment."

"There isn't one. The train's packed. What then?"

"I'd have to put up with it."

"But how would you feel, inwardly? What kind of resentment would be building up inside you?"

"I'm not blind, Miss Kemp, to the analogy you're trying to draw," Miles said after a pause. "But you know, lots of people have nighbors they find objectionable. They just have to grin and bear it."

"Why should they?"

"Or move."

"It's not always convenient or possible to move. And why should one be forced to? Especially when one has been living quite happily in a place for thirty years or more. Why can't it be the intruders who should have to leave?"

"If it were that easy."

"I'm certainly not saying it's *easy*. What I'm saying is, there's usually an answer if you look for it hard enough."

"Like playing silly games with the local Press?"

Hoisting himself out of the chintz upholstery, Miles advanced to confront Miss Kemp at close quarters. She shrank a little, but held firm. "Exactly how," he demanded, allowing his wrath to gain the upper hand, "did that performance of yours last Tuesday do anything to achieve what you had in mind? From your point of view, you'd have done better to stick to your original plan—left us to publish the faked report and see what happened. That way, you'd at least have been doing Mrs. Stanhope some harm, besides us."

Miss Kemp bowed her head. She remained silent.

He edged closer. "Shall I tell you what I think? I think you copped out. Having implemented this crackpot scheme which you hoped would embarrass the Stanhopes—though you were wildly optimistic, I fancy—you then panicked. You realized it might be traced back to you. So what course was left? Just one. You had to retrieve that bogus piece of copy before it got into print."

Still she said nothing. Her fingertips explored the dresser surface, as if for residual deposits.

"To do that, you had to see the Editor personally, explain the—" Miles's voice trailed away. He frowned. "You could have just come in and asked to speak to him. Why go through that pantomime with me? It doesn't make sense."

Miss Kemp lifted her face. A blush had risen to her cheeks, and a slight breathlessness was apparent when she spoke.

"It would have been such a letdown."

"I don't follow."

"It must be hard for someone else to grasp. I wonder if I can explain? I'd nerved myself, you see, to do this—over a long period. The pressure had been building up, you can't imagine. I felt there had to be some kind of relief. So I did it. But then—you're right, I did have second thoughts: I lost courage. I decided to backtrack."

She took a quick, nervous breath. "Even so, the idea of it just tailing off, petering out—" Enormous eyes gazed up at him. "I had to salvage something. Can you understand? It was a kind of therapy. I *enjoyed* my little charade. Somehow it made it all worthwhile."

"No, Miss Kemp. Sorry. I can't understand."

"Your Mr. Hartley did. He listened, and gave me a cup of tea, and was so kind. Particularly as I believe he wasn't feeling too grand himself at the time." Her gaze became more searching. "Didn't he explain all this to you afterwards?"

"He went sick. He's been off since Tuesday."

"I *see*. Poor man. I do hope it's nothing serious." Miss kemp reflected. "This accounts, then, for your coming round here this morning. You wanted to find out—I am sorry, Mr. Repton."

In a series of deliberate movements, Miles took a notepad from his hip pocket and a ballpen from his breast pocket, flipped the sheets, and began to scrawl. Miss Kemp watched with compressed brows.

"What are you doing?"

"I'm jotting it all down," he explained, "before I forget the exact wording you've used. As a journalist, I like my stories to be accurate."

Her body stiffened. "You're not intending to write a story?"

"You bet I am." Miles scribbled industriously. "How could I pass it up? *Bizarre behaviour by respected resident*. If this doesn't sell copies, I'm in the wrong business."

"I can't see that it's necessary." Her voice sounded calm, but tension lurked in the syllables.

"Necessary?" He glanced up. "Your histrionics in our front office were a trifle *un*necessary, wouldn't you agree?"

"Perhaps so." Miss Kemp fell victim to a touch of breathlessness. "I feel, Mr. Repton, I do owe you an apology for that. The entire thing was uncalled for. Will you please accept my most sincere and humble regrets?"

"Bit late for that, I'm afraid. You should have thought about it sooner."

Miles wrote on remorselessly. Another thirty seconds of crucifixion, he estimated, would do Miss Kemp no particular damage, and might help to knock some sense into her. In addition, it was therapeutic for himself. He recorded "The quick brown fox jumps over the lazy dog" before turning to the next sheet and making a start upon "Now is the time for all good men."

On the wall facing the dresser hung a gilt-framed mirror. In it, from the corner of an eye, he could see himself reflected, since he had half turned away as though to concentrate better upon his task. The mirror also showed him Miss Kemp, huge of pupil and openmouthed, stationed between himself and the pinewood dresser. He noticed that she was clutching the orange-and-purple vase.

She's about to dust beneath it, he marveled. In distress, take refuge in routine. Now she was raising it, as if to inspect the underside of the base. Her arms were stretched above her head. Unless she was careful, the vase would slip.

The massive ornament seemed to be hovering directly over him. His brain instructed him to pivot. Before his limbs could respond, he had time to see via the mirror that the vase was commencing a fierce, vertical descent, like a helicopter out of control.

Janwillem van de Wetering
Trumpetbird in the Cop Car

The patrol car was sluggish again that night long ago, in the era when police mechanics still repaired rather than replaced, and the Volkswagen shook and rattled every time the clutch was let out. At first the Inspector pulled faces. But after a while he responded by cursing, and when the shaking got worse he wanted me to swear, too. I did, every time. I was a constable then and lower ranks follow when officers guide the way.

The Inspector was a rat-faced gnome, but the two silver stars on his jacket shoulders changed him into a gentleman, never mind his looks—or his behavior, for that matter. My colleagues didn't care to serve under him, for the Inspector liked to look for trouble, but that particular night he seemed friendly enough. His foul language sounded almost tender as I obediently mumbled my repeats from the observer's seat as the car shook along through Amsterdam's empty alleys.

It was late at night with nothing much going on. The radio summoned another car to take care of a bar fight and we headed for the address, too, but it was all over when we finally got there. Broken glass on the floor, and subdued clients staring at the glass while our colleagues, lectured the bums on good manners. We saluted both parties and were back on our way.

We found a person of pleasure soliciting close to the Queen's very own Palace. A clear crime. Prostitutes are supposed to ply their trade in the Red Quarter, not where the Queen herself can snoop at them from her very own bathroom. We arrested Suspect, who turned out to be male, dressed in a dress, silk stockings, and high heels—most confusing. How to fill in the form? He/she explained it all—how he/she got that way and whatnot. The Inspector wandered off toward the canteen while I listened and nodded. "Right, dear." I had the form filled in after a fashion and he/she could be on his/her way again, but not before all the story was told. So I listened and sympathized. Why not?

By the time I got to the canteen, the coffee machine had broken down and the Inspector grabbed his hat. I made him wait outside until I was done with my soda, but when I folded myself back into the car I understood I'd better do something helpful.

"Motorcycle!" I shouted and pointed out the speeding machine. "Over there, sir—just passed a red light! Registration V for Victory, R for Roger. The number is unclear. Brand, Honda. Color, green. There he goes, sir, into the Palace Alley!"

"Yes, constable," the Inspector said and made the car turn away. "Not for us. This car's a bit slow."

I knew my duty and grabbed the microphone. Within ten seconds the message came back, directed at all cars. "Catch the green Honda. Victory. Roger."

"Waste of effort," the Inspector snarled. "No one listening but us. The colleagues are out of their cars, crowding the coffee machines in their respective stations. Quiet night, isn't that right, constable, old chap? The civilians have switched off their tubes and are ready for bed. Anything good on tonight?"

I said I didn't know, I didn't own a TV.

"So what do you do at night? You're not even married, isn't that right?"

I told him about my cat, leaving the bookcase and the record player out. The Inspector is rather down on culture.

He wasn't listening, holding up a small hand. "Hear *that*?"

I heard. A loud two-toned signal, but not the regular wail employed by us cop cars. "A siren, sir."

"Right! A bleeping siren. Where, constable, where?"

I pointed. "The silver Buick, sir, over there. There he goes again."

The siren called nastily in the almost empty square. The Buick faced a green light but was blocked by a compact suffering from starting troubles.

"*Right!*" The Inspector made our car jump. "That bleeper is done for! Sirens are illegal in all nonofficial cars!"

The Buick reversed, circumvented that stalled compact, and moved off at speed. A big truck, popped up from nowhere, got in our way. The Inspector made the VW climb the sidewalk and a kissing couple had to jump out of our way. I didn't foresee a successful pursuit and suggested informing the radio room. "This lemon can't catch a supercar, sir."

My superior knew a variety of four-letter words. I pushed the unused mircophone back and steadied myself against the car roof. A lot of trouble, to be totally unrewarded. A misdemeanor, worth twenty guilders maybe—what was it to us if the Buick bully hid a siren in his automated chariot? Did we have to turn ourselves into heroes, run risks, and frighten the innocent populace to catch him? I saw us headed straight for an old man crossing the street. When I opened my eyes again and looked round, the pedestrian had embraced a lamppost. I cursed the car's enthusiasm, for the clutch suddenly worked again and the speedometer was veering far to the right. If there had been a constable at the wheel, I would have pulled out the key.

I reached for the button controlling the car's top lights and siren. The Inspector knocked my hand away. "Leave that—the bastard isn't aware he's being followed yet."

"Sir," I whispered.

The Volkswagen produced a feeble grumble and actually managed to pass the Buick. I extended an arm through the window and moved it up and down in a stately and commanding fashion. The Buick put on her brakes and slowed to a halt. The Inspector jumped out and ran back to

face the vast driver who had gotten out, too, his fluffed and hairsprayed
mane shining in the lamplight. Under his mangy lion's head I detected a
three-piece tailormade suit and the latest-fashion turtleneck sweater.

Suspect was known to me. I marched back, too, and noted that I out-
sized him, which was good. Suspect was upset, just like the Inspector,
but my presence seemed to calm both parties somewhat. I folded my
hands behind me and arragned my facial expression, aiming for a suitable combination of curiosity and friendliness.

"So what the hell?" Suspect hissed. "So what the hell, hey?"

"Papers," the Inspector yapped.

I checked Suspect's papers. They were quite in order. The Suspect
was about to get back into his car when the Inspector growled, "Just a
moment. You got a siren in your vehicle. Open up the hood."

"Never," Suspect said. "I ain't got nothing and I don't show nothing.
I'm taking my girl friend home and you're hassling me. Let's have your
name and rank so I can complain to your chief." He checked the stars on
the Inspector's shoulders. "On your way, constable, get back in your
wreck."

The Inspector hopped. His short arms waved and his hands had
become little fists. "Mouthy, eh? You're under arrest! Get in your sleazy
rustbucket and follow us to the station. If you try to get away, every cop
car in town will be after you and I'll have you for escape. Constable,
make a note of that car's registration."

I handled notebook and ballpoint, put them away again, and saluted.

"So what do you have on me?" the Suspect asked, spittle dribbling
down his chin.

"That siren. We'll have a mechanic tear it out and we'll confiscate it."

The Buick followed quietly. It wasn't far. The Inspector grinned and
drummed his fingers tirumphantly on the wheel.

"Suspect is known to you?" I asked.

"Known now."

"'Blond Freddie," I said. "A pimp by trade. He used to keep a few
better-looking girls behind windows, but he's come up in the world,
runs a smart, cheap nightclub now. The Pink Balloon, in the Mad Nun's
Alley."

The Inspector laughed and nodded at the microphone. "Better and
better. Let's hear what's in his file so we can weight the charge a bit."

There was nothing down on Suspect right now, but the radio room
said Freddie had recently been in jail. Three months for pushing a client
around. Severe physical damage. Another three months suspended.

"Nice," the Inspector said. "Very nice indeed. I'll shake him loose in
a minute. If he pulls back for a swing, we'll soften his skull."

We had arrived, which saved me an answer.

I unfolded out of the car and banged on the sliding door next to the
station. We're next door to the Police Garage, which can be handy at
times. The doors veered open a bit and a bearded head stared.

"Open up, colleague, we've got a job for you."

"At this time of night?" the police mechanic complained.

I kicked the door. It finally slid away.

The Volkswagen burbled inside and the Buick flowed after it.

Blond Freddie got out and made an effort to look fierce.

The mechanic released the hood of the Buick and pushed it up.

"Right there," the Inspector shuted, "behind the radiator. Remove that stupid gadget."

The mechanic found the right wrench and released a nut. He wasn't in a hurry and I got a bit bored. I took a look at the Buick and saw the woman inside. She smiled a greeting, but I only saw her mouth—the rest of her face hid behind sunglesses, big ones. I liked her mouth and her thick brown hair, but I mostly noticed her blouse. The tight garment barely contained a majestic cleavage, pearly white in the neon light of the garage lamps. The lady wanted to get out and I opened the Buick's passenger door, putting on my best smile.

The mechanic paused before attacking the next nut and whistled. He seemed to be impressed by the woman's legs, which were long and tightly shaped. I was a constable first class, with one more stripe on each sleeve, so I stared him down and he got back to work. He knocked the little black box containing the siren free with the tapping wrench and handed it to the Inspector.

"Mine," Freddie pleaded. "Cost me money."

"City property now," the Inspector barked. "All ours, until we auction it off. Come along, it's time to fill in your ticket. There's the office! Forward, *march!*"

The woman looked at me. "Sir?"

She'd obviously dealt with the police before. Politeness pays off. We react well to respect.

I straightened up. "Miss?"

"Could you direct me to the restroom?"

The mechanic jumped. "Over there, Miss, behind the motorcycles. Let me show you the way."

She kept looking at me, so I gently pushed the mechanic aside.

She shivered when she passed the motorcycles. Our motor cops are tough. When they catch a punk, they cut off Suspect's hair, dip it in red paint, and attach the bloody hair to a piece of linen. The scalp gets hooked to the radio antennae on their bikes.

"It isn't real blood," I said.

She pointed at a kid's wrecked cart, crushed a few days ago by a truck in the city. The wreck was splattered with reddish stains. "That's isn't real, either," I said. I often lie so that things may look better.

I showed her the restroom door but she didn't go in. "Can I speak to you, sir?" I waited. The others couldn't see us, the corridor has a bend. "Can I trust you?"

I nodded. I'm the public's trusted servant.

She took off her sunglasses. One eye was swollen badly. The discolored bruise petered out in a deep scratch.

"Feddie?" I asked.

An impressive tear ran slowly down her face.

"I see." I kept my voice flat. I'd only had a few years on the force then, but they were bad enough and I hardened a bit—always stay calm, it's less fatiguing and makes it easier for everyone around.

"He's a pimp," she said. "He lives off my sin. That's illegal, right?" I agreed.

She was thinking. She smiled at me again, without replacing the glassess. "It's a crime," she said softly, "and you can do something if there's a complaint."

She was right, or course, and she had listened to a lawyer—or to one of us. Policeman are clients of the Red Quarter, too.

"Sure," I said. "Will you give us a complaint?"

They usually don't or retract the charge later.

"Yes," she said firmly.

"Will you throw in physical abuse?" That'a a nice charge, it makes the judge look up.

"Yes," she said again. "Poor Freddie"ll be all yours."

Her good eye looked at me hard. Maybe she sensed my hesitation. I would do all the paperwork and then she'd back out.

"Are you sure now?" I asked.

She turned and unbuttoned her blouse. I saw her back and the long wounds where the skin had broken, swollen up at the edges. "His belt," she said. "Last night. Because I asked for some money. I bring in enough and he keeps it all. He doesn't feed me well."

"Any proof?" I asked. It would be a customer's belt.

"Fred's belt," she said. "The one he's wearing now."

She buttoned her blouse again. She had no need to go to the restroom. When she started to walk past me, I put out a restraining hand. "Freddie isn't nice. We'll lock him up and he'll get out again. He'll remember the complaint. Some ladies finish up floating in a canal."

"I know. I won't be here. My passport is Belgian. I'll be going home."

"I'll take the case," I said.

I think Freddie knew what had happened between us. When the lady and I walked into the office, he grabbed hold of her. "Couldn't you hold your trap, silly sod?"

He had pulled back his arm, but I caught it before his fist connected. My other hand was flat and hit his head with a whap. The Inspector kicked his shins and the mechanic banged about with his wrench. Even so, Freedie didn't go down straightaway and we had to apply force before he kissed the floor and we could snap on the irons.

"All done, sir," I panted.

The Inspector sneered back at me with joy.

"And more charges, sir. Pimping and abuse."

The lady repeated herself, without looking at Fred. Fred protested a bit but the lifted wrench shut him up.

"Confiscate the belt," the Inspector said. "Don't handle it too much. Put it in a box so the laboratory can test the blood. Take the victim along. I'll throw Suspect into our worst cell and it'll be home for me after that." He grinned at me. "You're an intellectual—you phrase the report."

Freddie was marched off, prodded by the Inspector's stick. Suspect slouched and looked much worse for wear. I drove the lady to Head-quarters, in a car supplied by the mechanic. The lab people took their time with the belt while they stared at my catch. They dallied taking her blood. I took her home afterward. She lived in a dingy room at the rear of the nigtclub. She didn't want to stay. I waited for her to pack her bag and took her to a boarding house tucked away in a suburb. She moved close to me in the car and put her hand on my knee.

"Will you be looking me up?"

"Maybe," I said.

"When?"

I said I didn't know yet.

She kissed my cheek and I dented the car's fender on the way back, scratching a lamppost. Policemen should keep themselves apart from the public, but I'd been living alone for over two years, not counting the cat. The cat naps in my arms sometimes but I've been restless, anyway.

I retruned the car to the police garage. The mechanic was still on duty. He seemed amused. "You want to hear something?"

"Let's have it," I said.

The Buick's siren was attached to a wire and he unwound it into the street. When he pressed the switch, the siren howled softly. He turned up the volume and the screeching increased, blotting out the quiet of night, then sank back again and cut off with a low gurgle. the mechanic raised a hand. "Listen, colleague."

I heard the siren again, softer and from a distance.

The mechanic pointed at the trees across the road. "You know what's behind there?"

"The zoo," I said.

"There's something horrible out there," the mechanic said, "and I never knew it."

"Keep sounding it," I said, "I'll find out what answers."

Policemen have the right of way, and the zoo's watchman let me through the gate. The mechanic made Freddie's siren howl and I tracked the response. The watchman, a sharp-faced young man, came along.

We found the bird together. The nameplate on the cage lit up when I shone my flashlight. *Psophia Viridis*.

"Trumpetbird," the watchman said. "South American origin, *muy macho*." He told me he studied biology and worked nights at the zoo to help pay for his tuition. I looked at the specimen in the cage, determining the bird to be scraggly and possessed by a furious temper. He faced me bravely, the chicken-sized demon, before attacking the fence and scratching the earth, all hepped up to bury his beak in my throat.

I nudged the watchman. "What's up with him?"

"It's the siren that gets to him," he explained. "Male competition? Would you be trespassing on his turf?"

It was true that the bird calmed down when the mechanic got tired of playing with Freddie's gadget. He seemed ready to go back to sleep.

The watchman invited me into his shed. Daylight broke and I stayed for coffee, sharing my adventure and inviting the student's comments. He kept grinning at me.

"Amusing?" I asked. "A little weird maybe? You like battered woman?"

"Don't you see?" he asked.

"See what?"

"That, as usual, reality is not what we think it is? You're a cop—you think you serve, do a good job, that you care for others, right?"

"I don't?" I asked.

"Bah." The student shrugged. "You and your ratty Inspector. The Police. You lord it over us. The city is yours. You sound off your sirens as proof of your power. Now the other guy, ferocious Fred, contests your power. He sounds his siren and has the audacity to put his paws on a lovely lady. All our ladies are yours."

"Now now," I said.

He was still ginning. "Sex and uniforms. Look at yourself. Six feet four of official bully. Shiny buttons. A gun ready to draw."

I let that go. Civilians sometimes like to poke fun at us. We usually get them later.

"So?" I asked, encouraging him to have his full say.

"Biologists observe nature," the watchman said "We watch and try to see the truth."

"*We* are the truth," I said. "We uphold it. We represent the state."

"Yes, sir," he said. "You keep proving your strength. You beat the other fellow down, clink him in irons, drag him to a drafty cell, and then you take his woman, your rightful prey."

"Didn't she offer herself?"

He became thoughtful. "the female always manipulates the situation. She wants a strong mate, the fellow who is on top. She has to keep the species going."

I left. He walked me to the gate and suggested I should enjoy myself.

"Well?" the Inspector asked the next day. "Did you have a good time? Didn't I throw you nice spoils? Remember, Constable, the next one will be mine."

Jean Darling
A Little Late Theater

The most unpleasant aspect of running a boarding house for thirty young Broadway hopefuls was having to give a girl notice to vacate when her rent was four weeks in arrears. Several times Sadie Gold had relaxed the rule and allowed a particularly needy aspirant to stay longer, but without exception it had always ended with bad feelings on both sides. Now she was going to have to ask Lavenda Charles to leave. The young actress's rent was more than three weeks past due, and as far as Sadie knew she hadn't tried to find work since the musical, *Madcaps*, had closed after the opening night of its Boston tryout—at least she hadn't put her name down for any of the auditions posted on the callboard by the dining room.

It was man trouble, of course, and the worst kind: a petty crook and gambler who wasn't above being staked by his current girl friends. His name was Salvatore McCabe, and Lavenda wasn't the first Brownstone girl to fall for his compact Italian looks and the honeyed tongue he'd inherited from his Irish father.

Although Sadie was well aware that a gratuitous warning would fall on deaf ears, she had tried to tell Lavenda that Sal McCabe wasn't the ideal escort for a dancer on the first rung of the ladder. She even offered to give her the phone number of a young woman who had featured in some unsavory tabloid exposure from her involvement with McCabe in 1948, two years before. Lavenda, horrified by the very thought of checking up on her boy friend, had fled Sadie's office with her hands over her ears.

A few days later, Sadie looked up to see Lavenda standing in her doorway. The dancer's "Are you busy, Mrs. Gold?"—formal and dripping with ice—told Sadie she was still in the girl's bad books.

"Lavenda, wipe that scowl off your face and take a pew. Would you like a cup of coffee?" She gestured to the hot Silex on the table near the window. Lavenda shook her head, approached the desk, and slapped a twenty-dollar bill down on the open ledger on which Sadie was working.

"I got a job at the Golden Theater ushering for the Jonathan Furie show. It's only for six weeks but the money will keep me going and I can pay you off. She spoke harshly, but it was herself she was mad at, not Sadie. For a moment the two women looked at each other, then Lavenda turned and left the office.

Lavenda was aware that the other girls at The Brownstone thought she was grieving over the loss of her first solo dance in a Broadway-bound musical. It was true it could have been the break she was striving for, but she wasn't foolish enough to blame herself for the closing of the show. The whole cast had been expecting it for days. No, it hadn't been the show folding that had broken her heart. It was what had happened afterward that did that little job.

If she'd had the brains she was born with, she wouldn't have dreamed of catching the milk train for New York after the show closed, but all she could think of was getting away from Boston and back into the comfort of Sal's arms. She should have known a stud like Sal wouldn't be pining alone in his West Seventy-third Street walkup—so why was she surprised to hear a sultry voice telling him to get rid of whoever was there and come back to bed when he opened the door early that morning?

Nine weeks passed without a word from Sal, then Lavenda ran into him one afternoon when she stopped at the Astor Drug to buy a newspaper. "Hi, stranger," he said, taking her arm and leading her to the coffee counter. "I bet you could use a cup of coffee. I know I could."

Astonished at his assumption that nothing had changed between them, Lavenda allowed herself to be steered through the stream of customers. "Been out of town?" he asked two minutes later, stirring sugar into a steaming cup of black coffee. "I called you several times and left messages, but you didn't call back, so I hoped that meant you were away. —I've missed you, you know."

"If you say so."

"You're not still mad with me," he said , reaching for her hand. Pulling it away from him she called him every name she could think of. When at last she finished, he told her he knew now that she was the only girl in the world for him and begged for forgiveness.

And then they were in his apartment, sharing a pizza by candlelight while Lavenda told him of her imminent ejection from The Brownstone for nonpayment of rent. It was just the opening he was hoping for.

"Gee, baby, I wish I could help, but right now I'm in the same boat." He leaned over and kissed her. Best not to move too fast, he thought.

"I wasn't asking for anything," she stammered. "It just helps to talk to someone, you know?"

"Well—it's just a suggestion, Lavenda, probably nothing that would interest you, but I know they're looking for usherettes at the Golden Theater."

Spending two long hot afternoons waiting for Lavenda to show up at the Astor Drugstore, their old hangout, paid off. Lavenda Charles was still a trusting little girl from Butler, Pa.

For the first few performances, Lavenda hated wearing the uniform of white blouse and black skirt and showing ticket-holders to their seats. She was ashamed that the girls at The Brownstone knew what she was doing, even though most of them had some kind of part-time job to keep the wolf at bay until their all-important break. But after a while the privilege of watching Jonathan Furie perform in this one-man show took over and Lavenda began to enjoy herself. She found herself holding forth at meals in The Brownstone with her stories about Jonathan Furie.

The tales were first hand, gathered at the little "salons" Furie held between shows on matinee days. Though he was homosexual, there was nothing in the world the tall thin old man liked better than the company of young girls, especially when they were starryeyed and stagestruck like Lavenda Charles. And the girls themselves were charmed by his Old World gallantry.

But beneath his benign smile and venerable charm there dwelt a shrewd businessman. Jonathan Furie would not set foot on a stage until his sixty percent of the box-office receipts were delivered to his dressing room before each performance. The money was then put in a drawer and locked away in the heavy wardrobe trunk that had served as his bank ever since the Thirties' bank closure had wiped him out. It was one of the legends of Broadway, and as far as anyone knew no one had ever succeeded in broaching the most famous strongbox in the theater world.

Neatly dressed and flashing his thousand-watt smile, Sal McCabe picked Lavenda up after the show each evening. Sundays he took her to the movies. This continued for the first four weeks. On the Monday of the fifth week he was nowhere to be found when the show broke at ten-fifteen.

Lavenda waited outside for twenty minutes, then she went back along the alley to ask the stage doorman if she'd had any calls. When the old man shook his head, she dialed Sal's number on the pay phone by the callboard. There was no answer.

It was almost twelve when she finally decided he had stood her up. Still not wanting to believe it, she hurried back to The Brownstone, sure there would be a message waiting. Her box was empty.

The next morning she rang him half a dozen times, but there was no answer—and no call from him, although she didn't leave the house until showtime for fear of missing him.

By Wednesday night she was half out of her mind with worry—which was exactly the state Sal wanted her to be in when he appeared out of the shadows in the alley after the play, unshaven and disheveled. "Lavenda," he whispered and drew back into the gloom.

"Sal! Where have you been?" She hurled herself into his arms. "I've been going crazy—"

"Shhh, baby, baby, I couldn't, it wasn't safe."

"Oh, darling, what's happened? You look awful—" Lavenda tried to pull him into the light.

Glancing furtively right and left, he whispered, "I can't stay. They're after me."

"Who?"

He shook his head.

She studied him. "Is there someplace we can go? I'll get a cab."

In a booth in a small bar some blocks south, Sal told Lavenda that two weeks before, he sat in on one of Knuckles Malone's poker games at the Park Central Hotel. He had been on a high and won over eleven grand, then his luck had turned and he'd lost it all. "But you can't stop when you hit a losing streak, you've gotta keep playing until your luck changes. —Only mine didn't. I just kept on racking up IOUs. Finally Knuckles called a halt." Sal slumped, his head in his hands.

"How much do you owe?" Lavenda pressed him.

"Oh, baby, can you understand I never wanted to have to tell you? I've tried every way I know to get the money. I begged a few days' grace from Knuckles, but now I've run out of time." He paused to let the full meaning sink in. "I just had to see you once again—"

Lavenda clutched his arm. "We'll think of some way to pay, we have to."

"Oh, Lavenda—wake up, baby. Where could we get our hands on eleven thousand dollars?" The girl looked at him long and hard. So hard, in fact, that for a moment Sal wondered if he might have over-played his hand.

"We can't just let him kill you," she said—so fervently he was sure that the next words out of her mouth would be about Jonathan Furie's trunk full of money. He was wrong. It would definitely be to his advantage if the idea to rob the old actor came from her, but the one thing he hadn't reckoned on was the innate honesty of the girl.

In the end he had to spell it out for her. "All you have to do is make sure the latch is off the window in Furie's dressing room when the doorman locks up the theater on Saturday night. That's not so hard, is it?"

"It's not hard, Sal, but I don't want to steal from that wonderful old man."

"But, Lavenda, it wouldn't be stealing. Haven't you been listening? There's a big game on Saturday night. All I want to do is borrow a stake. If I can win enough to pay off Knuckles, and I know I can, we can get married. Oh, baby, can't you see? It's the only way."

"What did you say?"

"I asked you to marry me. But don't answer now." He put his fingers on her lips. "I have no right to ask."

"Oh, darling, of course I'll marry you. But I just can't steal—"

"Lavenda, it *wouldn't* be stealing, it would be borrowing. That's why I want you to do it Saturday night—I'd have the money back in Furie's trunk before the theater opens on Monday."

She held his eyes for a moment. "How can you open the trunk? Mr. Furie keeps it locked," she said. The resignation in her voice told Sal he had won.

He handed her a small box containing what looked to be putty. "You get the key, press it into this clay, make sure you wipe it clean, then put it back where you found it. I'll do the rest. It's not too much to ask a—wife to do, is it?" He kissed the tip of her nose. "You'll do it for me, won't you, baby?"

It was past four when Lavenda undressed for bed. The words of two drunks arguing down in the street were loud through the open window. Her roommate Nell Clements, her ears plugged and her eyes masked, was dead to the world.

Lavenda climbed into bed, knowing she wouldn't sleep. If only she had someone to talk to, someone to advise her. She could wake up Nell, of course, or go down and knock on Sadie's door. She could phone her parents. ("Hi Mom, I just called to let you know I'm going to rob the wonderful old actor whose show I usher for at the Golden Theater. My boy friend needs eleven thousand dollars to pay a gambling debt so he won't be killed and we can get married.") God, how stupid it sounded laid out like that, she thought, wondering how she could even think of violating the trust Jonathan Furie had placed in her.

For he did trust her. Only the week before, when his dresser, Nathan, was home with a summer cold, he had called her into his dressing room and asked her to do a favor for him. "My dear," he'd said, handing her a small key, "I have to run out for a few minutes. When the Mehron Make-Up lady comes, find out how much I owe. Ask her to wait in the hall, then close the door and take the money out of the trunk." She had asked him why he simply didn't leave some money on the make-up shelf and he had tousled her hair and said it was easier this way, and besides the woman might not even show up. Then, elegant in a white-linen suit, Panama hat, doeskin gloves, and cane, he'd left.

After over an hour of tossing and turning, Lavenda put on a leotard and went down to a practice room in the basement of The Brownstone, hoping a strenuous routine on the bar would dull her consciousness enough so she could get a few hours sleep.

On Friday night, Lavenda had no problem slipping into Jonathan Furie's dressing room while Nathan was in the wings waiting to help him with a quick change. She had no problem finding the key. The contents of the actor's pockets, including the key, always lay on the make-up shelf.

At eleven o'clock on the dot, she slid into the booth beside Sal McCabe and placed the box on the table in front of him. He dropped it into his pocket and bent to kiss her. She turned away.

"What's the matter, baby, did something go wrong?" She shook her head. "Well, then, we're almost out of the woods. You want a hamburger? I'm starved." He waved the waiter over to take the order and Lavenda watched, astonished. He seemed so cocky, so unworried, she couldn't believe he was the same man who forty-eight hours before had been terrified by the threat of a violent death. In spite of his still-disheveled appearance, it didn't ring true.

At first she attributed her feeling of doubt to nerves. After all, tomorrow she was going to leave the window open. Of her own free will, she was going to aid and abet a robbery. What guarantee did she have that Sal wouldn't take the money and run, leaving her to face the police? Knowing she had never done anything like this before, why hadn't he warned her to wear gloves?

In bed that night, she thought about the girl who had called to Sal from his bed. She thought of the nine weeks of tortune he had put her through before bumping into him at the Astor. The job at the Golden Theater had been his idea that very day. She thought of Knuckles Malone and wondered why she had never heard of him before. She'd heard of Lucky Luciano, Dutch Schultz, Legs Diamond, and others. How could she be sure there really was a Knuckles Malone who was threatening Sal's life? If she doubted this, how could she believe Sal really cared for her and she wasn't just being used?

Somehow Lavenda got through the matinee next day, as well as Jonathan Furie's ritual get-together afterward. She got through the evening performance, seating people and giving them programs. Then the show was over and she was standing outside Jonathan Furie's dressing room, still undecided about what to do. She could knock and stick her head in the door, say goodnight as usual, and go hide in an empty dressing room until he left. Or she could tell him about Sal McCabe. As she hesitated, Nathan opened the door with the star's laundry basket to bring it downstairs for pickup first thing Monday morning and Jonathan saw Lavenda's reflection in his dressing-table mirror.

"Ah, my dear, come in," he said. "I've been worried about you. You're looking peaky." He wiped off the last traces of grease paint with a damp flannel cloth and swung around to face her.

The gentle concern on his face was Lavenda's undoing and tears came. Like a bottle uncorked, she poured out the story of the planned break-in. "But he only planned to borrow the money. Honest, he planned to put it back—" she ended, pushing tears away with the heel of a hand.

"Well, if that's the case, don't you think you had better take the latch off the window as promised?"

"You mean you're going to let him—"

"Do as I say and don't worry. Go on, do it now." When it was done, he pressed several tissues into her hand, advised her to blow her nose, go home, take two aspirin, and go to bed.

When Lavenda was gone, the actor watched as Nathan set up the system of flashbulbs that were activated if the trunk was touched in their absence. The blinding flash of light when least expected had always proved unnerving to prospective thieves and they hightailed it out the there, empty handed.

It was almost nine on Sunday morning when Lavenda woke up and padded barefoot along the drowsy hall to the kitchen that belonged to the girls on her floor. Coffee was all she wanted, and to talk to Sal. Yet when she got downstairs to the pay phones near the desk where seventy-five-year-old Lily Bird protected Brownstone girls' virtue six days a week, Lavenda didn't ring him after all. She was scared. Scared that he wouldn't answer, scared that he would.

Suddenly one of the phones rang, shattering the silence. Lavenda grabbed up the receiver. "Hello," she almost shouted.

"Lavenda?" Jonathan Furie sounded amused. "Don't ask me any questions. Just get dressed if you're not and meet me at Rumpelmayer's for breakfast. Can you be there in half an hour?"

Lavenda could.

After the old actor seated her and the waiter poured coffee, she asked, "Did you call the police? Is—"

"First things first," Jonathan interrupted. "Do you remember when I asked you to pay the Mehron lady?"

Lavenda nodded.

"I did that as a kind of test, I'm ashamed to say. I had seen you meeting this rather unsavory-looking young man nights and I just wanted to make sure you were the girl I thought you were." He neglected to mention that his old friend Sadie Gold had phoned him about Sal McCabe and asked him to keep an avuncular eye on Lavenda. He went on to explain his flashbulb device and how it worked.

"So I gather from that Sal is in jail." She looked down at the plate of bacon and eggs Jonathan had ordered for her. "The condemned girl ate a hearty breakfast."

The actor threw back his head and laughed. "Please, Lavenda, spare me the histrionics and listen." He lit a filtered cigarette. "Last night you unlatched the window. Nathan set up the lights, and all was ready. He and I then sat in the dark until almost one-thirty, at which time Mr. McCabe arrived by way of the window. As soon as he touched the trunk, there was a blinding flash and Nathan grabbed your young man—who put up quite a fight. To answer your question, no, he is not in jail—nor is his life in any danger. There is no Knuckles Malone and there is no gambling debt, just the lure of my trunk full of money. Which, by the way, is a good publicity getter, like Bela Lugosi sleeping in a coffin. Most of my money is safely tucked away in tax-free bonds."

"No debt and no Knuckles. Sadie tried to warn me about Sal but I wouldn't listen."

"Well, not many of us welcome unsolicited advice. However, Nathan made drinks and the three of us discussed the question of whether to call the police. Naturally, Mr. McCabe did not fancy the police. So we compromised: if he agreed to leave New York, I would float him a small loan to help him on his way. And that was that."

Lavenda sighed. "As you say, that's that." Then she brightened. "I almost forgot." She rummaged in her handbag. "Here, read this." She handed Jonathan a message written in Lily Bird's wispy hand. "When I got home last night, I found this in my box. An audition next Tuesday for the Theater Guild."

"I wish you luck," Furie said.

Lavenda grinned. "I know. You've certainly proved that. Thank you." They smiled at each other. Then, feeling as though the world had been lifted from her shoulders, Lavenda launched into her cold but delicious scrambled eggs.

Ian Stuart

Roberta

Roberta studied her reflection in the mirror, touching her dark hair caressingly. Satisfied, she smoothed her skirt over her hips, tied a scarf round her head, and slipped on a coat. Soon, she told herslef, she would feel up to meeting people. Not to talk to, but casually to say good evening to if she met them in the lane. She wouldn't shrink back if anyone spoke to her. For the present she only went out after dark, and on the rare occasions she met a car coming the other way she still shielded her face instinctively.

Pulling on her gloves, she picked up her handbag, and went downstairs. The moon was nearly full, but most of the time it was obscured by the low cloud which had blown up during the afternoon, and it was dark when she let herself out by the back door. It was very still, too, here in the forest, the only sound the low rumble of the traffic on the main road half a mile away.

She walked down the short path to the lane, stepping carefully because the surface was rough. Sixty or seventy yards away she could see the dim glow of a light in Mrs. Bradshaw's bungalow. The bungalow and the cottage were the only buildings for nearly a mile, and hardly anybody came along the lane. There was another, shorter way to the village. Even the holidaymakers who flocked to the forest in their tens of thousands during the summer kept mostly to the other side of the main road.

It was for Roberta that Alec had bought the cottage. It was so isolated here.

The air was cold with the threat of winter coming, and she clutched her coat round her as she walked, her heels tapping on the metaled surface.

Mrs. Bradshaw, looking out of her bedroom window before she drew the curtains, heard them and stood watching. Roberta intrigued her. Where did she go on these evening walks? She and Mr. Carter had lived at the cottage over three months now, yet she had never seen her in the village. She didn't go to work. Had she a job she did at home—some sort of writing or designing, Mrs. Bradshaw thought with a rare flash of imagination? You only had to look at her tripping along on her high heels and in those smart clothes to see what sort of young woman she was. A real town girl, out of place here in the forest. Perhaps, even, she was foreign, Mrs. Bradshaw told herself.

She was sorry for Mr. Carter. He had to do all the shopping from the look of it. She had seen him carrying the bags in from his car sometimes. He seemed a nice young man, too, on the few occasions they'd spoken. Polite and friendly.

Mrs. Bradshaw drew the curtains, returned to the other room, and switched on the television to watch a film about a young husband who strangled his wife in order to marry an heiress. Mrs. Bradshaw liked a good murder.

A quarter of an hour later she heard Roberta pass the bungalow on her way home.

Alec was a junior partner in a firm of estate agents in Camford, the town seven miles away. (That was how he had come to hear about the cottage being for sale.) The next morning when he drove past on his way to work, Mrs. Bradshaw was standing at the bus stop on the main road waiting for the bus into town to do her weekly shopping. He pulled up.

"Can I give you a lift?" he asked.

"Oh, that is kind of you," Mrs. Bradshaw said gratefully. The bus was already five minutes late, and her bad feet and rheumatism made standing misery.

She wasn't a tall woman, but she was bulky, and she was carrying a wicker shopping basket as well as her handbag. It took her a little while to maneuver herself into the passenger seat. Having done so, and fastened her seat belt with difficulty, she settled back with a contented sigh.

"This is nice," she said. "You can't rely on buses these days. Sometimes they just don't come. And if I miss this one, there isn't another until the afternoon."

"Yes," Alec agreed. He was a small man, and he felt slightly overwhelmed by his passenger's size. Changing gear called for tact on his part and understanding on hers, he thought wryly. "Where would you like me to drop you?" he asked.

"Oh, anywhere in the center," Mrs. Bradshaw replied complacently. She knew Alec's office was at least a quarter of a mile this side of the town center, but he wouldn't want her to walk the rest of the way, she was sure. After all, having offered her a lift, he could hardly expect her to be worse off for it. "The bus is so handy for that," she added slyly. "It's no distance at all to the shops."

"No," Alec agreed.

It wasn't natural reticence but fear that perhaps it was too soon that made Mrs. Bradshaw hesitate before broaching the subject on her mind. She and Mr. Carter hardly knew each other, if he took offense she might never kow. But in the end curiosity overcame caution.

"I saw Mrs. Carter last night," she remarked.

Alec looked surprised. "Oh?" he said. "Where was that?"

"In the lane." Where else could she have seen her? Mrs. Bradshaw wondered, her curiosity mounting. "I was just drawing the curtains as she went past."

"Oh," Alec said.

"She doesn't go out much, does she?"

"Not very much, no."

"I mean, I've never seen her in the village, or shopping or anything. I was afraid she might be ill. But then, when I saw her last night—" Mrs. Bradshaw stopped delicately.

A school bus in front of them had stopped to pick up two small boys and a girl. "She's had a nervous breakdown," Alec explained when they were past it.

"Oh dear, I am sorry." Mrs. Bradshaw was a kindly soul at heart, and she meant it, but curiosity made her add, "It must be very lonely for her on her own all day while you're at work. Not being able to go out and meet people, I mean."

"Yes," Alec said. "But that's how she wants it. And the doctors say she mustn't mix with other people just yet. She's had a very bad time these last few months." He looked up at the sky. "It's supposed to be getting warmer today."

Mrs. Bradshaw wasn't ready to drop the subject of Roberta just yet, and, gathering her resolution round her like a warm coat, she said untruthfully, for all she had ever seen of Mrs. Carter was a glimpse of dark hair peeping out from under a scarf and shadowy features in the half light, "I am sorry. She looks such a pretty girl."

Alec, negotiating a congested stretch of road, was spared the necessity of saying anything. Damn the woman and her questions! he thought.

He put Mrs. Bradshaw down outside the vast concrete block of the new shopping center with a sense of relief. But it was short-lived. He knew he would never be safe while Roberta was around. And now there was Jan. Roberta would have to go.

He felt a slight regret, but no remorse.

The days passed, and Mrs. Bradshaw found herself listening for the light, quick tap of Roberta's footsteps passing the bungalow. But she didn't hear it. Was Mrs. Carter worse? she wondered. Perhaps she should go over and see if there was anything she could do. But if she was so bad. Mr. Carter wouldn't go to work, leaving her on her own. And he had said she couldn't see people yet. Not even neighbors if they were virtual strangers, Mrs. Bradshaw supposed.

On Saturday afternoon Alec played football for his club in Camford, and on Sunday morning Mrs. Bradshaw saw him in the garden burning rubbish on a bonfire. She toyed with the idea of walking over and asking after Roberta, but he would have come if they needed help. She had done her best to let him see she wanted to be neighborly that morning he gave her a lift into Camford and he had answered so abruptly it was almost rude. Changed the subject as quickly as he could. She had no intention of being rebuffed a second time.

There was no sign of Roberta that day. Nor on Monday or Tuesday. In the mornings, Mrs. Bradshaw heard Alec reverse his car out of his ramshackle wood-and-asbestos garage and drive off toward the main road. After he had gone, the cottage was silent, so quiet it might almost have been deserted, until he returned soon after six.

Mrs. Bradshaw wanted to meet Roberta. The younger woman was becoming an obsession with her. It was unnatural that anybody could live so near and still be a complete stranger. She tried to imagine Roberta shut away there in the cottage. What did she do all day while her husband was out? If she was well enough to go for walks, even if they were only down the lane after dark, she must be able to cook and do the housework, mustn't she?

On Wednesday afternoon, Mrs. Bradshaw could contain her curiosity no longer. Pulling on a coat, she walked up the lane.

A faint mist hung about the cottage, softening its square outlines and lending it an air of remoteness. It was an ugly building, well over a hundred years old, part brick from which the plaster was crumbling away, and part timber. A single chimney stuck up from one end of its slate roof. Mrs. Bradshaw pushed open the rickety little gate and walked up the path.

The front door was painted dark-green. Or rather, it had been once, a long time ago—now the paint was cracked and faded, and birds had left their marks on it. There was no bell, and she tapped with the old-fashioned iron doorknocker. Its sound echoed inside the house, but it brought no response. After a decent interval, she tried again, a little louder. Still there was no answer.

Mrs. Bradshaw told herself it was stupid to feel uneasy. After all, she was doing nothing wrong—indeed, she only wanted to help, if help was needed. Plucking up her courage, she walked round the side of the cottage to the back, the mist like the touch of cold, damp chiffon on her cheeks, and knocked on the back door.

Nothing happened. Through the net curtains at the kitchen window she could see there was no one there, and a pile of dirty crockery on the draining board. Was Mrs. Carter too ill to answer the door and do the washing-up? Nervous breakdowns were nasty things—Mrs. Bradshaw had a freind whose husband had had one, and he'd hidden when people came to the house. Even his brother had stayed away until he was better. Was Mrs. Carter like that? If so, perhaps she was in bed, and that was why the house was so quiet.

Quiet as the grave.

Mrs. Bradshaw would have been indignant if anyone had accused her of having too much imagination, but there was something about the cottage she didn't like. Something she had never noticed when the Jacksons lived there. An air of desolation. She shivered slightly, and despite her bad feet she walked a little faster than usual back to her bungalow. She was glad when she was inside, the door shut, and the kettle on for a nice cup of tea.

That night the weather turned still colder. Lights showed in the cottage windows each evening, but no footsteps passed the bungalow.

On Friday morning, Mrs. Bradshaw waited until she saw Alec drive off to work before she set out for the bus stop. She was prepared to miss her bus rather than face the possibility of his offering her a lift she could hardly refuse. To her relief, he left home early, and she caught the bus with a couple of minutes to spare. (She didn't know he had left early in order to avoid her.) The cottage looked just the same. It seemed to her it still had that desolate, slightly menacing air. How could it have changed in two days? she thought. Houses weren't like people.

The next morning, Alec was at home. He and his partners took it in turns to have one Saturday in four off and that week was his turn. About eleven o'clock, Mrs. Bradshaw saw him digging in the garden. It was the first time she had seen him doing more than clearing up out there or having a bonfire—he must have decided it was time he turned over the ground ready for the winter. Men everywhere were doing the same.

But there was something wrong. They dug a trench, forked in manure or compost, and filled it with soil from the next trench. Mr. Carter wasn't doing that. He was standing on one spot—there was a heap of soil beside him, and she could see his spade come up every few seconds, turning over and adding to the pile. It was nearly two feet high now, and growing steadily. He was digging a hole. He was nearly up to his knees in it. It was a big hole, too, she could see by standing on tiptoe and craning her neck. It must be nearly six feet long.

Why should he want to dig a hold like that over there on the other side of the garden where it was screened from the road by the cottage and the hedge that ran along the other boundary? Unless he was going to bury something. Something large. The hold was more like—

Mrs. Bradshaw let the curtain fall back into place. She was too shocked and horrified to move. The suspicion had been there at the back of her mind for days, she saw that now, but to come face to face with it, to have it confirmed—

She had thought all along there was something odd about Mr. Carter. No wonder he hadn't welcomed her questions about his wife that morning when he drove her into Camford. If she was his wife!

What should she do? It would be asking for trouble to rush over and confront him. Besides, he hadn't finished his gruesome work yet. Better to wait until he had buried—whatever it was he intended burying. It would be too late for him to hide the evidence then, he would be committed.

Mrs. Bradshaw made herself get on with her normal work. But she found it hard to concentrate on it. Her thoughts kept reverting to the sight of Alec up to his knees in that sinister pit, the heap of soil beside him growing steadily higher. The next time she looked out, he was still there, leaning on his spade, looking at the hole, and she thought she saw a grim smile on his face.

When she looked again, he had gone.

She didn't see Jan come some time after dark, and the first she knew of her arrival was when she noticed her bright-red sportscar outside the cottage the next morning.

Jan was a lecturer at the Camford College of Art. Alec had met her a few months before when he was acting as auctioneer at one of his firm's weekly furniture sales. Jan bought a Victorian tub chair. She had renovated it herself, and now it occupied pride of place in the living room of her flat.

She liked Alec and enjoyed being with him. Occasionally she wondered if there was any more to it than that, or if there ever would be. She enjoyed her life, but she was well aware that soon she would be thirty and she had never seen herself as staying single much longer than that. It was just a question of deciding which of her body friends she most wanted to marry. Alec was high on the list. He played football and cricket, both of which Jan hated, and he talked cars, but none of them dominated his conversation to the extent they did that of most of the others. Nor was he moody like Greg. He was intelligent, he had a sense of humor, he understood a little about her job, and he wasn't patronizing about it. She was happy when she was with him and enjoyed their lovemaking.

Alec was captivated by her. She had reddish auburn hair, fine green-blue eyes, a slim, nicely curved figure, and a flawless complexion. Whatever she was doing, her clothes always looked right. Her changes of mood, from cool and poised to carefree or enthusiastic, intrigued and delighted him. Being a modest man, he could hardly believe so lovely and desirable a girl should want to spend her time with him, but he was in love. Life without Jan was unthinkable.

It was her first visit to the cottage and she looked round with interest. Alec had warned her it wasn't much ("It's a dump," he'd told her, "I haven't had time to anything like finish it yet.") and when she'd seen the outside in the moonlight her spirits had sunk a little But inside, it was a lot better than she'd expected. The central heating was installed, the bathroom and living room modernized, and Alec had bought some nice old pieces of furniture. The kitchen was the worst. Trust a man to leave that to last, Jan thought.

"It's great, Alec," she told him.. "You're really off the edge of the world here, aren't you?"

"Really," he agreed. "There's only one other house for a mile."

"Who lives there?" Jean asked.

Alec frowned. "A nosy old woman named Bradshaw." He put his arms round her and she responded as warmly as he could have hoped. It was almost as if she has been waiting as impatiently to be with him as he had to be with her.

The next morning, he was out of bed first and went downstairs to cook breakfast while Jan bathed and dressed. When she came down, he was busy with a frying pan and there was an appetizing odor of cooking bacon.

"Is it breakfast or lunch?" she inquired, kissing him. It was after ten-thirty.

"Brunch," he answered, laughing, and extricating himself from her arms. "But it won't be if you don't watch it."

Jan perched on a stool and watched him. She had decided while she was in the bath that she liked the idea of being married to Alec. "Whose things are those in the spare room?" she inquired casually.

Alec's hand stopped, the bacon slice it was holding halfway to the frying pan, and he stared at her, his eyes blank. "Why did you go in there?" he demanded.

His tone startled Jan, it was so harsh. Almost hostile. Until now she had always considered him easygoing—too much so at times. Now, suddenly, she was seeing a different side of him. She found it slightly disturbing.

"I was interested to see what you'd done in there," she answered lightly. Maybe she shouldn't have looked, she told herself, but it was hardly a crime. She'd never dreamed Alec would make anything of it. "Sorry."

The sudden fear which for a moment had almost overwhelmed Alec subsided a little. "It doesn't matter," he said. "They're my wife's things."

Jan frowned. "I thought you said you were divorced."

"We are."   .

"But she still keeps some of her things here?"

"She's never taken them, that's all. I stuck them away in there when I moved here." The worst moment was over. Alec thought. She wants to believe me, so she will. He felt the tension easing away, and deftly transferred a fried egg from the pan to one of the plates he had been warming, following it with two rashers of bacon, some mushrooms, and a grilled tomato. "Does it matter?" he asked.

"Should it?" Jan countered. "I like to know where I stand, that's all."

"It doesn't." Alec filled the second plate and carried both through to the living room. "I haven't seen her since the divorce," he added, coming back for the toast.

Jan followed him into the living room. "Alec, you're playing straight with me, aren't you?" she asked.

Alec didn't miss the hard note in her voice. "Yes," he answered. "Honestly. She went off with a man she'd met at the drama group she belonged to. Don't you believe me?"

Did she? Jan asked herself. She wanted to, but there was something wrong. Maybe it was her imagination. All the same, suddenly she was afraid.

Alec seemed to have recovered his good spirits. He chatted and laughed, and gradually her uneasiness faded. After their meal, they went for a walk down the lane and into the forest. Mrs. Bradshaw saw them pass the bungalow, Jan with her arm tucked into Alec's, laughing up at him. Seeing them made her blood run cold.

When she fetched in her milk the next morning, Jan's car had gone. Mrs. Bradshaw made up her mind it was time she did something. Later that day she phoned the police.

A constable came first. He parked his car outside the bungalow, walked up the path, and rang the bell. Mrs. Bradshaw, who was waiting, opened it before the sound of the bell had died away.

The constable stayed ten minutes, taking down what she told him she had seen, and what Alec had told her about Roberta.

"He had a young woman there this weekend," she concluded. "They went down the road arm-in-arm, as if they hadn't a care in the world."

"Oh yes, madam?" The constable recognized malice when he heard it, and he thought he heard it now. Lonely old woman, he thought, living on her own here, no neighbors to chat to, and probably not enough to keep her occupied. A hundred to one there was nothing in any of it—she'd imagined it all, and this man Carter had been digging in his own garden at the weekend. Still, he'd better check. The sergeant would want a report and heaven help him if he hadn't done everything he should.

"With his wife ill in bed," Mrs. Bradshaw said indignantly. "If she *is* in bed. More likely—"

"We'll look into it," the constable said, standing up.

At least it broke the monotony. They hadn't had a report of a suspected murder for some time. Leaving his car where it was, he walked over to the Carter cottage, well aware that Mrs. Bradshaw was watching him from her doorway.

Although he knocked three times, there was no answer, and he walked round to the back. Two or three minutes later, Mrs. Bradshaw saw him return to his car and sit there, using his radio before he started the engine and drove off.

And what happens now? she asked herself.

She saw no more that day, although she went to her window every quarter of an hour or so to see if anything was happening. The police couldn't just walk away and do nothing, surely?

Then, about seven that evening, a car drove up, parked outside the cottage, and two men got out. Detective Inspector Walker, the older of the two, was middle-aged and lean. There was something about him which suggested he had seen enough of life's quirks to be surprised by very little that happened, and to understand a good deal. Detective Sergeant Benson was considerably younger. He liked to think of himself as a hard man. To him, people were either straight or crooked, honest or villains. Sometimes Walker almost envied him—thinking like that, life was so much simpler.

"Mr. Carter?" he asked when Alec answered his knock.

"Yes?"

"I'm Detective Inspector Walker and this is Detective Sergeant Benson. We'd like to have a talk, if we may. May we come in?"

"What's it about?" Alec hoped the alarm he felt hadn't showed in his voice. An inspector and a sergeant. It couldn't be a minor traffic offense.

Walker didn't answer. As if he was taking Alec's consent for granted, he stepped forward, and Alec gave way.

They went into the living room and sat down. Walker looked relaxed in his easy chair, but Benson gave the impression he had perched on his only for a moment, like some huge bird balancing on a fence. A bird of prey, perhaps, ready to pounce on its victim at any moment. It occurred to Alec there was something menacing about him. Benson intended it should.

"Is your wife in, Mr. Carter?" the Inspector asked.

Alec's hopes sank. They couldn't know, he thought. They couldn't. But Somehow they did. "No," he answered. "She's left me."

When did she leave you?"

"Some time ago. What's all this about?"

"We'll explain in a minute, sir. How long ago?"

Walker noticed the momentary pause before Alec said, "Two years. We were divorced last year."

"That was your first wife. You married again, didn't you? A few days ago you told one of your neighbors your second wife had had a nervous breakdown and she wasn't well enough to meet people. Is that right?"

Alec's heart was thumping and his mouth was dry. "Yes," he muttered.

"Where is she, Mr. Carter?"

This time the pause was longer. "She's left me, too." Alec said.

"Oh? When?"

"A few days ago."

"Although she was only just recovering from a nervous breakdown and couldn't face people? That's rather strange, isn't it?"

Alec turned his head to avoid Walker's eyes and found himself looking at the implacable features of his sergeant. "That wasn't true," he said. "She kept on about her, just being nosy. I told her that to shut her up."

"But your wife has left you?" Walker insisted. Alec nodded. "You must have been upset. After all, you hadn't been married long."

"Yes."

"You got over it quickly, though. You had a young lady to stay here this weekend, didn't you? Who was she, Mr. Carter?"

"Her name's Owen. She's a lecturer at the College of Art in Camford."

The Inspector made no comment. To Alec it seemed he was prolonging the silence deliberately, and he forced himself to sit still, resisting an almost uncontrollable impulse to clench his hands on the arms of his chair or stir uncomfortably. Perhaps, he thought, his tenseness didn't show. But he knew he was deluding himself.

"Where is your wife now?" It was the first time Benson had spoken. His voice had a rough edge to it.

"I don't know," Alec answered. It was true, but he could see they didn't believe him.

"Do you mind if we have a look round?" the Inspector asked. In contrast to Benson's, his tone was almost friendly.

"Why should I?" Alec said.

Benson stood up and walked to the door. Alec heard the heavy steps going up the stairs and crossing his bedroom.

"Are you fond of gardening?" Walker asked.

"Gardening?" The question took Alec by surprise.

"You've been doing some digging lately, haven't you?"

"Oh, that. I've been digging some holes ready to put a couple of fruit trees in."

Benson called from upstairs and the Inspector went out to the hall. Alec waited, his nerves on edge. The two policemen were moving about up there. Then, after a minute or two, they reentered the room together.

"We're going to have to ask you to come to the station with us, Mr. Carter," Walker said. "There are some more points to be cleared up to do with your wife's disappearance, and you'll be given the opportunity to make a statement."

"You won't find her," Alec said. He smiled.

He was right. The house was searched thoroughly and every foot of the garden explored. There was no trace of Roberta.

It was a bitterly cold night, and the frost, following a light drizzle earlier in the day, had made the surface of the lane treacherous.

For Alec, the last two months had been a terrible time. The police had questioned him repeatedly, for hours at a stretch, and he had had to endure the veiled accusations of the Press. People drove out to peer at the cottage, hoping for a glimpse of him. He no longer played football because he could sense the hostility of other members of the club and it seemed better to stay away.

His partners in the firm didn't know what to do. They liked Alec, and had always trusted him, but this business had come like a bolt from the blue, shocking them to the core. They didn't believe he and Roberta had been married. (Nor did the police. Alec had refused to tell them where or when the ceremony had taken place, and they were unable to trace any record of it.) If he chose to live with a girl, that was his affair, and it was understandable after the way his first wife had behaved. But why had he never mentioned Roberta to them? They were his friends. There was something underhand about that, and it made them uneasy. Moreover, it hadn't made life any easier for them, having the name of one of their partners plastered all over the newspapers, suspected of murdering his wife.

More than once, Alec had come to a point where the temptation to confess, to tell the truth and get it done with, was almost too strong for him to resist. At least then he would have a sort of peace. But he knew it would be the end. Better to keep his nerve, face this thing out, and eventually, sometime, it would be almost forgotten.

The worst time was when he knew he had lost Jan.

Mrs. Bradshaw hadn't spoken to him since the police came to the cottage that evening in November. It was as if by tacit consent they were avoiding each other. She might tell herself stoutly she had done only what any responsible person should have done, but she knew Alec wouldn't see it like that, and in a queer way she was more afraid of his resentment and dislike than of anything he might do.

This evening she had been watching the nine o'clock television news. The weather forecast was for the cold weather to continue for the next few days at least, with, possibly, snow showers in the East. She heaved herself to her feet and crossed the room to switch off the set. As she did so she heard something she had been sure she would never hear again —the light tapping of a woman's footsteps in the lane. Mrs. Bradshaw froze. Mrs. Carter: But it couldn't be Mrs. Carter. She was gone. Dead.

On these cold crisp nights, sounds traveled clearly, and the footsteps seemed louder than they had before. They were coming closer. Mrs. Bradshaw had never believed in ghosts, and she couldn't have said what she was afraid of now, but her fear was real. It was like a pain. She seemd to have stopped breathing.

The steps were level with the bungalow. She waited, tense, nerves on edge, as if she half expected Roberta to come to the door.

Then she had passed, going on down the lane. Mrs. Bradshaw breathed a sigh of relief. What had got hold of her? Of course it wasn't Roberta, it was some girl taking this way home to the village. Probably somebody had given her a lift to the corner.

The footsteps had nearly faded now, drowned in the noise of a car. It was coming too fast, Mrs. Bradshaw thought, much too fast with the lane slippery as it was tonight. Headlights blazed across her window as it roared past and she had a terrible sense of impending doom.

Afterward she could remember only the screech of tires, a thud she could hear in the bungalow, then the sound of the car accelerating away into the night.

Going to the door, she looked out. Everything was clear in the cold, silvery light of the full moon. Afraid of what she would find, she started walking along the lane after the car.

A hundred yards from the bungalow, the lane turned a little to the right. Halfway round the bend something was lying a few feet out from the left-hand bank, something that looked like a heap of old clothes. Mrs. Bradshaw made herself go closer, although she knew what she would see as certainly as if she had already looked down and seen Roberta's dead face.

She was dead, there was no doubt about that. Turning, Mrs. Bradshaw hurried home. It didn't occur to her to go to the cottage to break
the news to Alec, and even if it had she would very likely not have gone.
Panting, she telephoned the police.

Walker and Benson were still at the station when the call came
through, working late on a robbery case.

"We'd better go," Walker said.

"But—" Benson began. He was frowning, unable to believe what he
had been told. He had been sure Roberta's body was buried somewhere.
Had the old woman made a mistake, and it was some other girl who'd
been knocked down?

The ambulance had arrived when they reached the scene, and there
was a small knot of men in the lane. A constable was setting up warning
lights.

"Take a look, sir," the uniformed sergeant who had taken charge said
to Walker."

Together, the CID men squatted beside Roberta's crumpled body.
She was lying partly on her left side. Her coat was torn and stained and
her skirt pulled up round her thighs. There was a tear in her left stocking
and her right shoe was missing. Gently Walker turned her over. As he
did so, Roberta's dark hair slipped to one side, drooping in an obscene
grimace over her left eye. Underneath it was short, much fairer brown
hair. Carefully, Walker removed the wig and looked down on the dead
face of Alec Carter.

Beside him, Benson swore. "There never was a Mrs. Carter," he
exclaimed, his voice thick with disgust. "Carter was a bloody pervert."

Walker straightened up. Perhaps he hadn't heard the sergeant. Or
perhaps he was correcting him. "Poor bastard," he said quietly.

Nancy C. Swoboda
Hearts and Flowers

My name is Melva. Sit yourself down and I'll cook you up a burger. How 'bout them fall colors out there? Never thought I'd wind up here—kinda my own little estate, you might say. Raised my girl just like my grandma raised me, close to the land and the creatures. She knows every tree and plant, what berries are good to eat, how to make herb tea to cure most anything that ails you. Well, enough about that. It was fifteen years ago that my old man took off and left us. Francie was only two and I didn't know beans about nothing. Was just plain luck I heard about the college looking for a cook/caretaker for what they call The Cabin here in the woods at the edge of the campus.

Woodberry is a junior college for women, you know. Them buildings and the church are most a hundred years old. The Cabin is about the only place for recreation the girls have on week nights. They can come down here, dance to the jukebox, have a burger, and gossip. I see to keeping up the area and making sure there's plenty to eat for the students and faculty wanting a little break from the main-dining-room stuff or maybe only a change of scenery.

It's not very big, you can tell that, but our rooms in the back suit us fine. You wouldn't believe the things I see and hear while I'm behind the counter. Times have sure changed over the years. I'd like to tell some of them young girls that men aren't the end all to everything, that they'd better stick to getting a good education so they can be on their own if they have to. But I keep my lip buttoned.

Being as the campus is stuck way out here in the woods, you find that people sort out into some funny pairs and mixed-up groups. The faculty, especially. I swear, most of them have been here a hundred years! Any time new blood is hired, things get riled—like when a young rooster shows up in the hen yard, there's a lot of squawking and feather-ruffling until he settles into the pecking order and things calm down.

That last didn't happen when Randall Kincaid joined the facutly as the choir director and music teacher, though. Uh uh—with that mane of silver hair and rugged looks, he cut quite a figure. Most of the girls had a crush on him and got a sudden yen to sing. You could tell he liked the attention, but he was one of them men who pretend they can't understand why all the fuss.

The faculty arrives two weeks before the students to get their courses set up, and some of 'em come down here for a break, but the old timers would rather have tea up in their rooms. Miss Gilcrest, the botany teacher, was the youngest and I figure she was pushing fifty. The girls called her Miss Lonely Hearts.

You remember Dorothy Collins, the Lucky Strike girl? Well, Martha

301

Gilcrest reminded me of her, only plainer. She was the kind of woman who looks for the knight on the white horse but goes around with her knees padlocked together and a hatpin in her purse. I don't mean to put down morals, mind you—lord knows I've drummed 'em into my Francie—but at Martha Gilcrest's age, longing for romance like she did, it was high time she put a little spice in her vanilla pudding.

Well, anyhow, she wasn't to the point of sipping tea with the dinosaurs yet and that night she came down to The Cabin. It was the first I'd seen her since the end of semester last summer. She looked real nice, lost some weight. Them big blue eyes was still hopeful, but the rosebud mouth was set prim and proper, just like always.

"Hello, Melva," she said in her quiet voice. "Nice to see you again. It doesn't seem possible that summer's over and we're into the fall term again."

"Yep. Time gets away from you somehow." I was thinking more of her than college. "What'll it be, Miss Gilcrest?"

"One of your good hamburgers and a cup of coffee, please, Melva."

She went over to one of the booths and sat down with a notebook in front of her. I was just ready to put her burger on a plate when Randall Kincaid walked in. He had on a turtleneck sweater under a tweed jacket and grey slacks that showed off his narrow hips.

He strode over to the counter with his hand out. "Hello there, Melva. I'm Professor Kincaid, new hed of the music department. I understand you make the world's best hamburger."

Boy, was he smooth. He even flustered me a little, but I wiped a hand on my apron and shook his.

"Nice to meet you," I told him. "Shall I put one on the grill for you, Professor?"

"Please." He straddled a stool and leaned his suede-covered elbows on the counter. I happened to catch sight of Miss Gilcrest then. Her baby blues were saucers, her rosebud mouth was open, and I swear I could hear violin music floating from her booth.

The professor was looking at her, too. "Who's that?" he whispered.

"Martha Gilcrest, the botany teacher," I whispered back and took her burger over to the booth. Martha hardly saw it.

In one way, I was hopeful that love might finally have walked into her life, but I had a feeling about Mr. Slick Kincaid and I was afraid it would turn out to be something like trying to flag down the *Super Chief* with a candle. Before I could even hint at a little hard-earned advice, he'd come over and introduced himself.

He smiled at Martha. "Mind if I eat with you? Perhaps you can fill me in on the unwritten protocol here."

No bones about it, I listened as hard as I could. My ears are like radar according to Francie. Their conversation began about Woodberry and wandered off into how they chose their careers. I thought Kincaid was smooth, but old Martha slipped it in that she was unattached and found out that he was the same. They finished their hamburgers, dawdled over more coffee, and then left together. They walked real slow up the path to the main campus and I had mixed feelings about the way they'd taken to each other. Somebody was going to get hurt.

You'll be surprised to know that I thought it might be Professor Kincaid. I'd seen those doe eyes of Martha's turn to ice when someone crossed her. Even her students tried to keep on the good side of her. Halloween night the year before, some of the girls soaped her new Chevy and she was as mad as a boiled owl. She never let on to her students, though. Just continued in her usual sweet way until not long after that the girls saw a notice on the board that all botany classes would be required to go on a field trip on the very day everyone was geared up to drive into the city for a football game.

The romance seemed to get on real well. After the first month of classes, everybody knew that Randall Kincaid and Martha Gilcrest were an item. They came down to The Cabin at off times to sit in the corner booth and make googoo eyes at each other. Love was sure becoming to Martha. Her cheeks were rosy and her eyes had lost that lonely look. I still wasn't sure about Professor Kincaid, though. He had an eye for the young girls and I didn't like the look he put on them. There was one particular leggy blonde by the name of Ginger that you could see he fancied.

Sometimes he came down to The Cabin alone when most of the students were there. Ginger liked to play a hot tune on the jukebox and dance it up. Between her gyrations and her tight pants, it was quite a show, and she knew darn well Kincaid enjoyed it. I suppose it was only natural, but since he seemed to be courting Martha I smelled trouble.

Rufus, who looks after the stables, came down most nights for a cup of coffee and to shoot the breeze. He's got a steel-grey crewcut and looks like a retired wrestler, but you ought to hear him talk to them horses—he can gentle 'em into doing most anything. He'd taken a liking to Martha Gilcrest in a fatherly sort of way and taught her how to ride.

When he dropped in this one night, we were almost to the end of the first semester and the loving couple were still together. Rufus had his doubts, just like me. "I sure don't want to see that little lady get taken down the garden path," he muttered.

"I don't think you need to worry, Ruf. She's got a pretty stiff spine." I slid a piece of apple pie under his nose.

"Maybe. But I got an idea the only thing that silver fox is interested in is the challenge—and Martha sure is one."

"What's that mean?"

His craggy face got beet-red. "Melva, let's just say I hope the only time her feet leave the ground with him is horseback riding."

"Why, Rufus, you old rip. You're really worried about her, aren't you?"

He rubbed a big hand over his crewcut. "I seen what it can do to a

woman to be tricked into giving herself away. Kincaid had better watch
out else he wants to know what a horsewhip feels like."

Spring break came around. Martha Gilcrest was blooming right along
with the crocus outside my back door. I saw her one day on the path into
the woods. She had some little pots and stuff in a basket. I waved at her
and she came over. "Beautiful day, isn't it?" she said. "I'm going out to
cut some plant slips and collect a few lichen for my classes."

"Stop back and we'll have a cup of coffee." I hoped, being just plain
nosy, that she'd let me know how things were going.

"Maybe I will if I can find what I want without taking too long." She
held up the gold pocket-knife she wore on a chain around her neck.
She'd told me once it had been her grandfather's, she used it for cuttings
and the like. She said he'd been a florist and using the knife made her
feel close to him. I kind of liked that idea. Made me think of my grandma
and all she taught me.

Martha did have that visit with me and it all came out before she
could stop herself. She was just busting to tell someone. "Randall and
I are going to Meeker's Island over spring break. Please don't tell anyone, Melva. We've become unofficially engaged and we thought
Meeker's would be a nice quiet place to make our plans and talk things
over."

Just by her looks I knew what was going to happen on Meeker's and I
wanted to tell her to go slow, but I could see she'd made up her mind.
Out loud I did say, "That's nice, Miss Gilcrest. I hope you both get what
you want."

Well, that wasn't a very good remark, either, but it sure fit the
situation. I wondered if Rufus knew about their little trip. He'd blow a
gasket if he did.

I didn't see the two lovebirds again until about a week after classes
were back in session. When they came down to The Cabin together that
night, the first thing I looked for was an engagement ring on Martha's
finger. There wasn't even a cigar band. She caught me staring and got a
sheepish expression on her face. Kincaid acted different, too.

Oh oh, I thought, the bloom is off the rose in more ways than one.
They sat in the booth and talked, mostly about what to order, and then
he let Martha do it—like she should wait on him. She came over to the
counter and of course I had to aask. "Have a nice vacation?"

Her cheeks flushed and her eyes avoided mine. "It was wonderful."

"When's the big announcement?" I prodded.

"We've—decided to wait until the end of the term, then take our
honeymoon over summer vacation."

"I get it. Mum's the word for now, right?"

She gave me a little smile of relief. "Yes. Thank you for understanding. That's the way—we would prefer it."

Things seemed pretty routine for the next few weeks. Then I was out sweeping off the front porch one morning when I saw Rufus come chugging down the path like his boiler was ready to blow.

"I gotta talk to you, Melva. Let's go inside."

We sat in one of the booths and after Rufus pounded the table with his fist and said a few "damns," he settled down and told me what he was about to bust a blood vessel over.

"Last night I had to go to the tack room for something and I always try to be real quiet so's I don't stir up the horses. I heard this whispering and giggling. Well, that's happened before—some couple using my barn for a roll in the hay—but instead of backing off and lettin' 'em have their moment, I knew this time who it was and I hid and eavesdropped. It was Professor Kincaid and that Ginger. She was kidding him about having to work at romancing Miss Gilcrest, even up to promising to marry her. Kincaid said something about it having been quite a challenge getting her to come across, but at the end of the term he'd be gone, and that would be the end of it. Said Woodberry's too dull for him."

I remembered Ruf's concern about Martha the last time we talked. What he'd been afraid of had happened. Randall Kincaid had promised hearts and flowers when all he'd wanted was another notch on his gun.

"I'm gonna git him," Ruf growled. "I'm gonna fix him good."

"Hey, simmer down—you go horsewhip a member of the faculty and you'll be the one out on your rear."

"Okay, Melva, okay. You're right. But I'm sure as hell gonna warn Miss Martha off."

I fixed us a big cool glass of herb tea and we sat there stewing over what to do. I wished my grandma was there for a word of advice. But I knew what I'd do. Nothing.

I told Ruf as much. "Ruf, if you tell Martha she'll hate you for it. And you might cause her to do something drastic."

"But I can't sit still and watch her be used, Melva. I know her. She's the kind of woman who don't fall easy."

"Let time do it for you, Rufus. She'll be smart enough to realize what's happening and come out of it okay. If you tell her, you'll take away her dignity."

He was still shaking his head and talking to himself when he left, and to tell you the truth I was afraid of what he might do.

Soon it was time for the annual faculty picnic. The day was perfect—mild, with a clear blue sky. According to my almanac, a full moon would make it a real nice evening. Rufus came over and laid the wood for the wienie-roast fire and left as soon as he helped me set up the serving tables outside.

Francie and I took a hike in the woods and brought back enough hickory sticks for everybody to cook their hot dogs. I had a big pan of baked beans, a crock of potato salad, buns, and relishes all ready in no

time. The faculty wasn't that many, so I enjoyed making the little extra
effort to make a good spread for them. Besides, most of 'em could use a
little fresh air.

I was out back picking flowers to put on the tables when I saw Martha
Gilcrest on her way into the woods. She had on a pretty blue topcoat
and carried the basket over her arm. "Hi, Miss Gilcrest," I said.
"Coming to the picnic tonight?"

She smiled and waved. "I'll be there."

She seemed okay. Maybe things would work out in spite of what
Rufus had overheard. I hoped so. But it was time to frost my brownies
and get the posies in little vases, so my mind went on to that and the
other things that had to get done for the picnic.

We had a good turnout that night. The fire was just right for wienie-
roasting and it wasn't too chilly. The hot dogs and hickory sticks were at
the end of the table and after you speared and cooked your dog, you
came back and Francie and I served the rest of the food onto the plates.

In between dishing up, I kept an eye on Martha and Kincaid. They
really did make a nice-looking couple. They both acted happy and relaxed, and after they had their plates filled Martha got a mug of coffee
from the urn at the end of the table and stood waiting for Kincaid, who
was right behind her. She watched him pleasantly until he drew a mug
of coffee and then walked clean away from him to mingle with the rest
of the faculty. He shrugged and did the same. Good for you, Martha, I
said to myself. Give it back to that old silver fox.

By the time the moon was up, it began to turn cold. Some, including
Martha, came inside for more hot coffee, but Kincaid said he didn't feel
well and started up the path to the faculty housing. Before he'd gone
very far, he groaned, doubled over, and collapsed. I saw him because I
was outside gathering up the used dishes and stuff.

I ran inside, told Francie to phone the rescue squad, grabbed our
resident nurse, and went back outside with her to where Randall Kincaid was. The nurse got down on her knees and looked him over. Then
she stood up real slow.

"He's dead," she said in a low voice. "It looks like a coronary."

There's a little village, Montrose, about five miles down the highway
and their rescue squad is the volunteer type. But they arrived in jig time,
loaded Randall Kincaid into an ambulance, and went off with the lights
and siren going full blast. Montrose has a sheriff, a good old g.p., and a
ten-bed hospital, so I figured they'd do what was needed.

The next thing, though, was that somebody had to tell Martha what
had happened. Everyone had been rubbernecking and had some idea of
what was going on. I took Martha into the back and told her as easy as I
could.

Her face got real white and she said, "Oh." Then she kind of staggered over to a chair. I brought her a glass of water and she just held it.
"I'll be all right," she whispered. "I want to go to my rooms."

I had the nurse walk her back and get her settled. By then everyone else had cleared out, buzzing and chattering all the way up the path. Then something struck me. Where was Rufus? With all the red lights and the siren he should have come running. I called the stables and got no answer.

Before I could puzzle that over, the phone rang and scared me plumb out of my thoughts. It was Sheriff Cotter from Montrose.

"Melva?" he barked. "Don't do anything with the food you served tonight at the picnic. Don't serve any more of it and don't throw it out."

"What?"

"The doctor hasn't done an autopsy yet, but he will. He says it's probably heart, but he doesn't want to rule out poisoning."

After I hung up and recovered from that news, I got mad. No way could any of my grub be poison, ptomaine or otherwise. Oh, well—let 'em come and see for themselves. I put on a pot of coffee and waited.

Sheriff Cotter and two other men were here in fifteen minutes. They wanted a list of everyone at the picnic and took samples of everything we served, then Sheriff Cotter motioned me aside.

"Tell me what happened tonight, Melva. What you saw, who did what, and so on."

There was nothing in particular I could think of to tell him except I knew my food was in the clear. As to someone poisoning Kincaid, it was nigh onto impossible since Francie and I doled out everything but the wienies and who'd know what hotdog he was going to pick? Besides, I'd been watching him and Martha pretty close, enough to swear no one had the opportunity to slip him anything.

"Thanks, Melva. I'll let you know what we find out. Meanwhile, you'd better toss out all this food."

The hell I would! After they left, I put it all in containers in the icebox. When I went to make sure the back door was locked, I thought I saw a light moving out in the woods. Lightning bugs'll do that to you. I watched a little longer, but didn't see it again. Still, after what had happened it kinda bothered me. I went to bed and did a peck of wondering. A heart attack would sure be the simplest solution for everyone, but I had the feeling there was more trouble ahead.

At the crack of dawn, Rufus showed up on my doorstep. I pulled him in and over to a booth. "You look like you've been on an all-night binge," I said, pouring him some coffee. "Here, wash this down your gullet."

His cup did the dipsy-doodle between his mouth and the saucer, but he got most of the coffee inside him before he leaned back in the booth and shut his eyes. "I told Miss Gilcrest what a skunk Randall Kincaid was." His voice quavered. "I told her everything, Melva."

All of a sudden I developed a cold knot in my stomach. "Oh, Ruf! When? And where were you last night?"

He rubbed a hand over his drawn, stubbly face. "I told her a couple of days ago. As for last night, I was around. Just didn't show myself. Saw the whole thing, though."

The knot in my middle got tighter. Ruf hated what Kincaid had done to Martha and was skulking around last night. Could he have done something to cause the professor's death? And Martha! She'd known, but there she was, acting like everything was fine. But then I remembered the moment she'd coolly turned her back on him and joined the rest of the faculty.

"I probably shouldn't ask you this, but did you have anything to do with Kincaid's death?"

He dropped his head. "Maybe I did."

Before he could go on, the phone rang. It was the sheriff.

"Melva, I'm happy to tell you your food got a clean bill of health."

"I coulda told you that," I said. "Does that mean you know how Professor Kincaid died?"

"Doc says it was a coronary, all right, but he thinks something unnatural brought on the attack."

"Like what?"

"Don't know. He's sending samples to the lab at City Medical Center. Hard to do fancy stuff here with one microscope and a Bunsen burner."

An awful thought crossed my mind then . Rufus had syringes and all kinds of medications down at the barn to doctor the horses. There was a minute or two when Kincaid was out of sight on the path that Ruf could have got to him with a needle.

"Any marks on the body, Sheriff?" I asked.

"Not that we could find. Why?"

"Oh, nothing. Just a thought. Okay, Sheriff. Thanks for the call."

I went back to Ruf and stood over him. "What do you mean, maybe you had something to do with Kincaid's death?"

"I should have listened to you, Melva, and not told Miss Gilcrest anything. I'm afraid for her."

"You mean you think she might have done him in?"

"That's about it."

"Ruf, if she did, you can't blame yourself. Sooner or later she'd have found him out. She's responsible for her own actions."

He wasn't convinced and I decided the best thing to do was keep him busy.

"Come on, Ruf. Help me clear up outside. The tables need to be moved and you can clean up what's left of the fire. Then I'll fix us some eggs."

Most of the paper plates and plastic utensils had been tossed into the big trash bin the night before. I threw my wilted flowers in after them and set the vases on the porch. It was then that I spotted Martha Gilcrest striding into the woods. Ruf had his back in that direction and didn't see her.

"Keep at it, Ruf. I'll be back in a minute."

I went in the front door and out the back to follow Martha. She looked kinda funny, and after last night's events I wondered why she'd head out alone into the woods. Maybe she just wanted to walk and think. I do that sometimes myself, so I hung back to respect her privacy.

She sure seemed to have purpose in her direction, though. After a brisk walk, she started going in circles, stopping from time to time to bend down. There was a lot of brush between us so I didn't have a good view, but it finally dawned on me that she was looking for something. She really beat the bushes, so to speak, and from the look on her face when she started back she didn't find whatever it was.

I took a bearing on where she'd been searching and then headed back for The Cabin—Ruf would be wondering what happened to me. But my curiosity was up and later I meant to make my own search—for what, I didn't know. When I got back, sure enough, Ruf and Francie were looking for me. I got busy with some eggs and bacon, got her off to school, and sent Ruf to the stables to take a good hot shower and a nap.

Then I beat a path back to the woods and started poking around. Finally, I got down on my hands and knees. That's when I found Martha's gold knife half hidden under the leaves in a patch of plants that bloomed in purple and white blossoms. It was foxglove.

Oh the way back, it all came together. Life's not fair and Kincaid got what he deserved in my estimation, but I'm not the judge. I had to tell the truth and let those involved face the consequences. Grandma always said that the truth hurts some but in the end it's good for all.

It took all my gumption to call Sheriff Cotter. I told him about the love affair, how I figured she'd been searching in the woods that day for foxglove and the next day for the knife. I even tried out my idea with one of the brown ceramic mugs we used at the picnic before I called.

Even a fair amount of the liquid in the bottom of the mug was hard to see, especially if you weren't looking for it. Martha had filled her mug and put the stuff in another one closest to the urn. Then she waited to make sure Kincaid took it and filled it with coffee. Her only outward show of revenge was when she turned her back and walked away.

"That's it, Sheriff. I'll bet you one of my burgers the lab'll find digitalis as the cause of death."

Martha Gilcrest confessed in her usual quiet way when Sheriff Cotter faced her with the massive dose of digitalis they did find. I don't know if Rufus will ever forgive himself, but I mean to help him all I can. Seeing how sensitive he was about Martha's feelings kinda softened something inside of me, woke up the dreams I put aside years ago. We got married about six months later and so far it's working out just fine.

Antonia Fraser

Boots

Her mother used to call her Little Red Riding Boots, and eventually by degrees of use (and affection) just Boots. And now that Emily was no longer quite so little—the smart red plastic boots which had given rise to the joke were beginning to pinch—she still liked being called the pet name by her mother. It was a private matter between them.

Emily's mother, Cora, was a widow: a pretty, slight young woman, not yet thirty, but still a widow. When Emily was a baby, her father had gone away to somewhere hot on an engineering project and got himself killed. That at least was how Emily had heard Cora describing the situation on the occasion of her first date with Mr. Inch.

"And not a penny after all these years," Cora added. "Just a load of luggage months later. Including the clothes he was *wearing*! Still covered in his blood . . ."

Then Mr. Inch—not Cora—got up and shut the door.

Listening from her little bedroom, which was just next to the sitting room, Emily imagined her father getting himself killed. Or rather, she thought of the nasty accident she had recently witnessed on the zebra crossing opposite their house. Blood everywhere. Rather as if the old woman had been exploded, like you sometimes saw on the news on television. The old woman had been hit by one of the nasty long lorries which were always rumbling down their particular high street. Cora felt very strongly about the lorries and often spoke to Emily about them, complaining about them, warning her about the crossing.

Perhaps that was why Cora had let Emily go on watching the scene out of the window for quite a long time after the old woman was hit, in spite of all the blood.

Later, Cora explained her views on this kind of thing to Mr. Inch and Emily listened.

"You see, you can't protect a child from life. From the first, I never hid anything from Boots—Emily. It's all around us, isn't it? I mean, I want Emily to grow up knowing all about life: that's the best kind of protection, isn't it?"

"She is awfully young." Mr. Inch sounded rather doubtful. "Perhaps it's just because she looks so tiny and delicate. Such a little doll. And pretty, too. One wants to protect her. Pretty like her mother—"

On this occasion, also, Mr. Inch got up and shut the door. He was always shutting the door, thought Emily, shutting her out as if he did not like her. And yet when Mr. Inch was alone with her, if her mother was cooking something smelly with the door shut, even more if Cora dashed down to the shops, Mr. Inch used to take the opportunity to say that he liked Emily, that he liked Emily very much. And perhaps one day, who could say, perhaps Mr. Inch might come to live with Emily and her mother all the time—would Emily like that?

At this point, Mr. Inch generally touched Emily's long, thick, curly hair, not gold but brown, otherwise hair just like a princess's in a fairy story (so Cora sometimes said, brushing it). Mr. Inch also touched Emily's mother's hair in the same way: that was, of course, much shorter, which made it even curlier. But while Mr. Inch touched Cora's hair in front of Emily, he never, Emily noticed, touched her own hair when Cora was present.

Emily paused to imagine what it would be like if Mr. Inch got himself killed, like Emily's father. Would he explode like the old woman at the crossing? Sometimes Emily watched out of the window and saw Mr. Inch approaching the house: he was supposed to cross by the zebra, too (although sometimes he did not bother). Sometimes Emily would watch Mr. Inch just running toward the house, galloping really, on his long legs. When Mr. Inch visited Cora, he always brought flowers, sweets for Emily, and sometimes a bottle of wine as well. After a bit, Emily noticed that he began to bring food as well. He still managed to run toward their house, even carrying all these things.

When Mr. Inch ran, he looked like a big dog. A big old dog. Or perhaps a wolf.

By now Emily had really grown out of fairy stories, including that story her mother fondly imagined to be her steady favorite, Little Red Riding Boots. To tell the truth, she much preferred grown-up television; even if she didn't understand it all, she found she understood more and more. Besides, Cora didn't object.

That, too, said Cora, was a form of protection.

"The news helps you to adjust painlessly. A child picks and chooses," she told Mr. Inch. "Knowledge is safety."

"But Cora, darling, there are some things you wouldn't want your sweet little Boots to know—I mean, what have you told her about us?"

Since this time neither Cora nor Mr. Inch shut the door, Emily was left to reflect scornfully that there was no need for her mother to tell her about Mr. Inch, since she saw him for herself now almost every day, kissing her mother, touching her curly hair. And hadn't Mr. Inch told Emily himself that he hoped to come and live with them one day while touching her hair—Emily's much longer hair?

All the same, there was a resemblance between Mr. Inch and a wolf. His big teeth. The way he smiled when alone with Emily, for example. "All the better to eat you with." Emily could remember the story even if she could no longer be bothered to read it. Once, in spite of herself, she got out the old book and looked at her favorite picture—or, rather, what had once been her favorite picture—of Grandmother in her frilly cap, Grandmother with big teeth, smiling.

Little Red Riding Boots stood in front of Grandmother, and though you could see the boots all right, all red and shiny, just like Emily's own, standing in the corner of her bedroom, you could not see the expression on the little girl's face. Nevertheless, Emily could imagine that expression perfectly well. Definitely, the little girl would not be looking afraid—in spite of everything, in spite of Grandmother's big teeth, in spite of being alone with her in the house.

This was because Emily herself was not afraid of Mr. Inch, even when she was alone with him in the flat and he called her his little gir, his little Boots (which Emily firmly ignored), and talked about all the treats he'd give her "one day," a day Mr. Inch strongly hoped would come soon.

The girl in the picture was standing quite still. She knew that soon the woodcutter would come rushing in—as he did in the next picture—and save her. Then he would kill the wicked wolf, and in some books (not the version which was supposed to be her favorite) the woodcutter made a great cut in the wolf's stomach and out came tumbling all the other people the wolf had eaten. No blood, though, which was rather silly, because everyone knew that if you cut people open or knocked them or anything like that, there was masses of blood everywhere.

You saw it all the time in films when you were allowed to sit with your supper and hold your mother's hand during the frightening bits:

"Squeeze me, Boots, squeeze my hand."

Emily loved sitting with Cora like this, to watch the films on television, and it was one of the things she really didn't like about Mr. Inch that when he arrived Emily had to stop doing it.

Mr. Inch watched the films with Cora instead and he held her hand; he probably squeezed it, too. Sometimes he did other things. Once Emily had a bad dream and she came into the sitting room. The television was still on, but Mr. Inch and Emily's mother were not watching it. Emily's mother lay on the floor all untidy and horrid, not pretty and tidy like she generally was, and Mr. Inch was bending over her. His trousers were lying on the floor between Emily and the television and Emily saw his long white hairy legs, and his white shirttails flapping when he hastily got up from the floor.

Now that *was* frightening, not like a film or the news, and Emily didn't really like to think about the incident afterward. Instead, she began to imagine, in greater detail, how Mr. Inch might get himself killed, like the wolf—like her father. She didn't hold out much hope of Mr. Inch going somewhere hot, because he never seemed to go anywhere, and also Mr. Inch had plenty of money—lack of money was the reason Emily's father had gone somewhere hot in the first place. Nor was he likely to be killed crossing the road, like the old woman, if only because Mr. Inch was always warning Cora (and Emily) to take care. Even when Emily watched Mr. Inch running in their direction, she noticed he always stopped for the lorries and allowed plenty of time for them to pass. As for the woodcutter—which was a silly idea, anyway, because where would you find a woodcutter in a city?—even if you took it seriously, you couldn't expect a woodcutter to rush into their flat, becasue Cora saw so few people. She was far too busy caring for her little girl, Cora explained to Mr. Inch when they first met. Baby sitters were expensive, and in any case unreliable.

"I souldn't dream of trying to take you away from this dear little person," Mr. Inch had remarked on that occasion, flashing his big white teeth at Emily. "It was always one of my great regrets that I never had a daughter of my own."

No, Emily did not see how a woodcutter could be brought into the story. She wished that Mr. Inch would be famous, and then he would go on television and maybe be killed. But Cora said that Mr. Inch was not famous:

"Just a very good kind man, Boots, who wants to look after us."

"Now I've got two little girls to look after," said Mr. Inch once day. For a moment, Emily was mystified by his remark—she had a sudden hope that Mr. Inch had found another little girl to look after somewhere else. It was only when Mr. Inch took first Cora's hand, then Emily's, that she realized with a certain indignation that Mr. Inch's other little girl was supposed to be her mother.

After that, the caring and looking-after of Mr. Inch for Cora and Emily grew stronger all the time.

"I'll take very good care of her," said Mr. Inch when Cora asked him to go down to the supermarket with Emily, "and I'm sure you won't object on the way back if there's just one ice cream."

"Run along, Boots," called Cora from the kitchen, "and hold Mr. Inch's hand very tight. Especially crossing the road."

Actually, there was no need for Cora to mention crossing the road to Mr. Inch, because he held Emily's hand so terribly tight on the way to the shops that she had to stop herself squeaking. Then Mr. Inch cheated. He bought Emily not one but two ice creams. He took her to the new ice-cream parlor—Emily had never been inside before because Cora said it was too expensive.

Emily ate her ice creams in silence. She was imagining cutting open Mr. Inch with the woodcutter's axe. She didn't think the things inside Mr. Inch would be very nice to see (certainly no exciting people had been swallowed by Mr. Inch), but there would be plenty of blood.

Even when Mr. Inch asked Emily to come and sit on his lap and said he had something very exciting to tell her, that he was going to be her new daddy, Emily still didn't say anything. She let Mr. Inch touch her long hair, and after a bit she laid her head on Mr. Inch's chest, which is what he seemed to want, but still she was very quiet. "Poor little Boots is tired,' said Mr. Inch. "We'd better go home to Mummy."

So Emily and Mr. Inch walked along the crowded street, the short way back to their flat from the shops. Emily didn't say anything and she didn't listen to what Mr. Inch was saying, either. When Emily and Mr. Inch got to the crossing, they paused and Emily—as well as Mr. Inch—looked left, right, and left again, just as Cora had taught her.

This time Mr. Inch was not holding Emily's hand nearly so tight, so it was Emily who squeezed Mr. Inch's hand, his big hairy hand, and Emily who smiled at Mr. Inch with her little white pearly teeth.

It was when one of the really big lorries was approaching, the sort that Cora said shouldn't be allowed down their street, the sort that were rumbling their flat to bits, that the little red boots, shiny red-plastic boots, suddenly went twinkling and skipping and flashing out into the road.

Fast, fast, went the little red boots, shining. Quick, quick, went the wicked wolf after the little red boots.

Afterward, somebody said that the child had actually cried out: "Catch me! Catch me! I bet you can't catch me!" But Cora, even in her distress, said that couldn't possibly be true, because Emily would never be so careless and silly on a zebra crossing. Hadn't Emily crossed it every day, sometimes twice a day, all her life? In spite of what the lorry driver said about the little girl dashing out and the man running after her, Cora still blamed the driver for the accident.

As for poor Mr. Inch—well, he had died trying to save Emily, save her from the dreadful lorry, hadn't he? He was a hero—even if he was now a sad, sodden lump of a hero, like an old dog that had been run over on the road.

Emily said nothing. Now Boots expected to live happily ever after with her mother, watching television, as in a fairy story.

Brendan DuBois
The Warning

As Lucas loaded the shotgun by the light of the BMW's dashboard, he said, "Ron, one thing you always remember when working for the Firm is to keep the Firm's hands clean. Always."

Ron nodded as he watched Lucas's gloved hands carefully place each shell into the open magazine. Between his legs he cradled an identical pump-action shotgun in his hands.

"Understand?"

"Yes, I do," Ron said, feeling like the student he was. "That's something I learned the first day I started working."

Lucas finished loading and handed the gun to Ron, who kept both weapons upright. His hands were sweating in his gloves. He and Lucas were parked on a country road somewhere in Maine, next to a long stretch of woods. It was night and he felt uncomfortable—not because of the job, which was normal enough, but because of the woods. He hated the country. It was too quiet.

"Well," Lucas continued, "there's a difference between theory and practice. With me you'll learn a lot about the practice."

The rearview mirror lit up from an approaching car's headlights. Lucas reached down to the ignition but he stopped when the car passed by.

"Nissan," he murmured. "Martin Walker drives a Thunderbird."

They had been there for a half hour and Ron was bored, but he knew better than to say anthing about it. He concentrated on keeping both shotguns upright and he looked out at the woods, but after a while he glanced away. There were no street lights and he imagined he saw low and twisted faces among the trees, staring at him.

Lucas sat in the driver's seat, his face impassive, arms folded across his chest. His black hair was trimmed short, and in the glow from the dashboard light Ron saw a faint shadow of beard on the man's face. It was the only thing about him that was out of place.

"You've been with us six months," Lucas said, his eyes still staring out at the dark road. "What do you think?"

Careful, Ron thought, be oh so careful.

"It certainly is different," he offered. And how, it was. Like Lucas, he wore a tailored three-piece suit and a long cloth raincoat. They were the finest clothes he'd ever worn. In the past six months he had eaten at the best restaurants, had even learned how to order wine, and the women he had met— Seven months ago, his work clothes had been a T-shirt and a mended pair of jeans. He'd been doing similar work, freelancing, but now there was no more of the knife-edge tension, of wondering who

315

had hired him. The Firm took care of that, and many other things. Travel. Fine cars.

All in exchange for doing anything the Firm wanted, at any time, at any place.

"You know, your supervisors were very pleased with the way you handled the Taylor-woman matter. It was very well done."

"Thank you," Ron said, recalling the old woman. Was it only last week? He had an unusual talent—he never worried about the past, about anything he had done, and he certainly never worried about the future. The Taylor woman had been in her seventies and somehow she knew something embarrassing about an executive in the Firm. Rather than risk having the information get out,he had been sent to see her last month. He had visited her twice a week for three weeks, posing as a city health-care worker, until he had gained her trust.

Lights appeared behind them and a blue Thunderbird drove past.

"Here we go," Lucas said, starting the BMW and pulling out onto the roadway. Within a few seconds the taillights of the Thunderbird were in view. "About the Taylor woman—were there any difficulties at all?"

"No," Ron said, trying to keep the shotguns from striking each other. "By the end of the month she trusted me, and when I told her I was administering free flu shots she said she wanted one. I used an empty hypodermic and in a minute she was dead."

"Air embolism. That's always a good one. Was she in bed at the time?"

"Yes. She just closed her eyes and fell back. It was a hot day and I left all the windows closed. By the time anyone showed up it would be hard to find any trace of a needle mark."

Ahead of them the Thunderbird drove on, passing large homes set back from the road. Lucas kept the BMW at a constant speed.

"That's what our supervisors like to see. Clean hands. No way to tie a harmless old woman dying alone to the Firm. Did anything bother you about the Taylor woman?"

"No," Ron said, "nothng." It was the truth. A few hours after he left her stuffy apartment, he was on the other side of the city, having a leisurely meal with Sandra—Sandra with the bright eyes and soft mouth. By the next morning, he had completely forgotten about the Taylor woman and he hadn't thought of her again until Lucas had just mentioned her. A good way to live, he thought, letting the past and future take care of themselves.

The Thunderbird's taillights winked and the car turned to the right, into a driveway that rose up to a two-storey white house set among some large pines. A mailbox had COUTURE on the side and Lucas followed the Thunderbird, saying, "Get ready now, this is going to be a complicated one."

The BMW came to a stop and Lucas grabbed his shotgun and a satchel. He stepped out and Ron followed him, keeping his gun hidden in the folds of his raincoat. Lucas raised his shotgun up and a man who was stepping out of the Thunderbird turned and stopped, both arms rising slowly into the air. There was a loud clink as he dropped his car keys. Ron also raised his shotgun, and when he was with Lucas in the garage Lucas reached over and slapped a switch on the wall. The garage door rumbled down and Lucas said, "Well, Martin Walker, you may have changed your name and moved all the way out here, but the Firm always takes care of its own."

Walker was in his fifties and overweight, wearing a rumpled blue suit with a red tie. His hair was thin and brown.

He licked his lips. "It's been almost five years," he said slowly, his voice hoarse.

"Five or fifty, it doesn't matter," Ron said, enjoying again the surge of power he always felt on a job. "A half million dollars is a lot of money."

"Listen, I can pay it back, I'm doing very well out here—"

Lucas dropped the satchel and got to his knees, opening it with one hand. "Too late, Mr. Walker. Come on now. Five years later? Forget the interest on the money, forget the money, forget anything remotely connected to the money. You upset a lot of people in Los Angeles.

"Time to get dressed," he added, pulling out handcuffs and lengths of chain.

It went easier than Ron had imagined. He thought the man would kick and scream and put up a fight but instead he stood there, his head hanging, as Lucas gagged him and placed shackles around his legs and arms. When that was done, Lucas picked up the car keys Walker had dropped and opened the car's trunk.

"Give me a hand, will you?" he said to Ron.

Ron leaned his shotgun against a wall, and when he helped Lucas put Walker into the trunk the man started to react, kicking and mewling against the gag. Lucas grinned as he slammed the trunk lid down.

"Here you go," Lucas said, handing Ron the BMW keys. "I'll take your piece with me."

Ron opened the garage door and walked to the BMW. As he drove back out the driveway and toward the highway, the lights of Walker's Thunderbird followed him all the way. It was going fine, but what did Lucas have planned?

An hour later Ron felt shakened as he parked the BMW in front of a wooden cabin. He driven up a crumbling and bumpy road that rose steeply into the mountains and twice he'd had to slow the car to a walk as he negotiated some tight corners. Lucas pulled in next to him, and within a few minutes Walker was in the cabin chained to a chair, with only his arms a bit loose and the gag off. Ron sat across from him, shotgun pointed at his head.

Lucas was whistling as he went around the small kitchen, mixing a drink from a portable bar. He still wore his gloves, as did Ron. Lucas had told him that he chose this place because he owned a cabin only a few miles away and he knew the area was remote and almost deserted.

"Here's something to wet your whistle, Mr. Walker," Lucas said, placing the glass down on the kitchen table. "Sorry about the gag and all, but I know you understand."

Walker stared at the drink until Lucas said, "Oh, I get it." He picked up the glass and took a sip. "See? No poison."

Walker drank, his hand trembling slightly.

The kitchen had a door on Ron's left and one to his back which led to the living room. A gas lamp on a bench hissed and there was a black wood-range on Ron's right.

Lucas took a piece of paper from his coat pocket and unfolded it on the table. He handed the man a pen.

"This is a note we had typed on one of your typewriters at work, Mr. Walker. You really should have better locks there. It's a suicide note, expressing severe depression and an unwillingness to face the future. Just sign it right here."

Walker looked up and Ron saw his face was trembling. "Just like that, you vermin? Just sign it?"

"Oh, I know, I know. You don't want to sign it. Well, look at it this way. Sign it right now, with no more back talk, and we'll ignore your former wife, living at twelve ten Wall Street, Simpson, Oregon, and your two daughters, one of whom is attending St. Mary's Girls Academy and the other of whom is getting married next spring."

Walker chewed on his lower lip and then quickly leaned forward, scrawling at the paper in harsh motions, the links on his shackles rattling, then threw the pen across the room.

"There. For all the satisfaction it'll give you."

"A lot, I guarantee," Lucas said. "I'll be back in a moment."

He went outside and Ron looked at Walker. His eyes were red-rimmed and watery, and every few seconds his cheeks twitched as if tiny insects were landing on him.

"So. You're going to help him kill me."

Ron shrugged his shoulders. "Sure looks that way."

A small smile touched at Walker's lips. "I suppose the Firm is treating you pretty well, then."

"I've got no complaints."

"Yet. You have no complaints *yet*. Wait until you've been there a few years, wait until your bad dreams start and you begin dreading nightfall. Then see how many complaints you have."

Ron shifted in his seat but kept the shotgun straight and level. "I doubt it, old man. I'll forget your name by tomorrow. By next week I'll forget your face. The week after that I'll be hard-pressed to remember where I was when we did this job. It don't mean a thing, it's just a job. Hell, last week I took care of an old lady that was a lot nicer to be around than you and it hasn't kept me awake a second."

The lantern continued hissing. Its wavering light made Walker's skin look moist.

"You're a cold one, but that won't matter. There'll always be something that'll touch you and get inside you—"

"Listen, old man," Ron interrupted, motioning the shotgun toward him, "just shut your face."

"No, I won't." The small smile returned. "You can't stop me from talking unless you start hitting on me, and if you start hitting on me the coroner is going to wonder why a suicide victim has bruises on his face. No, you're going to have to listen to me.

"The Firm offers a lot, doesn't it? More money and other goodies than most can handle. But the Firm feeds on itself. Once you're listed as a liability or a problem, they'll cut you. No matter how good they tell you you are, no matter how good you feel you are, you'll be out, and even someone you trust, someone you've worked with, they'll use him to eat you."

Walker looked down at his hands, at the handcuffs and the short chain between them. "I had a friend in the Firm who remained a friend. He warned me that I'd made a certain list. I got out and in a week he was dead." He looked up. "A drowning. Very neatly done."

Lucas came in, carrying a stepladder and a coil of rope. "Sorry to interrupt your last words, Mr. Walker. Care for another drink?"

Ron was surprised, but Walker did have another drink as Lucas got on the stepladder and fashioned a noose from the rope, tying off one end to the exposed rafters. Sipping quietly from his glass, Walker stared at Ron—who looked away. Just another job, he thought. One more and I'm not counting. But he couldn't look at Walker's face.

He kept the shotgun trained on him until Lucas nodded and he got up, leaning the gun against the wall. Lucas moved a kitchen chair underneath the dangling rope and the two of them stood behind Walker. Lucas quickly blindfolded and gagged him again. There was a sour smell about Walker and Ron felt his stomach churn from the odor.

"Give a hand, then," Lucas said, reaching under one arm.

Ron grabbed the man's other arm, feeling the warmth through his gloves. Walker started making noises, muffled screams and moans from behind the gag, and the stench grew stronger as the two men lifted him out of the chair. Walker tried kicking and straining against the chains, making them clink and rattle, but in another minute they had him on the chair, standing and weaving.

"Hold him right there," Lucas said. Ron felt incredibly warm, his eyes stinging with sweat dripping from his forehead. Everything seemed too warm—his skin, the room, his raincoat. Lucas got up on the kitchen table and pulled the noose over Walker's head. The muffled cries grew louder and Ron felt the sweat trickle down his back as he tried to keep the man upright. Lucas pulled the noose snug. "Okay. Walk away. If he moves now he'll be dead anyway."

Lucas jumped to the floor and stood next to the chair. Walker's legs were shaking and the shackles on his wrists were rattling as he stood there, his face bright red. Lucas was grinning.

"So long, Mr. Walker," he said in a loud voice, and he swiftly kicked out with his right leg.

The wooden table flew over with a crash and Ron felt himself jump. Walker was still on the chair, strangled noises coming through the gag, and a wet spot appeared on his pants. Lucas was laughing.

"Not bad, huh?" he said to Ron.

"I don't understand," Ron told him.

"Never mind. Get your gun."

In a few seconds, Lucas went to work and Walker was seated back in the chair, the gag and blindfold off.

Lucas tossed two sets of keys into his damp lap. "Those are to your locks and your car," he said, pointing to the keys. "You have sixty seconds to free yourself and get the hell out of here before I change my mind and blow off your head."

Walker, who had been sitting motionless, blinking his eyes, drool running down his chin, started unlocking the chains in a frenzy.

"Tomorrow," Lucas continued, "someone from the Firm will be by your house to talk about a loan repayment. Will you be there?"

"Yes, yes," Walker said, his fingers fumbling at a lock on his waist. His eyes seemed to shine. "This was just a test, right? Something to scare me. Something to make sure that I'll repay the Firm."

"That's right," Lucas agreed. "This was just something to scare you."

Ron watched Walker free himself, resisting an urge to shake his head in disbelief. He had never seen anything like it. What was going on?

Walker stumbled to his feet and ran to the door, where he fumbled with the doorknob. When he got through the door, he left it wide open and the screen door slapped back after he left, sounding like a gunshot. Lucas said nothing, waiting for the sound of Walker's Thunderbird driving away.

"Well? What do you think?" he asked with a smile.

"I'm not sure what to think," Ron said, wondering what was behind that grinning face. "It seems like a lot of effort just to scare a man into paying back some money."

"Oh?" Lucas said, picking up the overturned table. "Then maybe you can understand this. While you were talking to Mr. Walker and I was outisde, I spent a lot of time working on his car. In another minute or two, while he's speeding down the side of this mountain, he's going to lose his brakes and steering. How does that sound?"

"Oh."

"So he's going to be very dead in a very short time, and the police are going to find a dead man with alcohol in his blood who went off a dangerous road. And here they'll find a cabin registered in his name, with only his fingerprints." He reached down and picked up the typed note from the floor. "And no suicide note. Just a dead drunk in an accident. Clean hands for the Firm."

Amazing. Ron thought he was good but Lucas was making him feel like an amateur. A hit was a hit, but a mind that could dream up something like this—Ron wasn't sure how much he should respect Lucas, or fear him.

Lucas turned off the lantern and the two men went outside. The night air was crisp and cool and Lucas stretched out his arms.

"God, I love these mountains," he said. He continued walking and looked over at Ron. "You know, I think I'm going to walk up to my cabin and spend the night there. It's a nice night, probably one of the few good ones left this year. You want to take the BMW back into town?"

Not a bad idea, Ron thought, walking along, his shoes crunching in the gravel. A chance to ditch Lucas and be by himself in the BMW, which was a nice car, a car with a lot of work put into it—a lot of work. Like Lucas, something unique.

Lucas, who'd had time to work on one car, and probably had time to work on another.

Even if they tell you you're doing a good job, Walker had said. Walker, who was probably bleeding to death right now.

Lucas was staring at him, smiling as if his offer of the BMW was some sort of challenge.

Ron licked his lips, which had suddenly become dry. "I'd prefer not to," he said, keeping his tone even.

Lucas's smile grew wider. "Don't worry, I was just funning with you. C'mon, we'll both head in. And I'll drive. In a week we'll be back on the West Coast."

A week, Ron thought, holding tight onto his shotgun. In a lot longer than a week he'd still remember Walker's name.

James Powell
A Baksheesh from the North

At that time of the afternoon, the only light in Achmed's American Bar came from the corner pinball machine. Plump, jolly Miss Chalmers, whom the Shaddocks had met on the bus from the airport, squinted at the tour literature and announced proudly: "The Beehive Mosque, seen it. Fatima's Fig Tree, seen it. The Grotto of a Million Bats." She shuddered deliciously. "Seen it. On deck for tonight, the quote 'unique sights and smells of the Goatherds' Bazaar' unquote."

Mr. Shaddock, a balding, small-boned man with a petulant mouth, grunted and rubbed the knee he'd hit groping to the table in the sudden gloom of the bar. "What I want to know is who's this guy Baksheesh," he said grumpily.

Mrs. Shaddock stared down into her rye and water to underline her lack of interest. "Who knows? Who cares?" she said.

Shaddock cared. Everywhere they went today a shabby crowd had dogged his steps shouting, "Baksheesh! Baksheesh!"

"He must be a real ringer for your Mr. Shaddock, eh, Mrs. Shaddock?" remarked Miss Chalmers.

"Big deal," said Mrs. Shaddock.

A shape rose up from a table in the shadows along the wall. A barrel of a man in a beige tarboosh stepped forward and smiled in the pinball glow. "Forgive my eavesdropping, messieur—demes," he declared. "May it please you to learn that Prince Baksheesh is the hero of Mokador's most beautiful legend." He tucked in his chin and looked down at them benignly. "Might I presume to tell his story?"

"Now isn't that nice now?" said Miss Chalmers, dealing everyone a smile.

"Don't let me stop you," said Mrs. Shaddock.

"Join the party. Have a drink," said Shaddock, who was curious. The fat man looked harmless enough.

"*You* must be *my* guests," the man insisted and pulled up a chair. Without turning his head he called, "Raki!" in a masterful voice that sent the pock-cheeked bartender scurrying for a bottle and glasses. "My name is Hakim," said the man. "Import-export."

"Shaddock," said Shaddock. "I run a chain of stereo shops out of Toronto. I came up with the name myself." He ran a finger along an imaginary marquee. "Mr. Speaker."

"Taint funny, Magee," said Mrs. Shaddock.

"Ingenious," said Hakim. He reread the marquee with a rumbling chuckle that made his body shake as if from falling rock within. Then he added, "How nice Canadians still visit Mokador."

"You mean after the disappearance of the "In the Footsteps of

322

Valentino' tour bus?'' asked Miss Chalmers. ''All those lady school teachers from Ontario?''

''Please do not slander my people with talk of abduction by force or white slavery,'' begged Hakim. ''In Mokador, we respect two things above all else: education and the abundant female form.'' When he leaned forward confidentially, they leaned to meet him. ''At this very moment in certain encampments to the west, fierce desert tribesmen smitten with love are mumbling their times tables and raising their hands for permission to leave their own tents.'' Hakim's glossy mauve eyelids dipped shyly. ''But how do you know all this, fair lady?'' he asked Miss Chalmers.

Miss Chalmers blushed. ''I teach school myself. The flu made me miss the trip. Ever since, I've felt like the kid who was left behind in *The Pied Piper of Hamelin*. You know: 'Rats! They fought the dogs and killed the cats—''

''About Baksheesh,'' intruded Shaddock.

''Ah yes, quite so,'' said Hakim, turning from Miss Chalmers regretfully. ''Prince Baksheesh was the sum of manly virtue poured into the most handsome of vessels. Where he trod the desert, green shoots started up from the ground. As he passed, the trees bowed down in leafy genuflection. And when Haroun al Rachid, Caliph of Bagdad, named Baksheesh his successor by bestowing on him the Sacred Scimitar in its jeweled scabbard, Araby hugged itself with joy.

''But the envy of Zendik al Mozawer, that traitorous vizier and vile magician, was aroused. He marched from his exile in the land of Sham with an army of sand devils and whirling dervishes and the sky ran black before him. So Baksheesh left the arms of his love, the most beautiful woman in Mokador, and, crossing the Bridge of Boats over the Tigris, strode out to meet his adversary. Baksheesh the Open-handed, the Evenhanded, the Helping-handed versus Zendik the Underhanded, the Highhanded, the Sleight-of-handed.

''When Baksheesh smiled, the white glory of his teeth made Zendik's host cast down their serpentine blades and monstrous-headed halberts and hide their eyes in the crooks of their elbows. Undaunted, Zendik let loose with black lightning bolts and fireballs of hellish greens and blues from his cursed arsenal. But Baksheesh's frank gaze turned all this aside and more. At last, his powers spent, his Army of Darkness in full retreat, Zendik groveled in the sand, begging for mercy with a tongue of silk, and offered his hand in surrender. Baksheesh, knowing no guile, took it willingly. But concealed in the magician's palm was a powerful talisman that pierced Baksheesh with invisible galvanic darts and made him shudder and dance from foot to foot. Baksheesh's faithful cupbearer, rushing forward to help, was himself caught in the talisman's grip when he touched his master's arm. With hideous laughter, Zendik clasped Baksheesh's hand tighter and tighter still until all life had left his body.''

"Well, we all gotta go sometime," said Mrs. Shaddock, looking at her watch. "And speaking of 'gotta go.'"

"Oh, the fashion show back at the hotel," groaned Miss Chalmers. "This gentleman's story was so engrossing I completely forgot." She gathered up her purse.

Shaddock hesitated. "You two go ahead," he said, pouring himself another drink. "I'd like a little chinwag with Mr. Hakim here. I'll catch up."

Hakim rose to bid the ladies goodbye. "Mokador is not so large that I must abandon hope of seeing you both again," he declared, his smile sad, his gaze tragic and all for Miss Chalmers alone. When they had left, Hakim took his seat again, adding, "A superb woman, don't you think?"

"You mean Baksheesh died and that's it, that's the whole legend?" demanded Shaddock.

"Well, hardly," said Hakim. He returned to his narrative.

"When the bird of Baksheesh's soul fled the nest of his skull, Zendik deftly caught it in his Cloak of Forgetfulness. The spirit of his faithful cupbearer, similarly caught, was sealed in a bottle and cast into the ocean. But the precious soul of Baksheesh was imprisoned in the bowels of a denizen of the vasty deep, a giant cachelot which, fluking mightily, dove down to an ocean cave to rest in bubbly slumber."

The man frowned, refilled his glass, and took a first sip before continuing a bit more brightly. "But it is written that one day the ancient whale will wake. It will rush to the surface for air and the soul of our Prince will escape in the spouting. Then Baksheesh will come back to us."

Hakim straightened and cupped a hand behind an ear as though hearing a parade in the distance. "And what a day that will be! Baksheesh will march around the world at the head of the Grand Army of Good Fellowship, showering sympathy and understanding on everyone, and neither king, corporation, nor commissar will be able to resist him. Then the desert will be green again. Then happiness and freedom will reign in every land and clime!"

"That sounds damn nice on paper," admitted Shaddock, "but I'm a hard-nosed businessman. Money makes the mare go. You're talking grass seed, uniforms, and band instruments for this Grand Army. You're talking radio and television spots and handbills to proclaim Baksheesh's return."

"Not to mention the priceless yard goods to clothe the Forty Musk Maidens of the Hadramaut, the anxious young brides-to-be of our glorious Prince," added Hakim. "Fortunately, unlike many other legends, ours had an attractive self-financing side to it. You see, in anticipation of Baksheesh's return, Haroun al Rachid hid the treasures of Bagdad somewhere in the Chiming Mountains. This is the Golden Hoard of which the ancients speak. He entrusted its location to the Thousand Elders of the

Poor, who to this very day walk the streets of Araby waiting for our hero's return. Only the music of Baksheesh's voice can open the mighty doors of the mountain treasure-vault."

Shaddock considered all this for several moments before asking off-handedly, "I guess Baksheesh won't be hard to spot, eh? A good-looking guy with charisma that won't quit?"

Hakim wagged a contradictory finger. "Just as Haroun al Rachid moved among his people in disguise, so Baksheesh will appear in our midst looking like the most commonplace of mortals. In fact, thanks to Zendik's Cloak of Forgetfulness, he won't even know he is Baksheesh. You see, when his soul escapes from the cachelot, it will take refuge in the body of some newborn male in a dark and distant land. There he will pass a childhood haunted by the dim certitude of his own uniqueness and teen years soured by a belief that he is hard-done-by, and by an acnelike facial excrescence called caliph's carbuncle. His early manhood will be plagued by unfulfilled dreams and his middle age marked by the profound conviction that—How can I put it?"

"That life is passing him by," said Shaddock flatly.

Hakim frowned. "Why, yes. Exactly." He gave Shaddock a long, hard glance before continuing. "All this is but a prelude to what legend calls The Great Dawning, that rosy-fingered glow on the horizon of his consciousness when Baksheesh is recognized by the Elders of the Poor, called by name and given the secret hand sign."

Shaddock looked left and right. "Listen," he whispered, wearing a grin that could turn into a joking smile if Hakim laughed, "what you were talking about, how Baksheesh felt growing up and everything, that fits me like a glove. I mean right down to the caliph's carbuncle. And all day since we arrived they've been dogging my heels shouting, 'Baksheesh! Baksheesh!' "

"You misunderstood," insisted Hakim curtly.

Shaddock shook his head. "I swear I didn't."

"You dare to mock our traditions?" hissed Hakim through clenched teeth.

"They shouted, 'Baksheesh!' " maintained Shaddock. "They went like this." He held his arm waist high with the hand palm up.

Eyes like saucers, Hakim leaped to his feet and shouted, "The secret hand sign! The Salute of Palms! Verily you are Baksheesh!"

The bartender was looking over at them. "Sit down, sit down," whispered Shaddock, giggling with embarrassment.

"Sit in the presence of my Baksheesh? Never!" shouted Hakim. Shaddock had to pull him down by the hem of his suitcoat. "But I am a stupid," said Hakim, pounding his brow. "The signs well all there. First the Sacred Scimitar appeared among us. Then Zhoftika, the Pride of Mokador, returns to us from abroad. Finally, last week, that unfortunate business with Mr. Mahoud, the lineal descendant of Baksheesh's faithful cupbearer. Obviously, the stage has been set for the Three Tasks to confirm Baksheesh's identity."

Shaddock was crestfallen. "You mean I don't just get the Golden Hoard and the Musk Maidens?"

"First, you must free your cupbearer from bondage. Second, you must possess the Scared Scimitar. And third, you must make love to Zhoftika, the most beautiful woman in Mokador," said Hakim.

"But my bus leaves at nine in the morning," protested Shaddock.

Hakim signaled for the check. "Then the first item on the docket should be clothes," he said, making a face at Shaddock's polo shirt. "Baksheesh should not be dressed thusly."

Remembering Baksheesh's legendary open-handedness, Shaddock reached for the check when it came. Hakim was horrified. "Once The Great Dawning has commenced, Baksheesh must never again soil his hands with the disbursement of moneys," he scolded. The fat man added up the bill and, muttering and casting black looks at the bartender, he paid it from a tattered wallet.

Half blinded by the stucco whiteness of the streets, Shaddock stumbled along after the trotting, puffing fat man. Though Hakim chose the narrowest and most deserted turnings, a shabby crowd shouting "Baksheesh!" was soon on their heels. Hakim tried to wave them off with curses. "Zendik is still with us," he explained desperately. "This restlessness among the natives will make him move against you before you reach the fullness of your powers. Unless you relish a return to the bowels of the Great Whale, come quickly!" Grabbing Shaddock's elbow, he hustled him through a shop selling enameled brassware, out the back door into the steaming kitchen of a working-class restaurant (or was it a laundry?), in the side door of a shop hung with red and yellow leather goods, and through the rosewater and witch-hazel smells of a native barbershop to the street beyond.

When at last they had to step for breath, only two curly-headed boys had endured the chase. Panting, Hakim went back, squatted down, and spoke to them in earnest Arabic. Shaddock smiled modestly as they examined him with bright black eyes across the fat man's shoulders. They haggled for a bit almost as though over price. Then the taller boy dashed off. Hakim brought over the other. "This is Ali," he said. "He and his brother Omar are your new squires. I've sent Omar on a little errand."

"Baksheesh," said Ali politely and gathered up a handful of stones to throw at whoever tried to follow them.

In this way they reached their destination, a narrow little shop, reeking of dried sweat and old galoshes. While Hakim spoke to the proprietor, an oily runt wearing a tapemeasure around his neck, Shaddock looked through the racks of old clothes. A bemedaled World War II Italian general's uniform in a smart green rather caught his fancy. But Hakim rejected it as run-of-the-mill. And he was right. They came across seven others on the racks, castoffs of Mussolini's Invincible Legion, which, smiling apologetically, had retreated in a shambles through Mokador in 1941.

"Hakim," asked Shaddock, "about the Forty Musk Maidens. I mean, how does that fit in with my being married already?"

Hakim scrutinized a navy blazer bearing the London School of Economics crest. "It is written that Baksheesh was married in his former life," he said. "To Al Harridan, the Unappreciative One, a figure of some derision in our popular folklore." Hakim compared Shaddock's head and a Borsalino hat with a wonderful brim. "Baksheesh will send her away. But she will live a long life and realize the full beauty of the man she was too blind to treasure."

Shaddock'a grin was too big for him to speak through.

The costume was now complete: mouse-grey jodhpurs, white shirt open to the navel, riding boots scuffed yellow at the toes, over-large pith helmet, and a black cape with torn red lining that tied at the throat with a silk cord. "But the cape's too long. It smells like a goat," protested Shaddock.

"Camel," corrected Hakim gently.

Shaddock struck a pose he remembered from a statue at home in Queen's Park.

"Baksheesh!" cried the others.

They crossed the roofs of Mokador on all fours—Hakim, Shaddock, Ali, and Omar, who dragged a shopping bag behind him. "Heads down," warned Hakim. "Caught spying into the Gardens of Earthly Delight where the women loll eating sweetmeats while being massaged with rich unguents, and our lives won't be worth a fig." But whenever Shaddock managed a peek, all he saw were areaways with garbage cans, clotheslines, and an occasional tethered donkey. Well, what if Hakim was a romantic? Shaddock saw no harm in that. In fact, if it didn't put too big a dint in the Golden Hoard, maybe Baksheesh would install a Garden of Earthly Delight in every backyard.

"There. The third floor." Hakim pointed across the street to a building topped with a battlement. "Mr. Mahoud is trapped behind the second window from the right."

Over the front door of the building flew the green crescent-and-comet banner of Mokador. Beneath it dozed a soldier in a camouflage burnoose, his rifle between his knees.

"But it's a prison," protested Shaddock.

Hakim hung his head. "You have been long in returning, O Baksheesh. It is hard to live always in expectation. Some despair. To earn his daily bottle of raki, a kindly old scholar like Mr. Mahoud was reduced to illegal trafficking in shameless postcards around the bus station." Hakim summoned Omar with a finger snap. From the boy's shopping bag he drew a fat coil of rope. He pointed to the battlement.

"Baksheesh must throw a loop over that merlon there."

"Merlon?" asked Shaddock.

"The parts that go up," explained Hakim. "The spaces in between are the embrasures. In time it will all come back to you." He patted Shaddock's arm reassuringly. "Next you swing across to the prison and hook your foot in the bars in Mr. Mahoud's window. This is for the bars." The shopping bag yielded a large rattail file. "Meanwhile, Ali and Omar will drive a cartload of melons underneath. You and Mr. Mahoud will jump into it and make your escape. The melons will no doubt break your fall."

Shaddock's jaw hung open. He snapped it shut. "This plan does not please Baksheesh," he said. "Baksheesh is not Douglas Fairbanks."

"Ah," mourned Hakim, "no doubt Baksheesh has a more ingenious plan." The best Shaddock could come up with was a sudden rush on the jail. Patiently, Hakim explained that the Three Tasks had to be performed by Baksheesh single-handed, adding, "Though my plan involves certain risks, the only other way is to bribe the guards. But of course Baksheesh cannot soil his hands with money."

"What about travelers' cheques?" said Shaddock. At Hakim's perplexed book, Shaddock pulled out a fat folder of cheques. "They're accepted everywhere like cash. But they're not really legal tender."

Hakim held one up to the light suspiciously. "Whose picture is here depicted, this man with the odd nose? What caliph? Whose vizier?" He shook his head in ignorance when informed it was Sir John A. MacDonald. But he admitted that the legend made no mention of travelers' cheques. Grudgingly he agreed to negotiate with the guards and crawled away.

Shaddock rested against a television antenna and tilted his pith helmet over his eyes. He felt great. He knew it would happen, and it had. He'd come home at long, long last. Fame, fortune, and home!

Hakim soon returned on all fours, shaking his head. "They are sons of camels," he hissed. "The guards demand fifteen thousand piastres for Mr. Mahoud. Eight hundred dollars!" he translated the figure for Ali and Omar, who made shocked, clucking noises.

"Well, that's just out of the question," laughed Shaddock.

"Good," approved Hakim. "I told them thusly and roundly so." He picked up the rope and snapped it between his fists. "Now, when you hit the side of the building, keep your knees flexed to cushion the impact. You'll have to carry the file in your teeth. Let us fondly hope the boys can find enough melons this late in the—" Tightlipped, Shaddock waved the signed cheques under Hakim's nose. Hakim took them with obvious distaste. "As Baksheesh commands," he said, bowing with a hand on his chest, and crawled away.

"You said the Sacred Scimitar was jeweled," insisted Shaddock. The notched blade with its coarse twine handle was bare of all decoration.

"I said the scabbard was jeweled," corrected Hakim. "But that's been lost for centuries." He hurried Shaddock away from the pawnshop window and back to the narrow passageway where Ali, Omar, and Mr. Mahoud waited. Mr. Mahoud, a toothless, stoop-shouldered man in fraying tweeds, wore a furry canteen on a strap across his chest. Whenever Shaddock looked at him he would make melodious noises deep in his mouth and offer the canteen to Shaddock, for whom its warm, stale contents seemed to be reserved. "Our friend Mr. Mahoud knows the shop well," said Hakim. "The owner keeps ruby tie-tacks in a drawer back of the counter. Ask to see them and when he turns, hit him with this." He pressed the rattail file into Shaddock's hand. But let the weight of the file do the trick, all right? Any muscle behind it and you'll crush his head like a sand plover's egg."

Shaddock handed back the file. "Correct Baksheesh if he's wrong," he said quietly, "but aren't the articles in that window unredeemed? And doesn't that mean the scimitar is for sale?"

"Please, my Lord Baksheesh," begged Hakim, "not those accursed travelers' cheques again. Surely they offend the spirit of the tradition if not the letter."

Shaddock snapped his fingers and Ali ran to him holding out a ballpoint pen, for he had been appointed Sacred Pen Holder. "The trouble with tradition is that it gets out of date," said Shaddock as he signed. "Besides," he added, giving the somber Hakim a jab in the ribs, "this gives me all the more time for Zhoftika, the pleasantest of the Three Tasks."

It fell to Hakim to go and haggle for the scimitar. But the pawnbroker ("That Saracen dog!" swore Hakim on his return. "That spawn of Zendik!") held firm at 20,000 piastres. Shaddock winced. As he pondered, Hakim emerged from a quick huddle with the others and announced, "All we possess is yours in this venture, O Baksheesh. Here are my life savings, a cheque for 5,247 piastres 415 rials which any office of the Euphrates Savings and Loan will honor when they open on Monday." From Mr. Mahoud came a soiled envelope containing postcard views of the Naughty Nineties ("Oo la la," said Mr. Mahoud half-heartedly). Omar offered a partial pack of Mephisto cigarettes.

Their simple faith caught Shaddock by the throat. And when little Ali tugged at his cape and shyly held up a rhinestone dog collar with a broken buckle, Shaddock's eyes went bleary and brimmed over. He cupped his nose in his palm. "Baksheesh is touched," he announced moistly. It was several moments before he was able to sign his name.

There was an ancient shrewdness in the deep, narrow streets. By late afternoon they had filled with cool, dark shadows. Now Shaddock could sit in an outdoor cafe shielded from the eyes of Zendik by a mere hedge of boxed greenery. Ali and Omar, having delivered the note to Shaddock's wife saying he wouldn't be back for dinner, were drinking fruit juice through straws and kicking their heels contentedly. Mr. Mahoud was working on a bottle of raki. Hakim's face was thoughtful.

"Hakim, is she really pretty, I mean verily?" asked Shaddock.

Hakim smiled wistfully and translated the question for Mr. Mahoud, who rolled his eyes. "Zhoftika is our treasure," said Hakim. "Skin without blemish, hair like the raven's wing, pomegranate lips. The most beautiful woman of all. Have you never dreamed of her, Baksheesh?"

It suddenly occurred to Shaddock that he had, many times. Though not recently. He nodded.

"And she of you," said Hakim. "The poor cry out for Baksheesh in the streets. The women cry out for him in their dreams. She will recognize you when you come. But do not be deceived. The winning of Zhoftika is still fraught with danger."

"I care not what it's fraught with," swore Shaddock.

"Her wicked stepmother employs two fierce and incorruptible Nubians to guard her and her sisters," warned Hakim. "Yet I know a secret way into the house through the sewers. This will light your journey." Hakim produced a candle stub, made a puddle of wax on the brim of Shaddock's pith helmet with a lighter, and planted the candle there. "A word of caution," he continued. "Mokador's sewer rats are notoriously aggressive. Should you meet one, whether in the deepness of the main sewer or on the forty-foot crawl through the drain into Zhoftika's cellar, freeze and above all show no fear. Understand?" Shaddock rubbed his throat and nodded unhappily. "Good," said Hakim. "Now, Zhoftika's room is there." To Shaddock's surprise, the fat man pointed to a fourth-floor window across from the cafe.

Shaddock had been watching that particular house with mild interest. In the doorway stood a hefty woman with hair like greasy black seaweed and a painted smile for every passerby. The first-floor windows framed younger if no less painted faces. "But, Hakim," said Shaddock, "it's a brothel. Zhoftika lives in a brothel."

Hakim jerked Shaddock back down behind the greenery. "Don't let the Nubian see you!" A big black man in a maroon suit, yellow shoes, and an incredible white shirt came to the door, peeling an apple with a switchblade. "The other one's inside," said Hakim. And as if on cue through the window came the sound of a piano playing "Honeysuckle Rose."

"But don't you see what that means?" insisted Shaddock. "All I've got to do is plunk down the old travelers' cheques."

"No," said Hakim sharply. "That would not be seemly." He looked around warily and then whispered, "Some would say that Baksheesh had acted the coward's part."

Shaddock sat bolt upright. "Do you think mere sewer rats and Nubian blades can daunt Baksheesh?" he said indignantly. "Yet have I the right to risk the life on which so many depend? Hakim, in these few short hours I've come to love your people. But Mokador has many things to learn from the Twentieth Century. Cautious heroism, to mention only one."

Visibly chastened, Hakim bowed his head. "If it must be this way, I will enter into the arrangements."

Twirling Zhoftika's garter (required proof of a fulfilled Third Task), Shaddock sauntered back across the street with a worldly arc to one eyebrow. "Baksheesh!" cried Ali, Omar, and Mr. Mahoud enviously. "And so quickly!" marveled Hakim.

Shaddock saw no need to tell them he'd bought the garter. It had cost him the few cheques left over from the gouging price demanded by the stepmother. But after being ushered into a room containing Zhoftika, the Pride of Mokador, a coy three-hundred-and-fifty-pounder with bad teeth, Shaddock had paid them out gladly and hurried back down the stairs with his cape fluttering majestically.

"Then the moment is at hand!" proclaimed Hakim. "Ali and Omar, search out the Elders of the Poor! Mr. Mahoud, take Prince Baksheesh to the Grove of the Manifestation! And I will bring Al Harridan thither from the Goatherds' Bazaar to witness your triumph." He looked away. "Perhaps Miss Chalmers might care to join us."

Shaddock placed a hand on Hakim's shoulder. "You like Miss Chalmers, eh, my friend? Come, don't deny it. Then you shall have her, courtesy of Prince Baksheesh. Tonight when I name you my Grand Vizier, I want her at your side". Hakim caught his breath. "Yes," said Shaddock, "Baksheesh rewards his loyal followers. Ali and Omar I intend to send to school in Canada, perhaps Upper Canada College. In fact, I may send all the children of the world to Upper Canada College. As for Mr. Mahoud, a denture to begin with. And after that, what? Perhaps his own distillery."

Once a staging area for caravans, the Grove of the Manifestation was now an auto graveyard. Among the rusting cars and trucks stood an old well and a single olive tree whose branches had entrapped the rising moon. Crosslegged on the stone lip of the well, Mr. Mahoud hummed a dreamy singsong, his elbow on the canteen, his cheek in his hand, the raki bottle a bulge under his coat.

Shaddock, watching from his seat on the runningboard of a Reo Speed-Wagon, felt a warm affection for this weak old man who was not to blame if he lacked the character for the part history and his ancestor had chosen for him. Who of us did? Shaddock himself had almost missed the real meaning of his own majestic role. At first it had only been Baksheesh, Master of the Golden Hoard, Darling of the Forty Musk Maidens, Baksheesh setting Toronto on its Royal Canadian ear as he rode down Bloor Street at the head of the Grand Army of Good Fellowship. Then in a rush he had remembered something dating back to way before The Great Dawning: a kid, all leather mitts and whipcord breeches, caught in an eighth grader's half nelson and dreaming—as late-afternoon snow was being crammed down his collar—of a far better world, where the bully would protect the weakling, the miser and the wastrel would share the same purse, and people just generally got along. Then it had seemed like a utopian dream. But he knew Baksheesh could pull it off!

Voices came along the road. Was it Al Harridan and the others? A circle of grey, ragged figures shuffled through the moonlit gate. Hopeful voices called "Baksheesh!" Shaddock's heart beat faster. Enter the Elders of the Poor. The great adventure had begun.

Shaddock stepped into the moonlight and struck a pose, chin high, cape back over his left shoulder, right foot forward.

"Baksheesh?" wondered the crowd.

Mr. Mahoud nodded vigorously and pointed at Shaddock with the canteen. "Baksheesh," he giggled.

But when Shaddock stepped forward, arms outspread, the crowd fell back, scattering a bit as it did. There were blind men with sticks, the lame on crutches, the hungry on withered legs. "My children, Baksheesh has returned," announced Shaddock in a voice choked with compassion. "The Three Tasks have been accomplished. Look, the Sacred Scimitar and Zhoftika's garter. And there is my faithful cup-bearer." Mr. Mahoud, solemn as an owl, toasted Shaddock with the raki bottle. Then he choked on a laugh in midswallow and fell over backward down the well. The quick splash was followed by whoops of echoing laughter.

The men looked over at the well and then back to Shaddock. "Baksheesh!" they cried patiently and made the Salute of Palms.

"Yes, Baksheesh," repeated Shaddock. "He is sorry he was been so long. But now your sufferings are over." Then awed by the wings of his own rhetoric, Shaddock painted the future for them on the canvas of the night. He spoke of the blooming desert and Gardens of Earthly Delight in every home and of the Grand Army of Good Fellowship, where the slumlord and the tenant bivouac together, the haves and the have-nots split their rations, the Jeremiahs and the Good-time Charlies drink from one cup, and the slicker and the hayseed march to the same syncopated beat.

The crowd leaned attentively at first. But when a single impatient voice in the back shouted, "Baksheesh!" the others picked it up. "Baksheesh!" they insisted.

"Baksheesh understands all your resentments, my children," smiled Shaddock. "He knows how much you have been put upon and oppressed. But that was yesterday. Today, Baksheesh—"

"Baksheesh!" The voice were angry now. Sure it was being mocked, the crowd surged forward. Shaddock started back in surprise and stepped on the hem of his cape. He fell and the crowd closed in around him.

Back at the hotel, Mrs. Shaddock, a cigarette snug in the corner of her mouth, played solitaire in her dim room. Down in the bright lobby, the fat man, reconsidering, removed two, then three travelers' cheques from an envelope, sealed it, and handed it to the desk clerk. "A Mr. Mahoud will call for this."

The clerk bowed. "Of course, Mr. Zendik. We trust you'll be coming back our way soon."

"Whenever the situation demands," said the fat man. He filled his arms with suitcases and walked out the door. Miss Chalmers smiled as he slid behind the wheel of the car and patted her on the knee. They started on their way through the twisted streets, bound for the Land of Sham, where each night before retiring fierce desert tribesmen sing "O Canada" while lady school teachers beat out the time with twelve-inch wooden rulers.

Rounding a corner, the car almost ran into Shaddock. His mouth and chin were bloody, his pith helmet crumpled and awry, and he'd been stripped down to his underwear. Blinded by the headlights, Shaddock staggered by without recognizing them. They saw him stop in the empty street to strike a heroic pose. They heard him shout up at the dark windows, "But it's me! I've come back! It's Baksheesh—Baksheesh!"

They drove on. They did not see a face glossy with sleep appear at a small high window over Shaddock's head. Or the hand with rings on it. Or the coins flash in the moonlight.

David Williams

Mr. Oliver

Claudia's flat was in Hampstead, not the posh side near the Heath, but nice enough. It was the converted upper floor of a small two-storey house in an old terrace on a side street. She had her own private entrance at the stairs beyond the front door. An old girl lived underneath. She was unsympathetic, I gathered, and allergic to noise, but you hardly ever saw her.

Of course, it was a lot different from the other place—when Claudia had been a call girl.

There are worse and better names for what she was them, but call girl about covers it. She wasn't exactly at it full time, and she never had to solicit, either—it was all done very discreetly through this so-called agency. That was how we met.

I was given the telephone number by my stockbroker. He'd never used it, or so he said. He'd got it from a high-up in the City. The system was all very reliable, very circumspect, very safe in every way—so my stockbroker advised me. There would be no need to give my name.

I was interviewed first, by appointment, in a service flat behind Park Lane. It had its comic side. There was this sixtyish lady of quality who sat beside me on the sofa of the chintzy drawing room while I sipped sherry, answered and asked a few questions, and leafed through the photograph album of available talent. Nothing pornographic, and only the most tactful reference to "preferences." And I was told that if the first introduction wasn't a success I could come back and make a new choice.

The "initiation fee"—payable there and then—allowed for three introductions if required. Even so, I was assured archly, it was a facility seldom used.

To avoid misunderstanding, clients were asked to make appointments with their lady friends as far ahead as was convenient, and always to pay on arrival the agreed rate for the time and services required.

Every client was supplied with a pseudonym—mine was to be Mr. Oliver. Total anonymity would be observed. I was given Claudia's address and telephone number, as well as a number to ring if not satisfied after our first encounter. The number was different from the one I had got from my stockbroker.

That was the last I ever saw of Lady Vi—as she was known to Claudia.

The arrangement worked perfectly from the beginning. Claudia was everything I'd been looking for, and even better than her photo promised—again in every way. She was tall, slim, wide-eyed, and twenty-nine—a dancer with too little work, a lot of wit, long black hair, athletic, and as sexy as you liked when you liked. The deal was expensive but it came without commitment, risk, or obligation. I could afford it and it didn't bother my conscience—it didn't hurt anyone.

I had retired early from the Ministry of Defense three years before. I received a substantial pension and I wasn't senior enough to have rated a knighthood if I'd hung on. Anyway, I'm an engineer—no Eton and Oxford background, not knighthood material. The consultancy I started worked harder than any Honour's List award.

My job had been in purchasing, with good contacts abroad, especially in Africa and the Middle East. A whole string of British and American manufacturers were glad to hire me as a roving extra salesman—and my services didn't come cheap, either. For once we seemed to have more money than we needed. It made a change.

I should explain that my wife Maud has been in a wheelchair for ten years. I am devoted to her. I would never have let her guess how much I yearned for the physical satisfaction she couldn't give me, or risk her finding out I was taking it from someone else.

I'm not promiscuous by nature. It wasn't until Claudia discovered how possessive I'd become—or perhaps always had been: it could be the two things were related. The fact is, after a year I still valued the lack of involvement, but I did want exclusivity.

So when Claudia told me one afternoon she'd been offered a permanent job running an aerobics class for pampered young house-wives, that the pay for two hours work a day would nearly cover her living costs, that it almost meant she could give up her other work—well, you can guess my reaction.

Of course, it meant she had to give up the tiny but very ritzy and rent-free apartment in Chelsea provided by Lady Vi. I gave her half the cost of the thirty-year lease on the place in Hampstead, plus a quarterly allowance—always in cash—for what we lightly agreed should give me reasonable access on an exclusive basis.

So, you see, the whole arrangement was made on trust. I didn't expect it would last forever. I accepted her word that I was enough "man in her life" for the foreseeable future and she accepted that I would never leave my wife. Our time together we enjoyed to the full. Individual problems of the kind that could have marred the relationship were not shared—her probable loneliness, my burden of a sick wife. These were never discussed, only sensed. And there were some not even sensed, I realized later—too late.

Perhaps the most singular aspect of the affair was that I remained Mr. Oliver, that Claudia never addressed me any other way and never showed the least curiosity about my real identity. There were dozens of ways she could have found out. But she didn't trouble and I suppose it suited me not to volunteer. "Lady Vi promised you total anonymity and that's the way it should stay," she said to me several times, even after the move to Hampstead.

Once I wondered if she was keeping her side of the bargain: only once, and she knew it. Before I asked, she'd volunteered. "The marks on my back—no one's been whipping me. My sunlamp's on the blink. It waffled me yesterday."

I believed her. In the "old days," she'd told me, she'd had an elderly client who enjoyed a mild bit of flagellation.

The black eye had been two or three weeks later. I don't even remember the details of the harmless explanation she gave for that—only that it sounded like a genuine accident. And I didn't link the two things with the only hint of trouble Claudia ever confided to me. Although it came soon after the two accidents, I suppose I was too tired to pay attention, too anxious to be pampered. That was the last time we met.

I'd done what I'd often done before—caught a night flight from New York to London. I told Maud I was taking a morning flight the next day—that way I wouldn't be expected home in High Wycombe till after midnight and I could spend a whole day with Claudia with an easy conscience.

I slept off my jet-lag for a couple of hours while Claudia did her aerobics class, shopped, and made us some lunch. We spent the afternoon in bed and walked on the Heath after tea. Then she gave me a massage—the world's best, I can tell you. We went out for dinner at a small, discreet place we liked close by, all candlelight and real French specialities. We made love again at the flat before I left.

We knew we couldn't be together again for two weeks—I had this African trip coming up. Claudia didn't want me to leave, it had been such a perfect day, and in the end I stayed too long, and drank too much. To be frank, I was bushed when we finally did part.

I knocked down the old woman in Willesden. At least it looked like an old woman. It was in one of a string of back streets I regularly use as a shortcut to my High Wycombe road. It was just habit to go that way—there wasn't much traffic at midnight on a Tuesday and I could have made straight for the main road.

The figure stumbled out straight into me from between some parked cars. She hit my fender, then sort of bumped down the passenger side. It was ghastly. Of course I braked, but I was going quite fast. I don't know how fast. When I stopped, I could see this bundle in the road through my rear mirror—also another car that had just turned into the street.

The other car had stopped immediately. The driver was already out and running toward the figure on the road. He didn't seem to be looking in my direction. I had to make the decision there and then—go back and be involved or drive on quickly and hope I'd never be identified.

It wasn't only that I'd drunk too much—that was bad enough. It was also that I had no excuse for being in Willesden—it's the opposite direction to my home route from Heathrow. What would I tell Maud? I honestly was more concerned about Maud than I was about the police at that moment.

If the person I'd hit was dead, then that was terrible but there'd be no helping her—only the near impossibility of proving the accident was her fault, there being no witnesses and my blood-alcohol level probably being over the legal limit. If she was alive, then help was already at hand, with nothing more that I could do.

I switched off my lights and drove away fast. The other driver was still bending over the figure in the road.

Later I stopped at a call-box. It was ten minutes since I'd left Claudia. She'd just gone to bed. I told her what had happened. I said if the police questioned me later I'd say I'd been with her till 12:30—it was then only 12:15. If I was questioned I promised to ring her again, except that might not be possible immediately because of Maud, not prudent if there was any chance the police might be with her when I called.

I told Claudia if the police did check with her she should ring me at home. I had to give her the number, and she had to write it down. Funny she'd never had it before. That was the way it had always been. I said if Maud happened to answer she should say she was Mr. Oliver's secretary phoning about an appointment.

There were other people I might have asked to give me an alibi, but not that many, taking all the circumstances into account. It would have been complicated, too—especially explaining things at that time of night, but I could hardly have left it till morning. And Claudia would be telling nearly the truth.

I wasn't worried about Maud. If in some way the authorities did get onto me, I'd fix it so I was interviewed alone in my study. Afterward, I could tell her the police had made a mistake. With my watertight alibi, that should be the last either of us heard about the matter.

They came next morning about 10:30: two of them—nice enough chaps. The senior one was a Detective Sergeant, quite young and very polite. They were both in plainclothes. I let them in and showed them straight to my study. Maud never even heard them arrive. She was in the kitchen.

It appeared there had been an accident. A woman had died the night before. The Sergeant hoped I might be able to help his North London colleagues with their inquiries.

I looked surprised, but said I'd help in any way possible. I invited them both to sit down.

"Could you tell us exactly where you were between midnight and twelve-thirty, sir?" the Sergeant asked.

"Certainly," I answered. "There's just one thing. I was with a friend—a lady friend. It would hurt my wife terribly to know that. She's an invalid, you see—"

"We understand, sir," he interrupted tactfully, nodding to the other one, who was younger still—a Detective Constable. "It's a question of elimination at the moment, sir. Anything you say will be treated as confidential."

So I gave him Claudia's name, address, and telephone number. I remember adding, "By the way, Sergeant, the lady knows me as Mr. Oliver."

"Indeed, sir." He looked at the constable as he spoke. "And you were with her till twelve-thirty?"

"I was."

"And you'll swear to that, sir?"

"Absolutely," I said.

There was silence for a moment, then both policemen stood up. I thought they were preparing to leave.

No one ever traced Lady Vi. The flat behind Park Lane was one you could hire by the day in between longer lettings. According to the landlord's badly kept books, it had been officially empty the day I went there. Neither of the telephone numbers I'd been given belonged to the flat. They were both answering services, and both discontinued some time before.

Claudia's old flat in Chelsea had been leased in her own name. Only I knew she'd never paid the rent herself.

She'd started to tell me Lady Vi's "agency" people were angry with her that morning when I got in—something about her not agreeing to go on paying some kind of penalty charge when she left them. They'd guessed she was going it alone with a client she'd met through them.

As I said, I was too tired to pay attention at the time and Claudia hadn't made it sound that important. I suppose she didn't reintroduce the subject later because she figured it was something she ought to handle on her own. It wasn't so much that she was independent, we just had this kind of tacit agreement we'd cope with our own troubles and problems.

The street accident never happened—not according to police or hospital records. Whoever I'd hit must have recovered. Whoever the other driver was, he hadn't reported to anyone. We even ran advertisements begging the victim or any witness to come forward. (By this time I'd told Maud the truth and she was very understanding.) I publicly pleaded to be accused of knocking someone over in that Willesden street at ten minutes after midnight.

Result—nothing.

Of course the marks on her back and her black eye hadn't been accidents. She'd been beaten up—by the enforcement members of Lady Vi's mob. And whoever Claudia had let in after I left had been intending to administer a progressively more hurtful lesson—before things had gone seriously wrong.

But why had she let anyone in at gone midnight?

The court took the view she hadn't had to let anyone in, that I'd been there already. The old girl on the ground floor had seen us come back after dinner. What's more, she'd seen me before, often, and had no difficulty identifying me.

I guessed what had really happened. Claudia had opened the door, thinking I'd come back after I'd telephoned, intending to make the alibi more convincing. If I'd come back I'd have used my own key, they said, the key I'd admitted owning—except a door key wouldn't unfasten the safety chain I'd pressed Claudia always to use.

She hadn't been beaten repeatedly—there hadn't been time. There were just the two marks of the rubber truncheon he'd used, one on her shoulder, the other lower down on her back. It was the fall against the bedroom mantelpiece that had knocked her unconscious, caused the commotion, and made him run for it.

The old girl's pet Scottie must have been roused by the vibration of the fall and it started barking. Its mistress got up and began shouting abuse in the hallway. She said later she'd heard screams and thought they were screams of delight because we'd always been noisy lovers, and sadistic—she'd noticed that black eye. The villain must have panicked and crashed out down the stairs. The old girl didn't see him, but she was sure it was me.

It was another seven hours before the stupid old bint realized Claudia's front door was still open. It was the dog that found her body.

The second truncheon blow had been much fiercer than the first. It had ruptured her spleen—chance in a thousand apparently, unless it had been deliberate, and, if so, very accurate. I don't believe whoever it was had been sent to kill—it wouldn't have made sense. Probably he'd lashed out hard, fast, and wild when she was trying to get away from him. That's when she hit her head.

Claudia died from internal bleeding. She'd come to at one point, but they figured she'd been too weak to move or shout for help—not loud enough to attract the old girl, anyway. But they were convinced she'd managed to do one thing.

It was how they'd got onto me. I here was nothing to connect me with Claudia otherwise. Despite our relationship, the total anonymity had endured.

Of course, I'd have come forward after the murder, whatever the consequences—but as a volunteer, not as what looked like the self-confessed perpetrator.

If it hadn't been for the damned-fool game of anonymity, Claudia would have known the number and wouldn't have needed to write it down-not after two years, and not so it looked like the victim's dying message.

Because that's exactly how they interpreted it. It was what had been on the message pad that fallen with the bedside table. The pad and pencil had been under her hand when they found her, with what she'd written before she'd been attacked—not after, as they supposed.

The writing was awkward-looking—naturally, as I explained, she'd been in bed, probably half asleep, the pad at an unnatural angle. They weren't interested. They were interested only in what she'd written—the High Wycombe number, Mr. Oliver—12:30. POLICE.

I lost again when we went to appeal.

Thomas Adcock
A Quaint Little Crossroads

One hour after the murder, Special Deputy Sheriff Torjesen's telephone-message slot contained twenty-two slips of bright-pink paper. Eva, his secretary, had checked the little square marked Please Return Call on each slip. She'd also entered, in a florid hand, the notation *Urgent* followed by five exclamation points per message. That amounted to one hundred and ten exclamatories, which was more excitement than Paint Creek had known in ten years.

Ten years, precisely to the day.

Most everyone had stopped talking about it—and had stopped talking, period, to the woman they hated for it. So far as the rest of the state was concerned, Paint Creek had settled back to normal as a quaint little crossroads along Lake Superior's Gunflint Trail.

Now this again.

Twenty of the callers were downstate reporters, mostly from St. Paul and Minneapolis. One was from Paint Creek's sole news medium, Duke Oelander and his 5,000-watt KOLD-FM, "the crisp voice of northern Minnesota," as he announced each broadcast day. The other caller was Torjesen's nominal boss down in the county seat of Duluth, Sheriff Fred Irons.

Irons was a friend who went back to the days when Torjesen was a Chicago detective who liked vacationing up in Minnesota. And Irons was a faithful reader of Torjesen's many paperback mystery novels, which he'd written from his police experiences with large dashes of vivid imagination. Two months ago, when Torjesen's wife divorced him, Irons convinced his old pal to become Paint Creek's first permanent deputy sheriff. A nice, peaceable plum of a job, Irons promised.

It was that. Torjesen had plenty of time to write and to fish and to sort out his pain and anger. He received a steady paycheck and all he had to deal with was the occasional drunk. Irons hadn't mentioned anything about that old business with Bridget Paige and her wolves. And Torjesen, like most outsiders, didn't think to ask about something dead and buried for a decade.

But now it was happening all over again.

Hokken Torjesen, more commonly known as Ken, sat at his desk inside the private office he'd fashioned. It was a writerly sort of inner sanctum within the small wooden building on Bay Street that Sheriff Irons had set up as Paint Creek's very own hostel of law and order, complete with flag and a cell in back in the event of a drunk with nowhere to go for the night.

Most of the walls of Torjesen's private office consisted of filing cabinets. A second-hand wooden desk, surplus from the post office, was set in the center of it. Taped to one of the filing cabinets was a spread from the previous Sunday's rotogravure section of the Minneapolis *Star-Tribune*, which included a half-page photograph of its subject: "Ken Torjesen, Northwoods Novelist-Sleuth."

Clouds of grey-blue tobacco smoke rose above Torjesen's enclosure. The deputy sheriff was in, but Eva knew better than to admit that to reporters on the telephone. He was hunched over an incongruously sleek IBM Selectric typewriter. He was a big man, well over six feet, and just fifty, the darkest birthday of any honest man's life. He wore a heavy plaid shirt over a turtleneck sweater and a shoulder holster packed with a .38 police special. His face was square and Finnish, his wispy red hair arranged in a pompadour, circa 1955. In his teeth, he clenched a black briar pipe, which burned a regional blend famous for its pledge to never bite—Barking Dog Tobacco.

Eva took all the calls and all the guff while Torjesen worked with his gently humming typewriter. Before starting on the machine, he'd made extensive notes on a yellow legal pad with a medium-point Montblanc Diplomat. The result of his detailed labors would be a homicide report more literary than the norm. He had begun it:

"Maybe I should have sensed that this morning would bring such a crime. Maybe I should have known it by the air—foul and stinking, like a shroud of wet wool hanging over the woods and the lake. Cemetery weather.

"The sun was a flat, dirty spot of orange low over the timberline. It didn't do much to light up anything. There would be a vicious snowstorm later, once the dry winds from Canada swept in. Just then, you could see your breath hanging in the dark air. There wasn't the slightest breeze to blow it away. People and dogs moved through their own frosted steam, cutting through the still mists as only somewhat darker outlines in the grey forenoon—their froms were like ghostly ships in a fogbound harbor.

"I left Flossie's Grill at half past eight with Pete and Einer from the railroad. They trudged off through the already snow-packed Bay Street to the depot and I headed the other way toward my office. I might have been a hundred feet from them when I heard Einer's screams.

"I turned around fast, but couldn't see a thing through the vapors. I only heard Einer's unearthly howling. Some dogs barked. There were a few amber lights low to the ground—the small headlamps of snowmobiles. One of them headed off Bay Street and out of town, the others converged on the place where Einer screamed. And I heard Pete start screaming, too.

"I ran toward that sound as fast as I could, ripping off my righthand mitten and reaching into my sheepskin for the .38 under my armpit. I've never drawn it on anything in the village but a stray bear or wolf, to shoo the thing away with a shot in the air. Now I felt something much more dangerous on the prowl.

"There was light in the windows of Flossie's place and I saw a mob of faces at the glass as I raced by. Then I heard the men who went with those faces pounding down the street behind me and I wondered whether I was leading a posse or being chased by one.

"Pete's eyes, as I'll not likely ever forget, stopped me in my tracks. I've never seen a man's eyes lit up by horror and hate like that. They glowed, I swear, and he didn't seem to know me. He pointed down to his mate on the street and I saw Einer Sorsa's huge body, face down and heaving, on top of someone else.

"I bent to touch Einer. His neck snapped back and he looked at me with a face full of hate, like Pete's. His lips were curled and he growled and wept and screamed again as he lunged at me. Pete held him back from me. And I saw what his body had covered.

"Einer's boy, eleven years old, lay there on the street with blood flowing from his slender neck, or what was left of it. His eyes were open, bulged with a very recent terror.

"The boy had been walking to school. Something had attacked him. Death came with no time for either a cry or a whimper.

"Pete and somebody else helped Einer get a grip on himself, which was quite a struggle because his body flailed with the strength of his agony. I touched the boy's wrist and it twitched reflexively. I touched his forehead and felt warmth. Whatever had killed him, it had happened only minutes ago, under our noses, under cover of the dark wet haze of morning.

"A few dogs sniffed around, but they didn't pick up any scent. If there had been any tracks, the small mob of townsmen had trampled away any chance of following them. The dogs lost interest and started chasing each other's tails.

"I was shaky and didn't know what to do, besides order some of the men I'd gotten to know from Flossie's to pick up the body and take it down to the funeral home until I could get a doctor up from Duluth for a postmortem.

"Then the sky cracked open and the storm began, like a white hell."

Torjesen stopped and read over what he'd written. He'd crafted the perfect opening to his next book and he felt guilty about it.

"Eva!" he shouted, louder than necessary. She jumped from behind her desk, smoothed down her tight skirt, and brought Torjesen his messages.

He looked through the pink slips and dropped twenty of them into a vinyl wastepaper basket. "Nobody in his right mind talks to reporters," he said. He kept hold of the messages from Fred Irons and Duke Oelander. "Speaking of out of his mind, what did Duke sound like when he called?"

Eva sat on the edge of Torjesen's desk. "He says for me to tell you that if you don't organize a hunting party right quick he's going to quote nail your big-city butt on the radio unquote."

Her free leg swung and Torjesen eyed it nostalgically. He sighed as a rush of the old mood passed, killed off as usual by the memory of his wife flying off for New York to take up with his now ex-literary agent and the two of them jetting down to a Haitian divorce court, where they'd turned him into a memory.

That was when Torjesen had closed up his apartment in Chicago and come north to lick his wounds in the solitude of trout streams, granite, and jackpines. When Sheriff Irons had offered him a reason to stay permanently, Ken had accepted the new life, lonely as it was. It didn't have to be lonely—Eva was his for the taking—but Torjesen wasn't up to giving just yet.

"First," he said to her now, "put me through to Duluth and I'll talk to Fred. When I'm finished, I want to ring up Duke and tell him to keep his pants dry."

Eva went back to the switchboard and worked at making the patchy connection to Duluth via the antique telephone system. Oelander had fought successfully against most modern inconveniences and Paint Creek was as free from idle telephone chatter as it was from fluoridated water. Like it or not, KOLD-FM and the crank who ran it called the shots around Paint Creek. And Oelander didn't much like the idea of a deputy sheriff in town, a situation he described often on the air as "a big-city power grab, mebbe worse."

If Oelander could keep calm, Torjesen planned to tell him how much he enjoyed one basic part of KOLD's programming. The Finnish tall tales. The rest was local news served up by Oelander, "news" that would have been prosecuted as libel anywhere else. Anyone who didn't agree with him was "a red stooge."

Finally, Eva got through to Fred Irons, whose voice came crackling over the wire from Duluth. Beyond the window the snow fell in sheets. Soon all utility and communication lines would snap in the storm.

"Ken!"

"I hear you, Fred."

"Can't make you, Ken," Irons said. "Speak slow and tell me what's going on up there. Half the state's calling me on it."

News never traveled so fast down in Chicago as it did along the remote stretches of Lake Superior's northern shore. "We got a killing, Fred. Maybe wolves, but I sure as hell don't think so."

"Oh, my God—" Irons said something else, but the static cut him off. The trunk line went dead.

Torjesen made a few more notes on his legal pad. Then he tried Oelander on the local line. No one answered in eight rings. Ken was about to hang up when the front door crashed open. "C'mon quick, Ken!"

It was Bert Musser, manager of the village-owned liquor store and tavern. His face was framed by the hood of his parka and nearly camouflaged by snow. Flakes hung in his eyebrows and beard like oatmeal globs. He carried a rifle. Outside, Torjesen could hear chain-bound tires creaking through drifting snow. And, distantly, the sound of new and bigger mob.

Torjesen laced up knee-high waterproof boots and checked the cylinder of his .38. Full up. He pulled on his sheepskin coat and fur hat, took a shotgun down off the wall, and followed Musser outside.

It had grown bitterly cold with the Arctic gales down from Ontario and Ken felt his lungs strain against air sharpened by snow crystals. His nose stung as he breathed, every inhalation like sucking up needles. He had to lift his knees high to step through the mounting snow. "C'mon," Musser shouted again, "you got yourself some help and we're going to get 'em this time!" He charged on ahead up the street. Ken followed in dread.

A circle of townsmen, about a dozen or so, stood in the middle of the street listening to their ringleader's familiar voice. "It's the wolves!" Duke Oelander croaked. "Tell you what we got to do, men, those of you that *is* men! We got to kill 'em now, once 'n for all! Ever' sire and bitch— and ever' cub, too. And while we're at it, just mebbe that hippie gal from the city who protects 'em!"

The mob roared, demanding blood and no questions.

Oelander's threat was directed at a state-protected preserve for wolves oeprated by Bridget Paige. She'd lived at the edge of Point Creek for twelve years, since leaving suburban Minneapolis to establish an ecological movement called HOWL, for Help Our Wolves Live. HOWL had raised enough money for a square-mile sanctuary off the highway leading to Paint Creek. Bridget lived in a caretaker's cabin on the grounds.

Ten years ago a gang of village boys had ignored the posted warnings against trespass and entered the preserve with guns. They had all been killed, their bodies found scattered through the forest, disemboweled.

"Kill 'em all!" Oelander croaked again. The mob was ready to move.

Torjesen took a deep breath, leveled his shotgun at Oelander's chest, and said, "I'm warning you, Oelander, in the presence of all these good witnesses—any further suggestion of a siege on the Paige preserve will land you smack in my jail on charges of inciting to riot. Understand?"

Oelander spat into the snow. "Yeah, I un'erstand only too well, Torjesen. You want to coddle this goddamn hippie gal who raises those goddamn wolves who kill our kids and even come into town to kill nowadays, and we're supposed to just sit back'n take it. Well, lemme tell you, city boy—we gonna kill us them wolves and we don't give a snake's fanny whether they're runnin' around that gal's woods or sittin' in her cabin like lapdogs!"

Torjesen took another deep breath. "Listen close, Oelander. You other men, too. You can go on home now where you belong, or you can go off into the woods. Anywhere but the Paige place, see? You might spot a wolf and you might be able to kill it. Probably, though, you're going to freeze if you don't get stone lost in this blizzard. Either way, I don't care—unless you set foot on that woman's property—in which case she'll blow your head off, or I will. The law's on her side. I'll write it up nice and neat for Duluth on an official report form, and after six weeks or so nobody's going to trouble himself to talk about you."

Oelander turned his head and spat again. Tough old coot. Torjesen wanted to lock him up then and there. He had grounds for arrest, but he knew that was sure to start the trouble he was trying to prevent. "I wouldn't get in the way if I was you!" Oelander growled.

"If I were *you*," the deputy sheriff shot back, "I wouldn't want to find *me* in your way."

Then Torjesen lowered his gun, knowing he'd confused the crowd by forcing some thought about the consequences of their violence. He'd accomplished what he could for the moment. He turned his back on Oelander and walked away.

At twilight, there was a break in the storm. Torjesen managed a telephone call to Bridget Paige, whom he'd not met. He told her to expect him out her way. He didn't say why, but he could tell from her voice that she must have heard the news, probably on KOLD.

He typed up a brief announcement for the press and instructed Eva to read it to whoever might be concerned, take it or leave it. Gassing up the four-wheel drive out back and filling the spare tanks, too, he headed off to the wolf preserve. The village was desolate in the wake of the storm and the slaying. The heavy snowfall had covered the crimson spot where Einer's boy had fallen. Torjesen said a prayer remembered from long ago.

By the time Ken reached Bridget Paige's place, darkness was complete. He spotted the narrow drive in the light of a slivered moon, turned in, and followed the rutted path, the sides of his rover scraping against blowing tree limbs. The winds rose and shadows made by the rover's headlamps danced through the night snow. The wolf howls were all around him, loud and sharp and maddening. Torjesen felt completely foolish for thinking anything that could live here needed protection from the likes of old Duke Oelander and his barroom hotheads.

He smelled a sweet wood smoke at the end of the drive, then there were lights in the clearing. A surprisingly large cabin was the source. He hoped there would be a large drink inside.

She appeared at the doorway the moment he climbed down from the rover. He stared at her. He hadn't expected Bridget Paige to be beautiful.

She was maybe forty, give or take a few years, with blue-black hair streaked handsomely with silver. She wore straight-legged jeans and a bulky sweater. There was a maroon kerchief at her throat, but her feet stuck out bare and tender. She shivered in the doorway and waved Torjesen to hurry on in.

The place was perfect. A huge blaze filled a slate fireplace, oak floors were softened by braided rugs, and the creased leather furniture invited a man to sit forever. The smell of venison chili reminded him how hungry he was. Books spilled across floor-to-ceiling shelving on two of the walls. A decanter of Scotch whisky and two glasses waited on a table at the hearth. The table also held a pile of Ken's books.

He leaned his shotgun against a wall near the door and unbuttoned his sheepskin. "Drink?" Bridget Paige asked.

He took a chair by the fire. She sat opposite in another. "A civilized visitor is a real occasion," she said.

"Do you know what brings me here?" Torjesen asked.

"I could guess if you like. But why don't you just tell me?"

Torjesen related the events of the morning and told her of Oelander's threats.

"So you're exactly what—my bodyguard?"

"I don't know." He honestly didn't know. "I can't tell you just why I'm here in Paint Creek. Can you?"

"I was a bored housefrau down in Minneapolis. So I quit. How come you quit being a cop?"

"Because I'd had to deal with too much of what I'm dealing with now. Then I managed to sell my first book. There isn't anywhere near as much money in that as people think, but it's enough to quit working. It's not nearly so debilitating as being a cop, which means every hour is two minutes of terror and fifty-eight minutes of boredom." He put down his glass. "Do you ever get bored staring at the woods up here and listening to wolves?"

She didn't answer him. Instead, she sad, "How about dinner?"

They enjoyed an especially good batch of venison chili, drank Moose-head lager, and talked about books and music they liked, including long Russian novels and jazz from the Thirties. And wolves.

"So they think the wolves killed Einer Sorsa's boy?" Bridget said. "Hah! You ask me, I think your killer's going to turn out two-legged. There are some up here mean and crazy enough, I know." Her head was back and her eyes were shut. "Besides, the legend of the big bad wolf is a crock. There isn't a nobler creature on earth. Wolves kill for food and in defense of one another. They don't murder. Wolves are infinitely more loving and loyal than men. Yet they're considered the epitome of evil. Why?"

Torjesen rubbed his eyes. He was woozy from the Scotch and the beer and the meal and he wasn't much interested in listening to Bridget Paige's screed on behalf of wolves so much as he was interested in the possibility of sleeping with her. "I don't know," he said weakly.

Bridget rose and turned on a radio. Duke Oelander's voice played over KOLD, reading a Finnish horror story about a mass murderer in

Helsinki who killed more than a dozen children before he was caught. The city had been paralyzed in fear of the monster in its midst. But his eventual identity, revealed with his capture, was an anticulimax. The despicable child-killer was a simple delivery man who brought milk to the city schools, and such an absentminded fellow that he was as surprised as the police to find parts of his victims' bodies in a wardrobe.

"There's no excuse for this," Bridget said, "tonight of all nights." She snapped off the radio.

Ken said something about getting back to town, even though he felt nailed to his chair. "You're not seriously thinking of driving back?" Bridget said. "I've planned on your staying." She poked the fire down to embers, then helped him out to a small room off the kitchen. There was a dresser and a bed heaped with quilts. Torjesen fell gratefully onto the bed on his back. He remembered Bridget removing his shoes and his gunbelt, then the smell of lavender as she kissed his cheek.

When he woke well into the next morning, the cabin was filled with the aroma of strong fresh coffee and a new fire. He refreshed himself with the warm water Bridget had set out in a basin on the dresser, then he strapped on his .38, pulled on his shoes, and met his hostess in the kitchen.

She was wearing a man's long woollen robe, a paisley scarf at her neck. Sunlight shafted through the window, sparkling her hair. She turned when she heard his step, smiled, and started to say something when a rock came sailing through the window behind her, glanced off the back of her head, and sent her sprawling to the floor in a shower of glass. Torjesen pulled out his .38 and dove to the floor beside her, covering her protectively. Her hands were bloodied by the glass shards and a trickle of blood welled up on the crown of her head.

"Stay down," Torjesen said. He ran to the front room after his shotgun. Dressing himself in the sheepskin and the boots, he ran back to the kitchen. Bridget lay where she'd fallen, her face pale and contorted more by rage than fear. The scarf had slipped from her neck to reveal an ugly, bluish line of scar tissue that ran from the base of her throat around to the back of her neck.

"Stay down," Torjesen said. "I'm going outside."

He hunched low behind snowdrifts and, looking to the trees surrounding the clearing, he spotted Oelander and six other men moving through white-tipped brush. "Halt!" he shouted. He fired off a round and the sound thundered in the air and echoed through the woods.

Oelander and his men turned and fled into the forest, with Ken in hot pursuit.

They crashed awkwardly through the snowy woods, seven villagers and Torjesen, whose heart pounded and whose mind reeled from things happening too fast to measure. One of the villagers stumbled, then cried out in pain when his leg snapped in a rut hidden by the snow. Torjesen ran to him and stopped. It was Pete. The fallen man drew a pistol from his coat, cocked back the hammer, and almost got off a shot before Ken cut him in half with a second blast of his .30/.06.

A bullet from behind whizzed past Ken's ear and thudded into a spruce tree. He dropped to the ground, flipped over, and drew a bead on his would-be killer with his .38. His shot went wild. He tried to get up and run, but another shot found its mark this time. the slug ripped into his thigh. Another opened his shoulder.

He tried crawling, but he was too weak. Then he heard wolves howling—and then a swift pack of them running toward the scent of his blood.

He heard the footsteps, too. Then his vision blackened and he couldn't move. A smaller man might have died, but Torjesen lived through the shock.

Two months of hospital rest and therapy, including psychological counseling, restored Torjesen to mobility and coherency. Surgeons had removed part of the bone from his leg, replacing it with steel. A plastic pin was put into his shoulder joint. He was back in Paint Creek as spring made a rare, brief appearance. But Ken had no time for it. He worked in his office from the notes he'd penned in the hospital. He was willing to pass off the story as another of his paperback fictions. Why burden people into thinking it was more?

And this is the conclusion of what he wrote:

"I was dying in that swamp of snow. I waited for the final bullet, but it never came.

"Instead, I felt a pair of strong, bare hands encircle my neck and fingers finding their way to my flesh, digging deep. I smelled lavender.

"Then there was something sharp on my neck. A knife? Then wetness, blood, and biting. I was fading. The blood flowing from my body seemed somehow a pleasant release from my pain. I felt myself floating senselessly again, as I'd floated off in the cabin the night before.

"With all my strength, I managed to open my eyes. I had to see the source of this sweet pain. And there was Bridget, her lips stained with my blood, a Bowie knife in her upraised hand—and a pack of wolves ringing me. My eyes sank shut.

"Then there was Duke Oelander's voice. 'Enough!' he shouted. An extended blaze of gunfire cut down most of the wolves, scattered the rest deep into the woods. 'I was right all along!' Oelander shouted. 'Witch! Killer!'

"There was another crack of gunfire. And a final, ghastly groan as Bridget crumpled next to me.

"I came to in the cabin. Oelender and the others had treated my wounds and told me a doctor was on his way by helicopter from Duluth, along with Fred Irons.

" 'What we had here,' Oelander said, 'was a case of the northwoods gettin' to somebody who couldn't handle it. City folks can't never take what they find here. No, sir. They think it's goin' to be heaven. But it ain't. It's more like to the other place.'

"I tried to speak, but my throat was on fire with pain. I touched my neck with my good arm and felt rolls of gauze tight around me.

"After they moved me to the hospital in Duluth, I had Fred Irons bring me the newspaper reports of the earlier killings on the Paige property. The police reports, too, such as they were. But I didn't begin to sort it out until Fred squared with me on a fact of life I hadn't run up against yet: 'Sometimes when civilization is spread thin, we have to make do with very flawed truths. And sometimes in a small town during a long winter, justice has lots of blank spots.' With that in mind, and with some information I coaxed out of Oelander and Eva, I filled in the blank spots.

"Ten years ago, Bridget Paige came across a gang of village boys on her land. The 'boys' were louts of sixteen or so, fully equipped for grown-up trouble. Despite what the clans of Paint Creek decided to believe, the boys weren't hunting for wolves—their prey was Bridget Paige, the divorcee from the big city. Only days before they died in the woods, Oelander himself heard two of them bragging it up at Musser's about how they planned 'to give that wolf gal what she needed most.'

"Bridget Paige had filed rape charges against the deceased, coolly dictating to a stenographer in Sheriff Irons' office exactly what had happened that day in her woods. During the course of the attack, she said, a pack of wolves came to the defense of their protectress. The boys couldn't fire fast enough and the pack soon took them down—but not before one of the boys had slashed open Bridget's neck with the knife he'd been using to overpower her.

"The animals had dragged the bodies off to various sections of the preserve and fed on their kill. KOLD's accounts of all this were lurid, vintage Oelander. From then on, when Bridget came to the village for mail and supplies, no one spoke to her directly. The women followed her up and down Bay Street, their voices raised in order to be overheard by her. 'If it's true she was molested like she went and claimed, she musta brought it on herself—' 'Big-city snob livin' all alone up here. Well, she ain't so desirable now with her neck all cut up, is she?' Teenagers insulted her and even the smallest child threw stones, not even knowing exactly why. Einer Sorsa's boy, not old enough to walk when Bridget was raped in the woods, became the most enthusiastic rock thrower by the time he was eight years old.

"For ten years, Bridget went about her business in Paint Creek shunned, stoned, and humiliated. She gave no outward sign of her building rage. But the ignorance and the sport of cruelty grew more powerful as the years passed, and while she had not once, apparently, entertained the notion of leaving her land, she became deranged—and for ten long years two evils twisted along a path toward the inevitable revenge. On the tenth anniversary of her violation, Bridget followed the Sorsa boy and took him down witth her knife—and then, as she had done to me, tore at his wound with her teeth. Chemical tests showed traces of her saliva mixed with his blood.

"The mob logic that morning was a continuation of the ignorance and myth that had ruled Paint Creek for ten years—the wolves had to be destroyed.

"But was I any wiser? I had sought to protect Bridget Paige, a psychotic murderer. I drank her whisky and ate the meal she set before me, a bowl of venison chili laced with just enough arsenic to render me physically defenseless in case she needed to kill me.

"But she'd let me live the night, a night I believed love could happen again. How banal evil is. How blinded to this disguise are its victims.

"Duke Oelander had formed a posse, this one nothing more than an alibi for murder, to get rid of Bridget Paige and her wolves under the cover of rescuing a fool deputy sheriff. And Bridget Paige figured she could charm this same fool and escape retribution for the murder she had committed.

"I've thought about leaving Paint Creek many times. But it's here I came to hide in the first place. There doesn't seem to be any percentage in running somewhere else. In my lucid moments, I understand the simple cop truth that makes everyplace the same. Life is sloppy and death does nothing to tidy it up."

H. R. F. Keating
Old P

Madelaine had loved "Old P" almost from the very beginning. As soon, that was, as she had got over her fit of wild gigles at the name that had jumped into her mind the moment she saw her. But when her big brother, fresh from passing his test the day after his seventeenth birthday, had driven up in this new acquisition, grinding and spluttering a little even then, and she had seen its numberplate, OLD 470P, she had come out with the words before she could stop herself. And "Old P" had stuck, for the whole of the year that Tony had had her, as her grinding day by day got grindier and her spluttering splutterier.

Because Old P was a banger, there could be no denying that. She had one door a whole shade lighter than the rest of her bodywork. Her roof leaked at the slightest rain. The springs in her back seat stood up like thrusting toadstools and, from the moment she got in motion, there was a curious, slow, ominous tocking sound like a grandfather clock needing a long while to make up its mind whether to tick on or not.

Other things, too, began going wrong with her almost from the start. One day the back numberplate dropped off and Tony somehow never managed to get it on quite straight again. Then the ignition key mysteriously refused to work and eventually she had to be started by holding the two ends of a piece of wire somewhere behind her dashboard. And the window on the driving side took to suddenly and unaccountably lowering itself. So altogether Old P was a mess.

But the more of a mess she became the more Madelaine came to love her. And the more angry Tony became about having bought her in the first place—especially after he began taking out the girl Madelaine always thought of as "That Janice." Plainly, Old P wasn't good enough for That Janice, which made Tony all the more angry about his "bargain" and Madelaine love her all the more.

"I just wish somebody'd steal the damn car and let me make a packet on the insurance," Tony would say—mostly to annoy her, Madelaine thought. Then he would add darkly, to annoy her more, "But who'd want to steal a wreck like that?"

But one day, after Tony had driven down to the local college where he was a student, he came back home unexpectedly early and announced that Old P—even he used the name when he wasn't talking about "that heap"—had vanished.

"I'd left her round the corner," he said jubilantly, "not even on a yellow line. And when I came back, no car. I've been to the insurance place and got a form to fill in. The only thing now is that I've got to tell the police and wait six weeks. And then I get the dough."

"I expect someone will bring her back, dear," Madelaine's mother said consolingly.

"That's the last thing I want," Tony retorted. "The bloody last thing."

"Don't swear, dear. You know your father doesn't like it."

But it seemed that, swear word or no swear word, Tony was going to be in luck. The days passed and nothing was heard of Old P. The days turned into weeks and still there was no news. The weeks turned into a whole month before there was news, of a sort.

News on television. There had been a big jewel raid first thing that morning, a raid that had completely fooled the police. What the thieves had done was to take off from the jeweler's with their haul—said to be worth half a million—in the usual fast car. But instead of speeding away with screeching tires, hoping to beat any cordon that might be set up, they had come to a quick halt just round the corner, had jumped out with the loot, and had been seen no more.

It had been pure chance, in fact, that their trick had come to light at all. The men had, the news said, slipped into the yard of a small factory that had gone broke years before, had got into a disreputable old banger of a car hidden there, and had cheekily driven this unlikely vehicle right through the police cordon. Nothing would have come out if there hadn't been an old woman vagrant sleeping rough in the yard, who had tried to earn a pound or two by saying what she'd seen.

The hunt was really on then, especially as the thieves had coshed an assistant in the jeweler's and badly injured him. In no time, the papers had headlines about "the banger gang" and before long jokes and cartoons were ten a penny.

But it was the description the old vagrant gave of the banger the gang had used that made Madelaine's ears prick up. "A green car with one door a much lighter shade than the rest." The old woman had not been able to remember the number, so Old P wasn't actually mentioned, but Madelaine was certain that the gang had stolen her, and when they were ready had taken her to the disused yard near the jeweler's, ready and waiting to make the getaway.

Even Tony reluctantly agreed that this was what must have happened, though he wouldn't ring up the police to tell them, much as Madelaine begged him to.

"What's the use?" he said. "It only proves Old P was stolen. I've half a mind to see if I can get the insurance money straight away now. Janice says it's hell not having wheels."

That might have been that, only a new girl called Tracey came to Madelaine's school and, because Madelaine was friendly to her, she invited Madelaine back next Saturday to her home. Soon after they arrived, she took her up to the attic of the house.

"I'm making a secret hideout," she said. "It's super. It's quite warm from the heating below and there's a little window to give some light."

It was looking out of that little window—you had to stand on tiptoe to do it—that led Madelaine to make her great discovery. She found she could see into the parking area behind a big block of posh flats in the next street, and there at once she thought she saw something familiar.

"It's Old P!" she exclaimed.

And then, when the two of them had got over *their* giggles about the name and she had explained everything, they went round to the parking area to make sure, and of course Madelaine was quite right. There was Old P, tucked away in the farthest corner of the parking area, with that telltale lighter door jammed up against some bushes.

"We'll have to tell the police," Madelaine said. "It's the getaway car. If they catch the banger gang, I'll come in for a terrific reward. It said so on telly."

So they went back to Tracey's house and rang the station. Madelaine was afraid they hadn't believed her because Tracey couldn't stop laughing in the background. But about half an hour later there came a knock on the door and there was a man who said he was Detective-Sergeant Peters, and with him was a woman detective constable.

Sergeant Peters led them round to the flats and they all stood for a little looking at Old P.

"Well," Sergeant Peters said, "it could be. It certainly could be."

And then, as a woman in a fur coat came out of a car she had just parked three spaces away, he said to the P.C., "Just ask that lady if she knows who owns this bit of a motor."

The lady did know, and what she said sent Madelaine's excitement fizzling out as if she had been doused with a bucket of cold water.

"Yes," the lady said, "I understand that wretched object is the property of Miss Janice Watts, whose parents live in Flat twenty-eight. It's been standing there for weeks, just where I like to park myself."

Janice, Madelaine thought. That Janice. So she lives here and she's known where Old P has been all along. That means she can't have been stolen, after all, and it must have been another banger with a light-colored door the gang used. Tony must have hidden Old P here just to get the insurance.

And then she realized she really ought to tell the sergeant everything. And that, if she was going to, she would have to do it straight away, while he was standing there.

But that would be giving Tony away. He'd been trying to cheat the insurance company. Could he be sent to prison? Yet if she didn't tell the sergeant, the police would think that Old P was truly the car the banger gang had used and the investigation would go off on the wrong track and the men who had nearly killed the jeweler's assistant would never be caught.

She felt her whole head in a whirl and wondered if she was going to faint.

But she didn't. And then she knew that she must speak now, or keep silent forever. She swallowed. "Please," she said. "Please, my brother

said that Old—that his car had been stolen, but I think he only hid
it here. You see, Janice Watts is his girl friend, and she was always
complaining he didn't have a good enough car, and so—Well, and so I
think he must have done that."

"Hid it here, did he?" Sergeant Peters said. "Where do you live,
missy? I think I'd better have a word with this brother of yours. He
sounds a right naughty boy."

At once, Madelaine realized what he must be thinking. Not that Tony
had just hidden Old P to get the insurance, but that he had hidden her
because he was one of the gang. The banger gang.

"No, no," she said. "No, you don't understand. Tony's not like that.
I mean, he may sometimes do things he shouldn't, but he wouldn't join
in a robbery."

"Not when he's got a girl friend he can't look after as well as he
wants?" the sergeant said. "No, you show me where you live, my girl."

Madelaine turned to lead the way, feeling a great heavy weight round
about where her heart was and a whole wash of tears ready to burst out
the moment she could keep them back no longer.

She gave a last look back at Old P. And then she noticed something.
It was only the tiniest thing, and if she hadn't loved Old P so much it
would never have registered at such a terrible time. But it had. She had
seen it. She knew it was so. She turned to the sergeant. "No," she said.
"No, look. Look at that. That proves it."

And she pointed to the car's numberplate, OLD 470P.

"It's on straight," she said. "Absolutely straight. And it never was
before. It was always a bit crooked ever since it fell off once. That
numberplate's been taken off on purpose and put back on again. And if
it was Tony who drove her after the raid, he wouldn't have changed the
plates—because if any of his friends had seen him go by they'd have
noticed. Because of the funny number."

"Well—" the sergeant said.

"And, besides, Tony was at home all that day. I remember him seeing
the first news of the raid on telly, because he tried to make out that it
wasn't Old P that was used. He must have thought it couldn't have been
because he thought she was hidden here. That's why he didn't want to
phone the police. Look at that plate. You can see the scrapes on it where
it's been put on again." She bent down to point them out.

"Stop," Sergeant Peters said, his voice cracking like a gunshot. He
turned to the woman P.C. "Be dabs on that, likely as not."

"Yes. And, Sergeant, I've just thought of something. Aren't these the
flats where Smiler Sutton lives?"

"By gum, you're right. And the Guv'nor's been wanting to lay his
hands on that mastermind for years. Seeing this old heap of a car here
must have put the whole idea into his head. It's just his style. With any
luck we've got him this time."

"And Tony?" Madelaine said hopefully. "You won't have to say anything about him hiding Old P? Or will you?"

"Well, I daresay if he's a good lad and tells the insurance people he's got the car back, we can turn a bit of a blind eye. This time."

And although Madelaine had to share the reward money with the vagrant who had seen the gang getting into Old P, she got quite enough to help Tony buy himself a much better car. But she never really got to love it, even though Tony, who'd broken off with Janice, was very good about taking her wherever she wanted.

"I mean," she said to Tracey one day, "you can't love a car that's called JWW 475V, can you?"

Charles Peterson
The Finishing Touché

Of the two dozen people at Roderick Croft's dinner party that night, I saw and knew less of what was going on than any of them. So it was ironic, to say the least, that I should wind up accused of killing him.

Naturally, it didn't help much when all the others swore they saw me do it.

What they saw, actually—well, this is the way it was described to me later—

Roderick Croft was alone, seated in a high-backed carved chair before the huge stone fireplace in the Great Hall of his country home, under a ceiling so high its uppermost beams were lost in shadow. His guests were all on the main central portion of the U-shaped balcony that overlooked three sides of the Great Hall at the second-floor level, busily demolishing the buffet supper laid out there and speculating about the possible appearance of the Casa Croft ghost that night. Croft's country home was once a Spanish castle, shipped over and reassembled in the 1880s by some railroad baron, and it's axiomatic that old castles come equipped with ghosts. This one was a Seventeenth Century cavalier who was said to prowl the halls with drawn rapier, seeking vengeance for something or other. Those who weren't speculating about the ghost were theorizing about why Croft had invited four theatrical producers and three agents to be present.

Then the lights went out.

In the shocked silence that followed, an eerie chill swept over the balcony, accompanied by a sound that was halfway between a moan and a sigh. Then someone whispered, "Look!" as there appeared a glow in the Great Hall, apparently emanating from the suit of armor standing near the fireplace behind Croft. As a figure began to take shape, somebody screamed.

Roderick Croft looked up, startled.

"Croft! Behind you!" a man's voice cried.

From plumed hat to cuffed boots, the figure was a spectral white, relieved only by a crimson sword-belt like a slash of blood against doublet and hose. The face was indistinct—a pale blur with a pair of sinister black holes for eyes and a thin cruel line for a mouth.

Croft glanced over his shoulder and half rose from his chair as this apparition became brighter and more distinct. It stepped forward menacingly, drawing its sword with ominous deliberation. A highlight glinted off the cold steel and there was a gasp from the onlookers as they realized they could actually see through the figure as it paced toward Croft, past the carved chairs and refectory table.

357

Croft, suddenly galvanized into action, sprang to the side of the fireplace and seized another rapier from the display of old weapons hanging there.

They say he had been a good fencer during his days on the stage, and at first he seemed to give a good account of himself. But he was, after all, well up in his sixties now, and though still lean and fit—well, what can anyone do against a ghost? The duel that developed was all the more terrifying for being soundless. There was no clang of metal against metal, no sounds of footfalls on the carpeted floor. And it was over in a matter of moments. A feint, a desperate parry, a thrust, and Croft staggered back with a cough of pain, rapier falling from one hand, the other clutching his chest as he collapsed on the floor.

The ghostly figure raised its sword in a mocking salute and, still facing the fallen Croft, retreated slowly to the suit of armor as the light faded and died.

The guests roused as from a collective trance. Cigarette lighters and matches were struck and eyes showed white in the feeble illumination. There was a rush toward the twin staircases that flanked the Great Hall at the far ends of the balcony, with everyone jostling and shouting in confusion, all trying to get down to the main floor at once.

Then the lights flickered on again.

I was back in the workshop, tissuing the white makeup from my face and thinking that it had all gone rather well, when I heard footsteps coming down the passage from the Great Hall. Croft, I supposed, since he was the only person other than myself who used it. But it turned out to be a chunky, florid-faced man of perhaps forty-five, with dark-brown hair and eyes that looked at me with surprise, succeeded at once by a steely glint. "Who the hell are you?" he demanded.

"I'm Scott Drake," I answered, "and who the hell are *you* and how did you get down here?"

"Don't wise off with me," he growled. "I'm Lindsay Fullerton, Roderick Croft's business manager, and—" His eyes widened as he took in the cavalier costume. I was still wearing the boots and hose, but the blouse had been thrown over a chair, along with the doublet and plumed hat, on top of the sword belt with its crimson rosette. "Aha!" he exclaimed.

"Aha what?" I said, irritated. "What's all this about, and why are you charging around here? Mr. Croft doesn't like people messing around his workshop."

Fullerton looked at me and shook his head. "Kid, you're a cool one," he said. "You'd better come along with me." He pushed me ahead of him into the corridor.

Back in the Great Hall, everyone seemed to be standing around looking uncomfortable. There was a group of policemen in the middle of the Hall huddled around something on the floor, and one of them—who turned out to be a lieutenant named Murdock—looked questioningly at Fullerton as we appeared. "Who's this?" he asked, and there was a stir among the guests as they caught sight of us.

"Here's your killer," Fullerton announced dramatically. "I caught him back in Croft's workshop, about to make his getaway."

"Killer?" I echoed, stupefied. "Getaway? What *is* all this?"

"I suppose you're going to tell us you didn't run Roderick Croft through with a sword less than half an hour ago?" said Fullerton.

"Yes," I said, "I didn't!"

"I *saw* you do it! Twenty other people saw you do it. We saw him plain as a pikestaff," he told the lieutenant. "Plumed hat, floppy boots, that red rosette holding his sword—all clear as day. And," he concluded, turning on me, "Roderick Croft is lying right there, stabbed through the heart."

And I always thought those mystery stories were a bit much—you know, the ones where the suspect is found standing over the body holding a smoking revolver he just happened to pick up. As if anyone with the IQ of a mushroom goes around picking up smoking revolvers at the scene of a murder. There's a standard line of dialogue that goes with the scene, and I uttered it with all the sincerity of pure desperation:

"But, Lieutenant, I can explain everything!"

I'd never heard of Roderick Croft before I answered the ad in *Variety* for a young man with some acting and fencing experience. At the time, I was waiting table in a midtown restaurant nights, attending dramatic classes afternoons, and haunting producers' offices any chance I got. It was in a producer's office that I met Roderick Croft. He was a tall thin man with wavy silver hair that made a deep widow's peak in his forehead and a pair of dark eyes that seemed to peer straight through to your cervical vertebrae. His long slim fingers appeared to have a life of their own, manipulating a coin as he talked, making it disappear and reappear in a dazzling manner.

"It's a pleasure to meet you, sir," I said.

A sardonic gleam appeared in those piercing eyes. "Indeed? Why?"

That stopped me for a two-beat pause. Then I took a shot in the dark. "I never met a famous magician before," I said. He looked gratified.

I investigated more fully later and found that in the heyday of the big traveling magic shows, Croft had been a headliner in the Thurston and Blackstone league. When that type of show faded, so did he, retiring to his country place upstate. That was over twenty years ago now. I learned, too, that the Casa Croft household included a much younger second wife named Annabel, a daughter Dina, and a son named Thurston.

Anyway, the upshot was that after demonstrating that I did know something about fencing, I was hired at a fee that justified my giving notice at the restaurant. A few days later, Croft drove me to his castle, installed me therein via a rear entrance that led to a small apartment next to his workshop, and informed me that I was henceforth a non-person as far as the rest of his household was concerned, except for his long-time dresser, a wizened little man named Seabury.

"Mr. Croft," I said, "I still have no idea what we're going to be doing for the next couple of weeks."

An expression of mirth crossed his face. "Rehearsing, my boy! We'll be rehearsing a murder!"

"Oh?" I said warily. "Whose?"

"*Mine*, dear boy," said Roderick Croft. "Mine!"

Lieutenant Murdock looked skeptical. "You're not going to try and tell me Croft arranged to kill himself?"

"No, no—nothing like that." What Croft had in mind, I explained, was an updated version of a venerable illusion known as "The Cavalier's Revenge." Croft had been tinkering with electronic gadgetry for years—his castle was gimmicked from turrets to toilets with doors that opened and closed themselves, weird plaster busts that chuckled as you went by, suits of armor that suddenly engaged you in conversation, skeletons in closets that waved hello when the door opened. What he had done was program "The Cavalier's Revenge" onto tape, lighting cues and all, so that the entire illusion could be set in motion and controlled from a few buttons in his chair.

"You mean that ghost thing was faked? It was a magic act?"

I nodded. "From the moment the lights went out. He was trying to work up interest in reviving his full-scale magic show, so he asked a bunch of producers and agents here tonight to give them some idea of what he could do, combining old illusions with these new techniques he'd worked out."

"But I could see right through you!" Fullerton said.

I shook my head. "You were looking at my mirror image in a partly reflective scrim that lowered between Croft and me when the lights blacked out. I was under the balcony, and when the lights came up on me you saw my reflection in the scrim." The entire scene was very precisely choreographed, I told Lieutenant Murdock, so that my reflection and Croft seemed to be engaging each other in a swordfight, though I was actually about twenty feet away out of sight of anyone on the balcony above.

"But I distinctly felt a chill when the ghost appeared!" Fullerton said.

"That was programmed, too. A blast from the central air-conditioning timed to coincide with the moaning—which, incidentally, covered any sound from the lowering scrim. Then at the end of the scene the lights dimmed on me, and in the blackout the scrim lifted again and I 'disappeared' by ducking down the corridor to the workshop before the house lights came on again."

Lieutenant Murdock looked as though he found the story hard to believe. "Sounds cockeyed to me," he said. "And it still leaves me with a dead body—and you the only person on the premises with a sword handy."

He hauled me over to the other cops and told one of them to keep an eye on me—perhaps to protect me from the guests, who were giving me dirty looks. The rest of the police shooed everyone else back up to the balcony while someone—I assumed it was the police doctor—knelt to examine Croft's body. Annabel Croft was weeping onto some gentleman's chest. A flabby young man with thinning straw-colored hair, Roderick's son Thurston, was standing next to his sister Dina, a pouty blonde in her early twenties. Her lavish use of makeup over a now-ashen complexion did very little for a face that was rather plain to begin with.

Lieutenant Murdock wa back, this time with the doctor in tow and a puzzled expression on his face. "Show me exactly where you were during this act of yours."

I led him beneath the balcony and pointed out the unobtrusive marks I'd used to spot my positions during the dueling scene.

"And you say you never varied your positions?"

"I couldn't. Otherwise the image would have looked wrong."

"And the whole routine was timed by Croft's taped control?"

"That's right. We had exactly two minutes and fifteen seconds for the whole scene."

Murdock was silent for several moments, then he said, "Well, Drake, you're probably the only one here who *couldn't* have killed Roderick Croft. Tell him, Doc."

The doctor cleared his throat. "You see, young man, in spite of what everyone thinks he saw, Mr. Croft wasn't stabbed at all. He died of a bullet wound, probably from a small-caliber rifle."

"And that means," Murdock added, "that any one of those folks upstairs could have sneaked over to the side balcony during the blackout and timed the shot to coincide with your sword thrust."

"That cough," I said.

"What cough?"

"Mr. Croft gave a kind of cough just as I was making my thrust. It wasn't in the script. That must have been when he was hit."

"But no one heard any shot—and it was dead quiet, they tell me."

"A silencer?" I guessed.

"Something like that." Murdock glanced at the balcony and sighed. "I'd better get busy and start taking statements from everyone up there. Somehow I don't expect much out of them."

"You may not need much," I said.

"How do you mean?"

"Well, the killer must have been familiar with the layout of the Great Hall and its balcony arrangement. And about the illusion Mr. Croft and I were working on. That should eliminate practically everyone except the members of the household."

"But you claim no one knew you were living here or that Croft was planning this stunt."

"Someone must have known."

"Any ideas?"

"A few. Mr. Croft was careful about getting meals to me, for instance, but someone could have noticed the extra food going to the workshop for his dinners. The cook, perhaps, or his major-domo, Seabury."

Murdock made a note. "Who else?"

"Someone saw Croft rehearsing his moves in the Great Hall yesterday. I was under the balcony when I saw him look up, kind of peering into the dark, and he said sharply, 'Who's there?' Then he said, 'Get out of here—I'm busy!' He added something about going through an exercise routine, probably trying to throw whoever it was off the track."

"*You* didn't hear this other party?"

"I didn't hear any voice at all—that time."

"There was another time?"

"One afternoon last week when we'd just started blocking the scene. All of a sudden Croft heard someone coming toward the Great Hall and he motioned me up the stairs to the balcony. By the time I got to the top, she was in the room."

"She?"

"Mrs. Croft. So I just froze in place behind the balustrade, knowing she'd probably spot any movement. I wasn't trying to eavesdrop."

"What did you hear?"

"Mr. Croft greeted his wife coolly. He said, 'You're home early. Bridge party over so soon?'

" 'I left early,' she said. 'Jane Thorpe took ill, so I drove her home. I've just come from there.'

" 'Jane Thorpe,' Croft mused. 'Would that be the same Jane Thorpe who telephoned shortly after you left to say she wasn't able to join you for bridge today?'

"There was a long pause, then Mrs. Croft turned and walked out."

Lieutenant Murdock gazed at me speculatively. "Any more tidbits to report?"

"Just one," I said. "A couple of days ago I was returning to the workshop from the Great Hall—I'd forgotten to bring the rosette that attaches to the sword-belt of my costume—and I heard Mr. Croft talking to someone on the phone." I tried to recall the exact words. "He was saying, 'I thought I was familiar with all the standard disappearing acts, but this is a new one on me. I want a full explanation at the dinner on Friday.' He listened and added, 'Certainly I expect you to make good—and soon.' He slammed down the phone. When I came in a little later, he didn't seem perturbed."

"Do you have any idea who he might have been talking to?" Murdock asked.

"I thought it might be his son, Thurston. He made a remark once about how much he'd been shelling out to pay up Thurston's debts."

"That's a lie!" said Thurston, his fleshy face trying to register a threatening scowl. "He's making it all up!" We were all on the balcony now.

"You deny you had arguments with your father about your debts?" Murdock said.

"Yes! No! That is, yes, we did dicuss them, but that was a couple of weeks ago."

"He refused to pay?"

Thurston's belligerence evaporated. He looked like a small boy caught in the jam jar.

"Well, not exactly. Not in so many words."

"His exact words," Dina Croft interrupted, "were, 'You need money? Get off your tail and earn it like anyone else. You're getting no more out of me.' "

The third family member, Annabel Croft, had been sitting, dabbing at her eyes. Murdock turned to her now.

"Mrs. Croft, can you tell me who benefits from Mr. Croft's will?"

"Oh, dear," she said. "I mean, at a time like this I can hardly—"

Lindsay Fullerton patted her hand. "Just take it easy."

She took a deep breath and nodded. "I believe Roderick set up half his estate in a trust with me the beneficiary. Except for some minor bequests to servants, the other half was divided between Dina and Thurston. His theatrical props were to go to some magic museum in California."

Lieutenant Murdock humphed. "So all three of you had a motive for murder."

Denials arose, Dina's the most strident, until Thurston silenced her with a venomous, "Listen to you! As if you had no interest in Father's money!"

"What do you mean by that, you pompous oaf?"

"What he means, darling," purred Annabel, "is that we're all well aware that the moment you get your hands on enough money, you'll be off with that sexy beachcomber you picked up in Florida."

Lindsay Fullerton turned angrily to Murdock. "Why are you putting the family through this?" he demanded. "It's obvious this actor had the best opportunity to kill Roderick." Apparently he didn't know the real cause of Mr. Croft's death, and as he spoke something clicked in my mind—a statement someone had made. And then I knew—and tugged at Lieutenant Murdock's sleeve.

Thus it was that, after order had been restored and the Croft guests allowed to leave, Murdock and I were left in the Great Hall with only

Mrs. Croft, Dina, Thurston, and Lindsay Fullerton. Murdock flipped through the statements taken in separate interviews and looked at me. "They all seem to agree on what they saw during the illusion. A figure in white with a plumed hat and floppy cavalier boots, slashed doublet and hose and wide-sleeved blouse, the only touch of color a narrow red sword-belt."

I had brought the costume in and placed it on a chair. "There it is—exactly as I left it in the workshop after the scene." I picked up the pieces and put them on in order. "And this is exactly what they should have seen from the balcony, because my right side was reflected in the scrim and I never turned around—Mr. Croft thought it was more theatrical if I walked backward to the point where I was to vanish in the suit of armor."

"Get to the point, Drake."

"The point is, at no time could anyone have seen the red rosette holding the sword at my left side unless that person happened to be on one of the side galleries and in a position to see the real me underneath the balcony. That person must be the one who shot Mr. Croft—and in all the statements you have the only person to mention it was Mr. Fullerton, when he was describing my costume after he brought me here to the Great Hall."

"Ridiculous!" sniffed Fullerton. "I noticed it in the workshop, of course."

"You couldn't have," I said. "It was out of sight underneath the rest of the costume. Exactly the way I brought it in a few moments ago."

If looks could kill, the world would have been minus one aspiring young actor. And the one on Lindsay Fullerton's face told Lieutenant Murdock all he needed to know.

Except, of course, for a few details that came out later. The rifle turned up in a search of the rooms off the gallery, since Fullerton had had no chance to dispose of it. It was a powerful air-gun of German make—one of several in Roderick Croft's weapons collection—that fired with little more than a discreet burp. It had been Fullerton on the phone with Croft that day, and the "disappearing act" was the one Fullerton had performed with a goodly portion of Croft's assets. And Fullerton again who had happened into the Great Hall as Croft and I were rehearsing and, knowledgeable as he was about all of Croft's stage properties, had no trouble deducing what Croft was planning—and the opportunity it presented to forestall further investigation into Croft's financial affairs. It appeared that the estate would be far less lucrative than Annabel, Dina, and Thurston hoped—a fact I found less heart-rending than you might suppose. Particularly since all I got out of the deal was the advance Mr. Croft had paid me at the beginning.

However, I noticed an ad in *Variety* this week for a young man with acting, fencing, *and* magic show experience.

Anthea Cohen

The Fixer

Desmond felt oil on his hands and wondered where it had come from. The wheel? He looked down at the wheel—no sign of any oil. He examined his hand and saw the shiny blob of slightly discolored oil on his palm. He cursed rather too extravagantly for such a small matter and gingerly started to maneuver his wheelchair toward the bathroom, using only the tips of his fingers so as not to get the oil on the tire.

Desmond was almost as fastidious as his wife. He could have wiped the oil away with his handkerchief but that would have marked its new morning whiteness and annoyed Annie. She wouldn't miss oil on a handkerchief, nor would she restrain herself from rebuking him.

He washed his hands, bending forward carefully, easing his cuffs up so as not to wet them. In his wheelchair he was too low to see his face in the mirror. He was not sorry—at eighty there wasn't much he wished to look at. He hated his face now. He had once been handsome, rugged. Women had—He dismissed the thought firmly. Annie was the only woman in his life now.

As he wheeled his way back to the little hall, he tried to imagine what it would be like if it were she who had been stricken with this injury—after all, they had both been in the car when he had crashed it—would he have been as irritable, as impatient with her as she was with him?

He had to have everything put out for him, everything, but once he was dressed and in his wheelchair he could manage. He hated the catheter, but it was a help. It drained into a transparent plastic bag, butter-yellow, jewellike, but sometimes it leaked. Sometimes, just before it needed changing—the male nurse did that—it leaked a little and the wet stained his clothes. This, too, annoyed Annie. She had the washing to do, she told him, as if he didn't know. He had bought her the washing machine.

Then his teeth. His jaw had been slightly injured in the crash—not broken, but his teeth would not stay up. Every time he tried to speak, they dropped, and when he was eating they sometimes almost came out. He would see Annie turn away in revulsion. Several visits to the dentist had done nothing to improve his dentures—and had not improved his wife's temper. She had missed two bridge afternoons and they were sacred.

Because of his inability to speak properly, he dreaded today's visit. Annie had gone to meet their son and his wife. Their visits were infrequent—they lived a long way away. Desmond loved to see them but dreaded their eyes appraising him, saying without words, Poor old Dad, he's lost a lot of ground since we were here last.

Desmond put the pad of his thumb firmly against the plastic plate and pushed it against the roof of his mouth, then clenched his teeth until it hurt. Just to see, he let his lower jaw sag and made as if he were about to speak. The teeth fell down immediately.

"Bugger it," he tried to say and almost turned his chair away, so as not to be there to greet them. Too late, the key turned in the lock and they all three were there in front of him.

His son looked as he himself had looked at forty—tall, upright, handsome.

"Hello, Dad." Michael pressed Desmond's shoulder, and his wife Jill bent down and kissed him, gazing into his face, her eyes blue, kind, inquiring. He smelled her perfume—light, flowerlike. She had short, curly, golden hair that fell forward and caressed his cheek. He felt tears come close, prick behind his eyes. God, crying now, maudlin, his brain going.

He tried to say something to Jill, but his bloody useless teeth got in the way and she withdrew her face from him, not showing disgust as Annie did, but so a not to embarrass him. Sometimes, in despair, when he and Annie were alone, he took the teeth out, but his wife would explode. "For goodness sake, Desmond, it's bad enough with them in. Supposing someone called unexpectedly?"

Next day, in the afternoon, the three decided to go shopping. "If you don't mind, Dad," his son said.

Desmond was hearty in his denial that he minded. "Of course not, why should I? Go and buy Jill a present from me and one for yourself." Desmond was sorry for his son. He knew Michael was longing to leave, probably hated the three days of the weekend, would have liked just to see his father and mother, check they were all right, and leave.

"But is it really all right, Dad? Are you sure you don't mind being left? Will you be okay?" Jill asked, and was quickly snapped at by Annie.

"Of course, it's perfectly all right. He has to be left. I can't be tied to the house day after day, you know."

Desmond felt like a dog, and he longed to say, "I'm quite trustworthy, I won't dirty the carpet," but this would have spoiled it for the children so he didn't say anything.

But when they had driven away, he cried. This crying was new, very frequent lately. Hardening of the arteries, Desmond supposed, senility. Though he tried to dismiss it, it made him afraid for his reason.

Hours later they were back, full of talk and laughter and carrying crackling paper bags.

Desmond was there again to greet them.

"I'll make a cup of tea."

Annie dropped her bags on the hall chair and made for the kitchen, ignoring Desmond's "I laid the tray, dear."

"Good for you, Dad," Jill said.

When they were all a little farther away from him, Desmond said, "Bitch, bitch, bitch, bitch," throwing the word softly at his wife's retreating figure.

"What did you say, Dad?" asked Michael.

"Nothing," mumbled Desmond.

"Oh." Did Michael look at him curiously as he passed him to take the parcels to their bedroom?

Jill followed Annie into the kitchen and Desmond was alone again in the hall.

He was about to make his way to the sitting room when he heard Jill's clear voice.

"Well, Mum, I think you're wrong. I think it's Dad's teeth that are the trouble. They don't fit and that's why he can't speak properly."

"Maybe so. That dentist—" He heard his wife bang the kettle down.

"Look, Mum:" It was Jill, rustling paper. "I got this denture fixative. It's new and they say it's great. You just spread it on like butter and it gets hard. Shall I give it to him?"

"No, you will not! That's all I need, that stuff on the carpet—he'll get it everywhere. Give it to me."

He heard another bang—the slamming shut of a cupboard door or a drawer, he couldn't be certain which. He wheeled himself into the sitting room and was there when they brought the tea, both the women, he noted, looking slightly grim. Desmond ate the cake with difficulty.

In bed that night he cried again. He couldn't stop, and that and the fact that he couldn't remember what day it was alarmed him. He lay there worrying, thinking. At last he ferreted it out. It was Saturday.

There's nothing worse than to doubt the mind's integrity, he said to himself, and the sentence reassured him. No one going off his rocker or losing his memory could come up with a sentence like that, he thought, and fell asleep.

Next day it rained all day. Michael was more cheerful and relaxed, no doubt due to the fact that he and Jill were going home tomorrow. Duty done, Desmond thought.

He had hoped the others would go to church and he would have the run of the house—the run of the kitchen to search for the fixative—but the rain kept them in. Annie couldn't bear him in her kitchen. If he offered to wash up, she would say, "You'll break more than you'll wash."

But he was intent on that fixative and that night he waited until they were all asleep and the bungalow was silent, then he got up, struggled into his wheelchair, and made for the kitchen. The faint buzz of snoring came from his wife's room—every night she took two sleeping pills. On the bottle it said, "One to be taken at night," but she took two and badgered her doctor when she ran out. She was so forceful, so dogmatic, she usually got them. She mostly got what she wanted.

Desmond was glad about one thing—the accident and the loss of mobility had cut down their visits together to shops and retaurants. It had always been a nightmare for him. Shop assistants, waiters, and waitresses hated Annie.

In the kitchen, Desmond searched in the drawers, under the sink, even in the trash. Annie could have thrown that packet anywhere.

The third drawer was full of kitchen knives. He cut the tip of his finger on one and felt the tears prick behind his eyes, but he felt something else—the fixer, in a box under the knives. It was a small box, containing a tube and a spatula.

He closed the kitchen door and switched on the light. The only sound was the harsh, metallic click of the electric clock. Desmond read the instructions on the box carefully, took his teeth out, dried them with a paper towel, spread the substance as directed, and put the teeth back. It was wonderful—they clung firmly to the roof of his mouth. He smiled and they stayed in place. He spoke softly and they did not drop.

He wheeled himself over to the refrigerator. On a plate were two chicken drumsticks—tomorrow's cold supper. He grabbed one and bit into the flesh—the teeth were beautifully stable. He finished the drumstick. That would pay the old bitch out, he thought. That would mess up their evening meal.

But fear suddenly overtook him, fear of being found out. He closed the refrigerator door, switched off the kitchen light, opened the door, and listened.

Nothing, not a sound.

Gently, he propelled his chair along the hallway, making only the slightest swishing sound on the carpet. He passed the guest room, arrived at his wife's door, and paused.

Later, he arrived at his own room and safety.

He took his silver-backed hairbrush to bed with him to use as a mirror. He switched on the bedside light and looked at his teeth. Great, wonderful. He put out his light, cuddled down with his teeth still in, and slept.

"Breakfast in bed, Dad?" Michael came into his room in the morning bearing a tray of poached egg, toast, marmalade, and coffee. Desmond preferred tea and hated breakfast in bed, but it was kind. He smiled at his son, conscious of his teeth, but Michael was leaving. "Going to fetch Mum's now," he called over his shoulder.

Desmond heard him go along to the kitchen and, a few minutes later, return and knock on his mother's door, then walk in. A few seconds later came his cry.

"Oh, my God! Dad! Jill! Get a doctor. Get—"

Desmond proceeded to eat his poached egg; he didn't want it to get cold.

There was more noise. He finished his egg, smiled into his silver-backed hairbrush, smoothed down his hair, got himself into his wheelchair, and joined his son in Annie's bedroom. "What's the matter, lad?" he asked.

Jill was in the hall, telephoning, her voice urgent. "Please be as quick as you can!" she was saying.

Desmond wheeled himself up to his wife's bed and peered at her. She was lying on her side, her head encased in its usual hideous hairnet. At the side of her neck, below her ear, was a gaping hole like a mouth, still oozing what was left of her blood. It looked as if an animal had bitten through her carotid artery while she slept.

Michael pulled his father's chair back from the bed. "I wish you hadn't come in here, Dad. What in God's name can have happened to her?"

Desmond was sorry for his son. As he looked at his white, stricken face, he felt remorse, but then his son hadn't had to live with her. "Can't think, lad," he said. He turned his chair around and went back to his room to finish his toast and coffee.

Ron Goulart
Eavesdropping

Psychotherapy helped him a great deal more than he'd expected. After only a few visits to the psychiatrist's office, some of his major problems vanished and his whole life seemed to change for the better.

George Norkin wasn't anticipating anything like that the first Thursday morning. He arrived at Dr. Walter Matterheim's waiting room about ten minutes early for his eleven o'clock appointment, feeling glum and depressed. And on the brink of poverty, he was thinking. How can I even afford this guy? A hundred bucks a visit. And he wants me to come twice a week. Plus I need a fat fifteen hundred each and every month in alimony for Wendy and Veronica. I can't even smile any more because the crown of my canine tooth fell off. And if I don't get a new muffler for the Porsche soon, the Santa Monica cops are going to run me in.

There was no one else in the small paneled waiting room. No nurse and no receptionist. Only a bleak sofa and a table spread with magazines. Not *Time* or *People*—just last year's psychology journals and tabloids devoted to making the world safe for ecology.

He sat. That wasn't a bad line about ecology. If he wasn't in such a slump that he couldn't even write any more he might have used it someplace.

Imagine, he told himself. A year ago he was headwriter on the #2 comedy show on television. Headwriter on *Take a Flying Leap*. He'd won an Emmy three years ago for *The Mary Alice Muggin Show*. He was the creator, for heaven's sake, of *Drunk Tank*. Now he was about six weeks away from abject poverty. He was lugging around enough anguish and despair to make Kierkegaard look like Little Miss Sunbeam.

George glanced at the door of the therapist's office. He had become aware that he could hear what was being said in there. Coughing, he started thumbing through a slick-paper magazine devoted to world-wide famine. The wooden door obviously wasn't soundproof. George wondered if Dr. Matterheim knew that. Supposedly, he'd only been in this new building about a month.

Or maybe the doctor did know and this was a test for patients, to see if they could refrain from eavesdropping or how they reacted to other people's problems.

No, George decided, the most logical explanation was that he didn't know he and his patient could be heard out here.

On the other side of the door a woman with a pleasant voice was saying, "It's difficult for me to accept the fact that he still hates me."

"Hate's a strong word, Marcia."

"Not when applied to my ex-husband. See, Walt, he really and truly believes he invented the dolls. He's obsessed with the idea and—well, he's an extremely nasty and violent man."

"Yet he's going through the courts about his claims on your RagTag Kid dolls, isn't he? That seems rational."

"I'm afraid he's too impatient to wait for the court to decide. When we were married, Peter was—well, he hit me a lot."

"That was then," reminded Dr. Matterheim. "But you got yourself out of a bad marriage, went on to start your own business, and you've become extremely successful. So—"

George eased along the low sofa, moving nearer to the closed door. That has to be Marcia Westerly in there, he thought. She manufactures those halfwit RagTag Kid dolls. They look like starving ghetto children dressed in rags. And they're outselling everything but Killer Marine robots. All that money and still she's got problems.

"See you on Thursday, Walt."

"Have fun until then, Marcia."

A moment later, a slim dark-haired woman of thirty or so came out of the inner office. She was very pretty, and when she took a tissue from the pocket of her designer jeans to dab at her eyes George was touched.

If I wasn't in such a slump, I'd offer to help her out, George thought, watching her guardedly as she crossed to the outer door.

"George?" Dr. Matterheim was beckoning to him.

"Yes, Dr. Matterheim," George said, shaking hands and stepping into the office.

"Call me Walt," said the therapist.

The next Tuesday morning, George arrived at the psychiatrist's waiting room a full fifteen minutes early. Picking up a tabloid dealing with Zen agriculture, he seated himself as close to the office door as possible.

Sure, it's eavesdropping, he said inside his head, but it's beneficial. Thinking about somebody else's problems takes my mind off my teeth and the damn alimony and my ailing car and the fact my creative powers are about on the par with those of a doorknob.

"The police didn't seem to take it all that seriously," Marcia was saying in her lovely voice.

Wendy, George's first wife, hadn't possessed a lovely voice. Well, maybe it had started out lovely but by the time it was rerouted through her nose it didn't come out that way. And Veronica had one of those voices you could use to shatter wine glasses.

"It might be," Dr. Matterheim said, "only a prank."

"No, it's more than that," she insisted. "Maybe I should've brought it to show you, Walt. He'd gouged the two button eyes out of a girl RagTag Kid, then left it sprawled on my bed with a hand-lettered note pinned to its little chest. 'Just a friendly reminder.' That's scary, Walt."

"How could he have gotten into your house?"

"I don't have a burglar-alarm system. Though I'm going to see about having one installed now," Marcia answered. "Up until now I've felt fairly secure up in that part of Beverly Hills. For all I know, I didn't even lock up the place when I went out last night."

"How about servants?"

"I have a maid and a cook, but neither lives in. So the house is empty most nights."

"Did the police find anything?"

"No evidence of forced entry. No fingerprints on the note. The paper's from a cheap tablet, lettering you can't identify."

"You think it was Peter Westerly."

"How many other vicious psychopaths do I know? Of course it was Peter."

"Have you contacted him, asked him about this?"

"Oh, no. That would be giving in to him," she said. "In that devious brain of his, Peter really believes all this garbage his idiotic lawyer intends to bring up at the trial next month—that it was Peter who designed the RagTag dolls and I'm only a clever seamstress who sewed up a model and sold it after we'd divorced."

"No truth in any of that?"

"None, Walt. I divorced Peter because I was tired of being punched around. When I married him, he was a second-rate-ad-agency art director. He remained that throughout our three years of sex and violence, and he's that now. I thought up the RagTag Kid dolls after he was long gone and he's not going to rob me now. The millions those dolls bring in belong to me. All the friendly reminders in the world aren't going to move me to settle out of court with him."

"It might be a good idea to have that alarm system put in," Walt said.

"I'm already on the waiting list."

"Meanwhile, you can call me any time, Marcia."

"I know, and I appreciate it."

She was wearing a grey suit and looking very attractive. This time, as she crossed the waiting room, she smiled at George and said, "Hello again."

"Same here," he muttered, dropping his tabloid and getting to his feet.

This is sort of nutty, George advised himself that evening.

He was sprawled out on his stomach on a wooded hillside above the large Moorish-style home of Marcia Westerly. He was watching the house and grounds through a pair of night binoculars. The glasses he'd borrowed from a photographer friend and Marcia's address he got through a friend on the Los Angeles *Times*.

He felt a little sheepish about what he was doing, but he was actually, aside from that, feeling better than he had in weeks. Some of that, a little anyway, he supposed was due to his sessions with Dr. Matterheim. But the chief source of his improved mood was the interest he'd taken in

Marcia Westerly and her nasty former husband. He'd gone to the library and done research in back issues of *Time, People, Mammon*, and *Business News Weekly*. About Marcia's life and business he now knew a great deal. All he could find on her in the back issues tended to confirm the impression he'd been getting from eavesdropping at Dr. Matterheim's. She was a bright, clever woman being harassed for a share of her very successful doll company by a husband who was fifteen years her senior and noted for his violent temper.

"The thing is," George was talking to himself aloud now, "somebody's got to look after her. She's too stubborn and independent to get outside help and the nitwit cops are too dim to understand what's really going on."

George had always admired bright and self-sufficient women. He'd never gotten around to marrying one yet, but he'd worked with several in his ten some years of writing television comedy shows.

"When it comes time to live with somebody or marry somebody, I end up with the dim, completely dependent ones," he told himself aloud now. Both of his wives had been like that. And Wendy was on the heavy side as well. "Obese is probably the apter word," he corrected himself.

Marcia Westerly was thirty-three and still had the same slender figure she had when she'd majored in English at the University of California at Berkeley back in the Seventies.

George did quite a bit of thinking up on the weedy hillside among the trees as he watched the maid leave and the cook depart. He saw Marcia herself drive off in her Jaguar at nine and return at a few minutes after eleven. Nobody else came near the place.

The next night was virtually the same, except that a chill drizzle fell on him during the last two hours of his vigil. Marcia went out at eight and came home at eleven-thirty. No one prowled the grounds or tried to break in. He could see the whole layout from up where he was and he was certain of that.

George's Porsche, which was nearly six years old, after all, stalled on him twice en route to Dr. Matterheim's office Thursday morning. And even though he jogged from the parking lot to the waiting room he didn't get there until ten minutes to eleven.

"It's too disgusting to bring here and show you, Walt," he heard Marcia saying as he dropped down on the end of the sofa.

"Even so, I would have liked—"

"He slashed the RagTag Kid open, ripped out the stuffing, splashed it with blood-red paint and left it on the floor of my living room with the same darn note—'a friendly reminder.' I almost got sick, but I wouldn't allow myself."

"You locked up before you went out last night?"

"Yes. He smashed a patio window and got inside that way."

"Marcia, do you think you could get him here to talk to me?"

"I won't contact him. I mean, that's what he wants. No, I can't do that."

"His behavior is making me increasingly uneasy," said the psychiatrist. "Peter may be building up to—"

"He's only trying to upset me, make me offer him some kind of settlement. He knows his claims about being the real creator of the RagTag Kid are crazy."

"Did you contact the police about what happened last night?"

"Yes. I think maybe they're finally starting to think I'm not imagining things after all."

"Have you suggested to them that Peter's behind the incidents?"

"Well, when they asked me who might have a grudge against me, I put his name right at the top of the list."

"You're handling this pretty well, Marcia. But don't be afraid to call for help."

"I won't, Walt."

"See you next Tuesday. Have a good safe weekend."

Marcia smiled in George's direction while crossing the waiting room. He returned the smile without letting his eyes meet hers.

Nobody could've broken into her house last night, George told himself as he trailed Marcia's Jaguar through the Southern California evening. I didn't doze off, didn't miss anything. Peter Westerly sneaking across the grounds, smashing a window and depositing a RagTag Kid, ripping it apart—nope, that I would have noticed.

Puzzled as to what was actually going on, he decided to ignore Marcia's house tonight and follow her instead.

She drove to a small beach town just beyond Malibu. Parking her car on a rundown side street, she walked a block uphill.

That's where Peter Westerly lives, George realized, driving on by the hurrying woman and ditching his car around the next corner. He'd obtained Westerly's address two days before from his friend on the *Times*, figuring that he might come out here and warn the guy to leave his former wife alone.

George moved carefully toward the small white ranch house where Marcia's former husband lived, keeping in the shadows as much as he could. At the high hedge fronting the place, he halted. There wasn't a light showing anywhere in the house.

Wait now, he told himself. There was a glimmer of something over in the garage. Crouching low, he skulked over to the closed garage. He moved silently along its stucco wall to a window and risked a look inside.

Marcia was in there, carrying a lantern-type flashlight. On the workbench before her was a small keg and a scattering of empty shotgun shells.

Skeet shooting. Right. That's Westerly's hobby. George had read that in one of the old magazine stories. The guy apparently loads his own shells with powder. But why does she want to sneak in here and steal a cupful of gun powder?

With the metal cup in her gloved right hand she was scooping black powder from the keg. On the work table next to the keg was a length of pipe about a foot long. It was capped at one end. The light from the lantern she'd set down showed also a small electronic clock and some flashlight batteries, a couple of firecrackers, and RagTag Kid with its chest ripped open.

Holy Hannah, realized George, she's making a pipe bomb!

Very quietly and carefully, he worked his way out of Westerly's yard and back to his car. He moved his sluggish Porsche to a new position across the street from Marcia's Jag. He sat and waited.

When she returned to her car a half hour later, she was carrying a brown-paper bag that looked to hold a RagTag Kid with a bomb in its middle.

Now she's got herself a bomb made chiefly with ingredients taken from her erstwhile husband's workshop, George noted to himself. He started his car, keeping the lights off for a while, and followed Marcia as she drove away. What the hell is she going to do? Blow herself up and make it look as though Westerly did it? Not much advantage in that.

What she actually did was drive to a parking lot behind an office building down near the ocean in Santa Monica.

"That's where Peter Westerly's ad agency is," George told himself in the mirror. "She must know he's working late tonight."

Marcia moved on foot across the dark unattended lot. Opening the trunk of what must be her former husband's car with a key she probably had from when they were married, she put the paper bag inside and shut the door.

"That's it, that's it," said George. "Here I've been feeling mushy and heroic about her and she's a murderess. She's been convincing Dr. Matterheim and the police that Westerly is on the verge of going bonkers, that he's so goofy over his delusion that he's the true creator of the dolls he finally cracked and intended to kill her with a RagTag Kid loaded with gunpowder. The point of all this must be that the guy really did invent the dolls and she's afraid she'll lose millions when the court rules against her."

He sat in his car and watched Marcia stride back to hers and drive away.

"What the cops were supposed to think when they found the remains of Westerly was that the poor crazed simp had the bomb in his car, ready to deliver to his wife's, but that it went off too soon," George said to himself, shaking his head. "Boy, it's damn lucky I decided to get involved in this whole mess."

The following Tuesday, George entered the waiting room at five minutes shy of eleven. He was smiling and humming the theme from one of his award-winning comedy shows.

He settled onto the sofa, crossed his legs, and relaxed.

Nothing but silence was coming out of the psychiatrist's office.

At exactly eleven, Dr. Matterheim opened the door. "Come in, George."

"I didn't expect to see Mrs. Westerly here today." George sat in the chair facing the therapist's desk. "I saw the story on the news and in the papers."

"It was very unfortunate," said Matterheim. "I was fairly certain the man was deranged. The law being what it is, though, there wasn't much I could do."

"In a way," suggested George, "things worked out well. Poetic justice sort of thing."

The psychiatrist nodded slowly. "I suppose so. Peter Westerly blowing himself up with a bomb he'd obviously intended for his ex-wife. Still and all, Marcia Westerly was very upset when the police notified her."

"I imagine she would be, sure."

Clearing his throat, the psychiatrist said, "I sense something more positive about you, George. You're looking less sad."

"Yes, I *have* been feeling less depressed."

"Any reason?"

George smiled. "Well, my sessions with you are certainly part of it, Walt. And then, too, I've just come into some money. Quite a lot of money, actually."